Nonparametric
Methods
in Statistics

CE

Nonparametric Methods in Statistics

D. A. S. FRASER

Associate Professor
University of Toronto

New York · John Wiley & Sons, Inc.
London

To Jean

Preface

NONPARAMETRIC STATISTICS IS CONCERNED WITH THE TREATMENT of standard statistical problems when the familiar assumption of normality is replaced by general assumptions concerning the distribution form. One of the oldest nonparametric methods is Karl Pearson's χ^2-test of fit proposed in 1900 (Reference [1], Chapter 3). Another is the classical sign test. Development of nonparametric methods was slow until the second war years, but since then their growth has touched almost every phase of statistical activity. This book is an attempt to collect and unify these diverse developments. Preliminary to this, the first two chapters provide a survey of the general techniques of estimation and hypothesis testing.

The book is intended as a second course in mathematical statistics. Prerequisites are a knowledge of calculus and familiarity with an introduction to statistics such as is found in Hoel—*Introduction to Mathematical Statistics*. A knowledge of measure theory is not necessary, the essential ideas of measure being introduced with a statistical interpretation. The first two chapters are used at the University of Toronto for an undergraduate course surveying recent small sample methods, while the remainder of the book covers material for a graduate course on the applications of these methods in the nonparametric branch of statistics.

Many of the names of contributors to the development of nonparametric theory appear in the references and bibliography at the end of each chapter. In particular, Professor Erich Lehmann has contributed much by collecting the results of his own and others' researches in his two sets of mimeographed notes on estimation and hypothesis testing.

Completion of this book was made possible by the generous support of the United States Office of Naval Research during the spring of

vii

1955. At that time I enjoyed a visiting appointment at Princeton University, and I wish to express my appreciation to Professor Wilks and Professor Tukey for their encouragement.

D. A. S. FRASER

University of Toronto
October 1956

Contents

CHAPTER 1

Probability Concepts

1. INTRODUCTION

In Chapter 1 we introduce the notion of probability and discuss some concepts that are naturally associated with probability. In Chapter 2 we add the necessary mathematical structure for statistical decisions and treat in some detail the methods of estimation, hypothesis testing, confidence regions, and tolerance regions. In these two chapters the purpose is to have a treatment of the more important ideas of general statistical inference and therefore to enable the development of the remaining chapters with the emphasis on the methods particular to the field of nonparametric theory.

2. MEASURABLE SPACE

In constructing a probability model for an experiment, the first step is a consideration of what are the possible outcomes of the experiment. We assume that all possibilities for the outcome can be foreseen, and we refer to this aggregation of outcomes as the *sample space* and designate it by a capital script letter, say $\mathscr{X}$. An arbitrary *outcome* or point of this space is designated by x, of the space $\mathscr{Y}$ by y. As an example consider the tossing of a single coin. The outcome could perhaps be considered in some detail, but usually interest is restricted to a description of what face shows after the toss. Accordingly, if we designate the two outcomes in the obvious manner, we have $\mathscr{X} = \{H, T\}$; or if we envisage the possibility of the coin standing on edge, then we have $\mathscr{X} = \{H, T, E\}$. As another example consider a sequence of five measurements of the gravitational constant. An outcome then is a sequence or ordered set of five numbers, $\mathbf{x} = (x_1, \cdots, x_5)$, and the sample space could be the Euclidean space of five dimensions, $\mathscr{X} = R^5$. Of course, not all points in R^5 are possible outcomes, but what is essential is that $\mathscr{X}$ *contain all* possible outcomes.

1

The probability model of an experiment is based on a certain phenomenon observed, not in a single performance of the experiment, but in a long sequence of repetitions under as nearly identical conditions as possible. The phenomenon is concerned with the frequency with which the outcome falls in any particular subset of the space $\mathscr{X}$. It would be satisfying if the later development of the mathematical model would permit us to consider the phenomenon, and its analog in the model, for arbitrary subsets A of $\mathscr{X}$. However, in general this is not possible. Accordingly, we associate with the space $\mathscr{X}$ a class $\mathscr{A}$ of subsets A of $\mathscr{X}$, these subsets to be referred to as *measurable sets*. We shall impose some natural restrictions on the class $\mathscr{A}$, but first we introduce some notation.

If x is a point in (or element of) A, we write $x \in A$; and if x is not in A, we write $x \notin A$. If each point in a set A is also in a set A', we say A is contained in A' and write $A \subset A'$. The set consisting of each point either in A_1 or in A_2 (or in both) is called A_1 *union* A_2 and is designated by $A_1 \cup A_2$. $\bigcup_{i=1}^{n} A_i$ is the set consisting of all points belonging to any of the sets $A_1, \cdots, A_n$. $A_1 \cap A_2$ is the set of points that belong to both A_1 and A_2, and is called the *intersection* of A_1 and A_2. Similarly $\bigcap_{i=1}^{n} A_i$ is the set of points belonging to each of $A_1, A_2, \cdots$. $A_1 - A_2$ is the set of points belonging to A_1 but not to A_2 and is called the difference. A particular difference is $\mathscr{X} - A$ and is called the *complement* of A. $\{x \mid \text{condition}\}$ is the set of points satisfying the condition following the vertical bar; for example, we can write $A_1 - A_2 = \{x \mid x \in A_1, x \notin A_2\}$.

The restrictions imposed on the class $\mathscr{A}$ are such that, if we apply the simple operations of union, intersection, and complementation to sets in $\mathscr{A}$, then the resulting sets will also be in $\mathscr{A}$. We require that $\mathscr{A}$ be a *σ-algebra* of subsets of $\mathscr{X}$, that is, $\mathscr{A}$ be nonempty and satisfy:

(i)   *If $A_1, A_2, \cdots \in \mathscr{A}$, then $\bigcup_{i=1}^{\infty} A_i \in \mathscr{A}$.*

(ii)   *If $A \in \mathscr{A}$, then $\mathscr{X} - A \in \mathscr{A}$.*

It is easy to show that these conditions imply that $\mathscr{X} \in \mathscr{A}$, and that, if $A_1, A_2, \cdots \in \mathscr{A}$, then $\bigcap_{i=1}^{\infty} A_i \in \mathscr{A}$. See Problems 1 and 2.

The combination of a space $\mathscr{X}$ and a σ-algebra $\mathscr{A}$ of subsets of $\mathscr{X}$ is called a *measurable space* and is designated by $\mathscr{X}(\mathscr{A})$. The term measurable is used merely to indicate that this is the structure upon which a measure or probability measure can be defined. (We shall consider measures in the next section.) In many cases the classes $\mathscr{A}$ will not be mentioned explicitly. For example, if $\mathscr{X}$ consists of a finite number of points, then $\mathscr{A}$ will always be the σ-algebra consisting of all subsets of $\mathscr{X}$. Also, if $\mathscr{X} = R^n$, the class $\mathscr{A}$ will almost invariably be the class of Borel sets or the class of Lebesgue measurable sets. We define the Borel sets when $n = 1$; an analogous definition applies when $n > 1$. The class of Borel sets is the smallest σ-algebra containing the intervals $[a, b] = \{x \mid a \leq x \leq b\}$ for all a, b. Problem 3 shows that it is meaningful to speak of a *smallest* σ-algebra. Lebesgue measurable sets will be defined in the next section. In the sequel some familiarity with Lebesgue measure and integration would be helpful, and for further reading see Monroe [1] and Halmos [2].

Frequently a number of experiments are considered simultaneously, in which case the over-all outcome is the sequence of outcomes from the individual experiments. Therefore, we define a product space $\mathscr{X}_1 \times \cdots \times \mathscr{X}_n$; it consists of all n-tuples $(x_1, \cdots, x_n)$ where $x_1 \in \mathscr{X}_1$, $x_2 \in \mathscr{X}_2, \cdots, x_n \in \mathscr{X}_n$. If each $\mathscr{X}_i$ is a measurable space $\mathscr{X}_i(\mathscr{A}_i)$, we now consider whether there is a natural σ-algebra $\mathscr{B}$ to be associated with the product space. If $A_i \in \mathscr{A}_i$ for $i = 1, \cdots, n$, then we might well be interested in whether the over-all outcome $(x_1, \cdots, x_n)$ was such that each coordinate x_i was in the corresponding set A_i: that is, whether $(x_1, \cdots, x_n) \in A_1 \times \cdots \times A_n$. Accordingly, we require that $\mathscr{B}$ contain all the *product* or rectangular sets,

$$A_1 \times \cdots \times A_n = \{(x_1, \cdots, x_n) \mid x_i \in A_i \qquad (i = 1, \cdots, n)\},$$

and, in fact, we define the *natural* σ-algebra $\mathscr{B}$ on the product space to be the smallest σ-algebra containing all the product sets $A_1 \times \cdots \times A_n$, and we designate it by $\mathscr{B} = (\mathscr{A}_1, \cdots, \mathscr{A}_n)$. See Problems 4 and 5.

In analyzing an experiment the statistician frequently does not need to consider the outcome as such with all the detailed information it contains, but may be content with a condensation or function of it. We now consider formally the procedure of condensing the outcome of an experiment. Let $\mathscr{X}(\mathscr{A})$ and $\mathscr{T}(\mathscr{B})$ be two measurable spaces corresponding, respectively, to the outcome and its condensation. Then for the statistician to obtain a condensation he needs a function, say $t(x)$, which maps $\mathscr{X}$ into $\mathscr{T}$. Thus, for each $x \in \mathscr{X}$, $t(x)$ is a unique point in $\mathscr{T}$.

For the space $\mathscr{X}(\mathscr{A})$ we confined our attention to the sets belonging to $\mathscr{A}$. Correspondingly we have a natural restriction to impose on the function $t(x)$. For, if the statistician investigates the frequency with which the condensation $t(x)$ falls in a set $B \in \mathscr{B}$, he could just as well have observed the frequency with which the original outcome x falls in a set A defined by

(2.1)
$$A = t^{-1}(B)$$
$$= \{x \mid t(x) \in B\};$$

A is the inverse image of B under the mapping $t(x)$ and consists of all points that are mapped into B by $t(x)$. Since we have confined the statistician's attention to measurable sets, then, if he considers a set $B \in \mathscr{B}$, certainly the inverse image set $A = t^{-1}(B)$ should belong to $\mathscr{A}$. This is our requirement on $t(x)$, and a function satisfying this requirement we call a *measurable function* or *statistic*.

A function $t(x)$ from $\mathscr{X}(\mathscr{A})$ to $\mathscr{T}(\mathscr{B})$ is a statistic if, for every $B \in \mathscr{B}$, $t^{-1}(B) \in \mathscr{A}$.

Sometimes we shall have a function $t(x)$ from a measurable space $\mathscr{X}(\mathscr{A})$ into a space $\mathscr{T}$ and would like to define measurable sets on $\mathscr{T}$ so that $t(x)$ is measurable, is a statistic. First we make the trivial restriction that $\mathscr{T}$ consist only of points obtained under the mapping $t(x)$; i.e. $\mathscr{T} = t(\mathscr{X})$. We define a class $\mathscr{B}^*$ to consist of all sets $B \subset \mathscr{T}$ whose inverse images $t^{-1}(B)$ are elements of $\mathscr{A}$.

$$(2.2) \qquad \mathscr{B}^* = \{B \,|\, t^{-1}(B) \in \mathscr{A}\}.$$

As soon as we have verified that $\mathscr{B}^*$ is a σ-algebra on $\mathscr{T}$, it is obvious that $t(x)$ is a statistic from $\mathscr{X}(\mathscr{A})$ to $\mathscr{T}(\mathscr{B}^*)$. The proof that $\mathscr{B}^*$ is a σ-algebra (Problem 7) is easily obtained from the following relations:

$$(2.3) \qquad t^{-1}\Big(\bigcup_\alpha B_\alpha\Big) = \bigcup_\alpha t^{-1}(B_\alpha),$$

$$(2.4) \qquad t^{-1}\Big(\bigcap_\alpha B_\alpha\Big) = \bigcap_\alpha t^{-1}(B_\alpha),$$

which are given for proof in Problem 6. This σ-algebra $\mathscr{B}^*$ is, in fact, the largest σ-algebra on $\mathscr{T}$ for which the function $t(x)$ is measurable.

In condensing the outcome of an experiment, the important thing to a statistician is a knowledge of which x's will produce a given value of the function and not the particular designation or name for that value. Thus, for n real numbers, $x_1, \cdots, x_n$, the sample mean $\bar{x}$ is just as useful as $n^{1/2}\bar{x}$ or Σx; and conversely. The value of each can be obtained from the value of any other. Thus from some points of view the essential idea of *statistic* for the statistician is given by a partition of the space $\mathscr{X}$ into disjoints sets $T(x)$:

$$\mathscr{X} = \bigcup T(x)$$

where $T(x)$ is the set containing x, and for any two points x and x' either

$$T(x) = T(x')$$

or

$$T(x) \cap T(x') = \phi$$

where ϕ is the empty set. The statistician obtains his condensation by recording the set $T(x)$ which contained the outcome x and forgetting which x in the set $T(x)$ was the actual outcome. The space $\mathcal{T}$ for the mapping $T(x)$ has as elements subsets of the space $\mathcal{X}$. A set B will belong to the σ-algebra $\mathcal{B}^*$ induced on $\mathcal{T}$ if, when its elements are considered as subsets of $\mathcal{X}$ and their union is taken, the result is a subset belonging to $\mathcal{A}$.

3. MEASURES AND PROBABILITY MEASURES

In Section 2 we described the aggregation of outcomes of an experiment by the sample space $\mathcal{X}$, and the class of subsets of $\mathcal{X}$ to which we restrict attention by the σ-algebra $\mathcal{A}$. In this section we introduce the idea of probability.

If in a series of repetitions of an experiment we observe a *frequency ratio*, the proportion of times that the outcome x falls in a set $A \subset \mathcal{X}$, then it is an empirical result that in many types of experiments this ratio becomes quite stable as the number of repetitions is increased. Experiments possessing this property are called *random experiments*. The stability of the frequency ratio naturally leads us to hypothesize the existence of a number or *probability* to be associated with that set A. This number is the value about which the frequency ratio seems to settle in an extended series of repetitions.

Thus, to each set $A \in \mathcal{A}$, we can associate a number or probability. We require that these probabilities obey some simple rules corresponding to rules obeyed by the frequency ratio. We have, then, an example of a measure: For each set of $\mathcal{A}$ there is a number which *measures* the "probability" that an outcome falls in that set, a number which represents the frequency ratio for that set in a long series of repetitions of the experiment.

Before talking in detail about probabilities we introduce the general idea of a measure.

$\mu(A)$ *is a measure over* $\mathcal{X}(\mathcal{A})$ *if*

 (i)   *For each* $A \in \mathcal{A}$, $\mu(A)$ *is a real number.*

 (ii) *For each* $A \in \mathcal{A}$, $\mu(A) \geqslant 0$.

 (iii) *For* $A_1, A_2, \cdots$, *which are disjoint† and belong to* $\mathcal{A}$,

$$\mu(\bigcup_{i=1}^{\infty} A_i) = \sum_{i=1}^{\infty} \mu(A_i).$$

† Sets are disjoint if there are no points that belong to more than one set.

Because $\mathscr{A}$ is a σ-algebra, $\mathscr{X} \in \mathscr{A}$. Then, from conditions (i), (ii), it follows that $\mu(\mathscr{X})$ exists and is a non-negative real number; also from (iii) it follows that

$$\mu(A) + \mu(\mathscr{X} - A) = \mu(\mathscr{X}),$$

where each term is non-negative. Conditions (i), (ii), (iii) thus imply that the values of $\mu(A)$ are bounded by $\mu(\mathscr{X})$. More precisely then, we should call a function satisfying the conditions above a *bounded measure*. We obtain the definition of an *unbounded measure* by relaxing the first condition (i) above to

(i)′   *For each $A \in \mathscr{A}$, $\mu(A)$ is a real number or $+\infty$.*

As an example of an unbounded measure, consider Lebesgue measure defined over the Borel sets on the real line R^1. If we associate with any interval $[a, b]$ its length $b - a$, we have then a *measure* of that interval. But it is obvious that the intervals do not form a σ-algebra. The smallest σ-algebra containing the intervals is the class of Borel sets defined in the previous section. Now it can be shown that the definition of a measure over a class of sets together with the conditions (i)′, (ii), (iii) uniquely defines a measure for all sets in the smallest σ-algebra containing this class, and of course this measure agrees with the given measure for sets in the original class. This is called *extending a measure*, and for the details the reader is referred to Cramér [3], p. 19 and Halmos [2], p. 54. Lebesgue measure then is the extension to the Borel sets of the simple measure of an interval as given by its length.†

For $\mu(A)$ to be a probability measure we add the one additional condition:

(iv) $\mu(\mathscr{X}) = 1.$

However, when a measure is a probability measure, we shall usually designate it by $P(A)$ rather than $\mu(A)$. It is to be carefully noted that each of the four conditions or axioms for a probability measure corresponds to a similar condition satisfied by the frequency ratio.

As a simple example, consider the tossing of two unbiased coins. We can designate the possible outcomes by HH, HT, TH, TT, where for example HT stands for heads for the first coin and tails for the second.

$$\mathscr{X} = \{\text{HH, HT, TH, TT}\}$$

† If we add to the Borel sets any set contained in a Borel set having Lebesgue measure zero and then take the smallest σ-algebra, we obtain the Lebesgue measurable sets. The Lebesgue measure extends uniquely to this larger algebra. This is an example of the *completion* of a σ-algebra with respect to a measure.

The probability measure that seems to fit experimental results best is given by

$$P(HH) = 1/4, \qquad P(HT) = 1/4,$$
$$P(TH) = 1/4, \qquad P(TT) = 1/4;$$

the measure of a set containing more than one point is obtained by applying condition (iii) to the values in the above equations.

If $\mathscr{X}$ is a Euclidean space R^n, it is frequently more convenient to describe the probability measure by means of a *distribution function* $F(x_1, \cdots, x_n)$ defined by

$$(3.1) \qquad F(x_1, \cdots, x_n) = P\{(x_1', \cdots, x_n') | x_i' \leq x_i \quad (i = 1, \cdots, n)\}$$
$$= P\{]-\infty, x_1] \times \cdots \times]-\infty, x_n]\}$$

where $]a, b]$ is the interval from a to b, open on the left and closed on the right. Now it is quite easy to show that $F(x_1, \cdots, x_n)$ satisfies the three conditions:

(i)* $F(x_1, \cdots, x_{i-1}, -\infty, x_{i+1}, \cdots, x_n) = 0.$

(ii)* $F(+\infty, \cdots, +\infty) = 1.$

(iii)* $\Delta_{x_1}(a_1, b_1) \cdots \Delta_{x_n}(a_n, b_n) F(x_1, \cdots, x_n) \geq 0$
$$\text{for } a_i \leq b_i \quad (i = 1, \cdots, n).$$

The operator $\Delta_{x_i}(a, b)$ is defined by

$$\Delta_{x_i}(a, b) F(x_1, \cdots, x_n) = F(x_1, \cdots, x_{i-1}, b, x_{i+1}, \cdots, x_n)$$
$$- F(x_1, \cdots, x_{i-1}, a, x_{i+1}, \cdots, x_n).$$

It is quite easy to show that the expression occurring in condition (iii)* is the probability

$$P(]a_1, b_1] \times \cdots \times]a_n, b_n]).$$

Conversely, a distribution function $F(x_1, \cdots, x_n)$ satisfying (i)*, (ii)*, (iii)* uniquely determines a probability measure $P(A)$ defined for the Borel sets of R^n. The proof of this provides another example of the extension of a measure. We note that $F(x_1, \cdots, x_n)$ by virtue of (iii)* provides a non-negative measure for every rectangular set of the form $]a_1, b_1] \times \cdots \times]a_n, b_n]$. Then, just as the Borel sets are obtained from these rectangular sets, so also is the probability measure for the Borel sets.

Often we shall want to construct a measure on a product space $\mathscr{X}_1 \times \cdots \times \mathscr{X}_n$ from measures μ_i on the component spaces $\mathscr{X}_i(\mathscr{A}_i)$. In general, this can be done in many ways, but we consider now a natural way corresponding in statistics to independence between the experiments recorded in the components spaces $\mathcal{X}_i$.

The product measure $\mu(A)$ on $\mathcal{X}_1 \times \cdots \times \mathcal{X}_n$ obtained from the measures $\mu_1(A_1), \cdots, \mu_n(A_n)$, respectively, on $\mathcal{X}_1, \cdots, \mathcal{X}_n$ is given by

$$(3.2) \qquad \mu(A_1 \times \cdots \times A_n) = \prod_{i=1}^{n} \mu_i(A_i)$$

for all $A_1, \cdots, A_n$ belonging, respectively, to $\mathcal{A}_1, \cdots, \mathcal{A}_n$.

This definition for product sets together with the conditions for a probability measure uniquely determines the measure $\mu(A)$ for all sets $A \in (\mathcal{A}_1, \cdots, \mathcal{A}_n)$, the natural σ-algebra on the product space. This is yet another example of the extension of a measure.

If the measures μ_i are probability measures, then quite obviously μ is also a probability measure. For probability measures the above definition has the following meaning in terms of frequency ratios. If there are n experiments with the outcomes recorded, respectively, in the n spaces $\mathcal{X}_1, \cdots, \mathcal{X}_n$, and if there is no dependence or connection between the experiments, then the frequency ratio for the set $A_1 \times \cdots \times A_n$ is found in a long sequence of repetitions of the combined experiment to approximate the product of the frequency ratios of the individual sets A_i. This phenomenon we refer to as *statistical independence* and hypothesize that the probabilities give an exact equality; this is the definition above.

Let $t(x)$ be a statistic from $\mathcal{X}(\mathcal{A})$ into $\mathcal{T}(\mathcal{B})$. If $t(x)$ is used to condense the information in the outcome x for an experiment over $\mathcal{X}$, and if $P(A)$ is the probability measure descriptive of the outcomes in a sequence of repetitions, it is natural to inquire what probability measure governs the values of $t(x)$ in a sequence of repetitions. In analogy with an equivalent relation for the frequency ratio we define *a probability measure $Q(B)$ over $\mathcal{T}(\mathcal{B})$ induced by the probability measure $P(A)$ over $\mathcal{X}(\mathcal{A})$.*

$$(3.3) \qquad Q(B) = P(t^{-1}(B));$$

that is, the probability measure for $t(x)$ in B is the probability measure of the set of all outcomes mapped into B by $t(x)$. Of course, for the definition to be meaningful it must be shown that $Q(B)$ is really a probability measure and satisfies the four conditions; this is given as Problem 14.

The induced probability measure $Q(B)$ of the statistic $t(x)$ is sometimes called the *marginal probability measure*. The reason is that in some simple examples the outcomes can be arranged in a table with rows and columns and a given value of a statistic might correspond to all the outcomes in a row. Then the probability for that value would be obtained by adding the probabilities in the row and perhaps placing the total alongside "in the margin."

The term *random variable* is quite inessential to the mathematical model, but, on occasion, it can lead to considerable convenience of expression. We therefore define:

X, a random variable, is a symbol for a measurable space $\mathcal{X}(\mathcal{A})$ and probability measure $P(A)$ over $\mathcal{X}(\mathcal{A})$.

The symbol X can be associated with the result of a future performance of the experiment, the future outcome.   However, the only way to give any meaning in the model to such a statement is by means of the probability measure, and for this the "random variable" is superfluous.   The convenience is that we can use the expression $t(X)$ to stand for the random variable of the induced distribution.   Then we have a symbolic analog of X an outcome from the experiment on $\mathcal{X}$ and $t(X)$ an outcome for the condensation by the statistic $t(x)$.   If we wish a single symbol for the random variable $t(X)$, we shall capitalize the letter giving the statistic and write

$$T = t(X).$$

It is also convenient to speak of the probability that a random variable fulfills a condition and to write $\Pr\{X \text{ condition}\}$.   By this we mean the probability measure of the set of points fulfilling the condition, and, for example, we would have

$$\Pr\{X \in A,\ X \in A'\} = P(A \cap A').$$

The term probability distribution is also frequently used in statistics. It is a general term for a "distribution of probability" and does not refer explicitly to the measure that defines the "distribution" or if the space is Euclidean to the related distribution function.

4. EXPECTATION AND CONDITIONAL PROBABILITIES

To introduce expectation and conditional probability we need to define integration with respect to a measure $\mu(A)$.   One of the standard definitions for the Lebesgue integral can be extended in a straightforward manner.   Also many of the properties of the Lebesgue integral carry over to the more general form.   The derivation of some of these properties is given as problems in Section 8.

Let $f(x)$ be a real-valued statistic over $\mathcal{X}(\mathcal{A})$, and assume for the moment that it is bounded, $B < f(x) < C$.   Also, let $\mu(A)$ be a bounded measure over $\mathscr{X}(\mathscr{A})$. Then we define *the integral of $f(x)$ with respect to $\mu(A)$ by*

(4.1) $$\int_{\mathscr{X}} f(x) \, d\mu(x) = \lim_{\substack{n \to \infty \\ \epsilon \to 0}} \sum_{i=1}^{n} M_i \, \mu\{x \mid M_{i-1} < f(x) \le M_i\}.$$

where $B = M_0 < M_i < \cdots < M_n = C$, $M_i - M_{i-1} \le \epsilon$ for each i, and ϵ is taken to zero as $n \to \infty$. It is straightforward to prove that the limit exists; see Problem 15. The integral can be viewed approximately as a sum of values of $f(x)$ weighted with the measure of the points giving those values to the function; and, if $\mu(A)$ is a probability measure, as a weighted average of values of the function.

The definition of the integral can be extended to unbounded functions. Let $f(x)$ be an unbounded function and $f_{BC}(x)$ be $f(x)$ altered to satisfy the lower and upper bounds B, C:

$$\begin{aligned} f_{BC}(x) &= C & \text{if} \quad C &\le f(x) \\ &= f(x) & \text{if} \quad B &< f(x) < C \\ &= B & \text{if} \quad f(x) &\le B. \end{aligned}$$

Then if $\int f_{BC}(x) \, d\mu(x)$ approaches a finite limit as $B \to -\infty$ and C separately $\to +\infty$, then the integral of $f(x)$ is said to exist and

$$\int_{\mathscr{X}} f(x) \, d\mu(x) = \lim_{\substack{C \to +\infty \\ B \to -\infty}} \int f_{BC}(x) \, d\mu(x).$$

The integral over a measurable subset A of $\mathscr{X}$ can be obtained directly from the definition of the integral over $\mathscr{X}$. For this we define the characteristic function $\phi_A(x)$ of the set A:

(4.2) $$\begin{aligned} \phi_A(x) &= 1 & \text{if} \quad x &\in A \\ &= 0 & &\notin A. \end{aligned}$$

Obviously $\phi_A(x)$ is measurable. From the result in Problem 16, $\phi_A(x) f(x)$ is also measurable. Then we define the *integral of $f(x)$ over the measurable set A by*

(4.3) $$\int_A f(x) \, d\mu(x) = \int_{\mathscr{X}} f(x) \, \phi_A(x) \, d\mu(x).$$

It is sometimes possible to give a definition of the integral with respect to an unbounded measure $\mu(A)$. Suppose we can find a monotone sequence of sets $A_1 \subset A_2 \subset A_3 \cdots$ such that $\mathscr{X} = \bigcup_{i=1}^{\infty} A_i$ and $\mu(A_i) < \infty$ for each i.

Then within each set A_i the measure $\mu(A)$ is bounded, and the integral over A_i can be defined. If the limit,

$$\lim_{n \to \infty} \int_{A_n} f(x) \, d\mu(x),$$

exists and is independent of the sequence $A_1, A_2, \cdots$, then that limit is defined to be the value of the integral

$$\int_{\mathscr{X}} f(x) \, d\mu(x).$$

If X is a random variable for $P(A)$ over $\mathscr{X}(\mathscr{A})$ and $f(x)$ is a real-valued statistic, then we define *the expectation of $f(X)$ to be*

$$(4.4) \qquad\qquad E\{f(X)\} = \int_{\mathscr{X}} f(x) \, dP(x)$$

if the expression exists; otherwise we say the expectation does not exist. If probabilities are visualized as frequency ratios for an extended sequence of repetitions of an experiment, this expectation then appears as the average of the values of $f(x)$ for that sequence. Kolmogorov's theorem to be mentioned later adds theoretical weight to this experimental interpretation. For, if $f(X_1), f(X_2), \cdots$ is the sequence obtained by repeating the experiment, then *with probability one* the average $n^{-1} \sum_{i=1}^{n} f(X_i)$ converges to $E\{f(X)\}$ as $n \to \infty$.

The random variable $f(X)$ in formula (4.4) is a real-valued random variable, and hence has a distribution on the real line, R^1. If we designate the random variable $f(X)$ by Y and its measure by $Q(B)$, then we could consider the simple function y and the corresponding expectation,

$$(4.5) \qquad\qquad E\{Y\} = \int_{R} y \, dQ(y).$$

Since $f(X)$ and Y are the same random variable, we should hope that (4.4) and (4.5) are equal. That they are equal can be obtained directly from the definitions of the two integrals; see Problem 23.

The idea of conditioned probability has its origin in a simple experimental situation. If an experimenter knows that an outcome fulfills some condition, then what probability measure represents the outcome? The interpretation in terms of the frequency ratio is of course possible only when there is a positive probability that the condition will be fulfilled. We first define conditional probability in this simpler situation.

Let C be a subset of $\mathscr{X}$, and suppose that $x \in C$ is the condition the experimenter knows the outcome fulfills. If $P(C) > 0$, then we define the *conditional probability of A, given C*:

(4.6) $$P(A|C) = \frac{P(A \cap C)}{P(C)}.$$

It is easily seen that $P(A|C)$ is a probability measure as a function of A. The frequency interpretation of probabilities requires that the left-hand side be the ratio of the times that the outcome is both A and C to the total times that it is in C. The right-hand side expressed in terms of frequency ratios clearly reduces to this. In the notation of random variables we could write

(4.7) $$P(A \cap C) = P(C)P(A|C)$$

in the form

$$\Pr\{X \in A, X \in C\} = \Pr\{X \in C\}\Pr\{X \in A | X \in C\}$$

Thus for the conditional probability $P(A|C)$ we can speak of the probability that the random variable X falls in A, given that it is in C.

We do not attempt to define conditional probability given C, when $P(C) = 0$. In fact, any definition whatsoever could be used and would not violate the distribution of probability as given by the measure $P(A)$. However, if we have a statistic $t(x)$ and if $C = \{x \mid t(x) = t\}$, then a definition is possible in relation to the statistic $t(x)$. Here again there is a degree of arbitrariness in that the conditional probability may remain undefined or arbitrarily defined for a set of values of $t(x) = t$ having probability zero.

To obtain the more general definition of conditional probability we need some results from measure theory. We define *absolute continuity* for measures:

$\nu(A)$ is *absolutely continuous with respect to $\mu(A)$ and written $\nu(A) << \mu(A)$ if, whenever $\mu(A) = 0$, also $\nu(A) = 0$.*

Consider a few simple examples of absolute continuity; the proofs are given as problems in Section 8. First, the binomial distribution has a probability measure absolutely continuous with respect to the Poisson but not with respect to the normal. Second, the normal distribution measure is absolutely continuous with respect to Lebesgue measure. Third, all the distributions on R^1 given by a simple probability density function,

$$P(A) = \int_A f(x)\,d(x),$$

are absolutely continuous with respect to Lesbesgue measure.

The Radon–Nikodym theorem is a powerful theorem concerned with the property of absolute continuity. We state the theorem here but do not attempt a proof. For the proof and further reading, see Halmos [2].

THEOREM 4.1. (THE RADON–NIKODYM THEOREM). A necessary and sufficient condition that a measure $\nu(A)$ be absolutely continuous with respect to a measure $\mu(A)$ is that there exist a non-negative function $g(x)$ such that

$$(4.8) \qquad \nu(A) = \int_A g(x)\, d\mu(x)$$

for every $A \in \mathscr{A}$. $g(x)$ is determined uniquely except on a set having μ measure zero.

The last sentence in the theorem has the following interpretation. If there are two functions $g_1(x)$ and $g_2(x)$ satisfying (4.8), then those functions will be different at most on a set having μ measure zero.

Consider an example of the above theorem. Let $P(A)$ be the measure of the Poisson distribution with parameter m. Then for a non-negative integer x,

$$P(x) = \frac{m^x}{x!}\, e^{-m}$$

Let $N(A)$ be the number of non-negative integers in the set A; it is easily seen that $N(A)$ is a measure. Now, if the set A has $N(A) = 0$, then there are no non-negative integers in it, and therefore the Poisson measure $P(A) = 0$. By the Radon–Nikodym theorem there must exist a function $g(x)$ satisfying

$$P(A) = \int_A g(x)\, dN(x),$$

and by taking A to be a typical non-negative integer it is seen that

$$P(A) = \int_A \frac{m^x}{x!}\, e^{-m}\, dN(x).$$

We now extend the definition of conditional probability. Let $t(x)$ be a statistic from $\mathscr{X}(\mathscr{A})$ to $\mathscr{T}(\mathscr{B})$. See Fig. 1. Also let $P_X(A)$ be a measure over $\mathscr{X}$, and let $P_T(A)$ be the measure over $\mathscr{T}$ induced by the statistic $t(x)$. As an example of conditional probability by our definition above, we have

$$P_X\{A^0 \cap t^{-1}(B)\} = P_X\{A^0 \,|\, t^{-1}(B)\}\, P_X\{t^{-1}(B)\},$$

or equivalently

$$(4.9) \qquad P_X\{A^0 \cap t^{-1}(B)\} = P_X\{A^0 \,|\, t^{-1}(B)\}\, P_T\{B\}.$$

In words the equation says that the probability that $X \in A^0$ and $t(X) \in B$ is equal to the probability that $t(X) \in B$ times the conditional probability that $X \in A^0$, given $t(X) \in B$. In attempting to obtain $P_X\{A^0 | t^{-1}(B)\}$ when B reduces to a point, we might look for a function of t, $P_X\{A^0 | t(x) = t\}$, which gives the right answers in the sense that it satisfies the relation

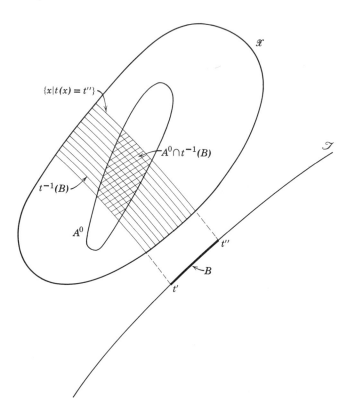

Figure 1. The probability mapping for conditional probability.

$$(4.10) \qquad P_X\{A^0 \cap t^{-1}(B)\} = \int_B P\{A^0 | t(x) = t\} \, dP_T(t)$$

for all $B \in \mathcal{B}$. The Radon–Nikodym theorem will give us the function $P\{A^0 | t(x) = t\}$.

We obtain a new measure on $\mathcal{X}$, say $\nu(A)$, by deleting all the probability that is not contained in A^0:

$$\nu(A) = \int_A \phi_{A^0}(x) \, dP_X(x)$$

$$= P_X(A \cap A^0),$$

where $\phi_A(x)$ is a characteristic function defined in (4.2). Now by the Radon–Nikodym theorem, $v \ll P_X$; in fact, this relation is obvious since actually $v(A) \leqslant P_X(A)$ for all A. The measures on $\mathcal{T}$ induced from $v(A)$ and $P_X(A)$ are, respectively,

$$v_T(B) = v(t^{-1}(B)),$$
$$P_T(B) = P_X(t^{-1}(B)).$$

Now these induced measures also satisfy the same relation of absolute continuity, $v_T \ll P_T$. This is easily seen since $v(A) \leqslant P(A)$ implies $v_T(B) \leqslant P_T(B)$, and hence $v_T \ll P_T$.

Now, applying the Radon–Nikodym theorem to $v_T \ll P_T$, we have the existence of a function of t, say $P(A^0 | t)$, such that

$$(4.11) \qquad v_T(B) = \int_B P(A^0 | t) \, dP_T(t).$$

Since v_T depends on A^0, in general the integrand furnished by the Radon–Nikodym theorem will also depend on A^0, and we have indicated this. Noting that

$$v_T(B) = v(t^{-1}(B))$$
$$= P_X\{A^0 \cap t^{-1}(B)\},$$

we can rewrite (4.11) as

$$(4.12) \qquad P_X\{A^0 \cap t^{-1}(B)\} = \int_B P(A^0 | t) \, dP_T(t)$$

where $P(A^0 | t)$ is uniquely determined except at most on a set having P_T measure zero. This is the equation (4.10) we set out to obtain.

In exactly the same manner it is possible to define the conditional expectation of a real function $h(x)$ with respect to a statistic $t(x)$ and a random variable X over $\mathcal{X}$. If $h(x) \geq 0$, the Radon–Nikodym theorem gives the existence of $E\{h(X) | t\}$ to satisfy

$$(4.13) \qquad \int_{t^{-1}(B)} h(x) \, dP_X(x) = \int_B E\{h(X) | t\} \, dP_T(t)$$

for all $B \in \mathcal{B}$. $E\{h(x) | t\}$ is uniquely determined except on a set of values of t having P_T measure zero. If $h(x)$ is not necessarily positive, it can be written

$$h(x) = h^+(x) - h^-(x),$$

where $h^+(x) \geq 0$, $h^-(x) \geq 0$, and

$$\begin{aligned} h^+(x) &= h(x) && \text{if } h(x) \geq 0 \\ &= 0 && \text{otherwise,} \\ h^-(x) &= -h(x) && \text{if } h(x) \leq 0 \\ &= 0 && \text{otherwise.} \end{aligned}$$

Then (4.13) can be shown to hold in general by applying it to the two components of $h(x)$. If B is taken equal to $\mathscr{T}$, (4.13) can be written

$$E_X\{h(X)\} = E_T\big\{E\{h(X)\,|\,T\}\big\}.$$

It is perhaps natural to hope that $P(A\,|\,t)$ as a function of A be a measure on $\mathscr{X}(\mathscr{A})$. However, in general this is not true. Doob [4] has shown that, if $\mathscr{X}$ is Euclidean, then it is possible to determine $P(A\,|\,t)$ so that it is a probability measure for all t except perhaps for t values having probability zero. It is straightforward to prove that $P(A\,|\,t)$ has some properties of a measure:

(i) $P(\mathscr{X}\,|\,t) = 1$, except perhaps for t in a set having P_T measure zero.

(ii) $0 \le P(A\,|\,t) \le 1$, except perhaps for t in a set having P_T measure zero.

(iii)   If $A_1, A_2, \cdots$ is a sequence of disjoint sets, then $\displaystyle\sum_{i=1}^{\infty} P(A_i\,|\,t) = P\left(\bigcup_{i=1}^{\infty} A_i\,\Big|\,t\right)$, except perhaps for t in a set having P_T measure zero.

The difficulty is that we would want these conditions for *all* $A, A_1, A_2, \cdots$ to hold *simultaneously*, except for t values in a set of measure zero.

Conditional expectation can also be defined directly from a determination of conditioned probability. Consider the expectation of $h(x)$ relative to the statistic $t(x)$ and the probability measure $\mu(A)$ over $\mathscr{X}$. Let

$$(4.14) \qquad s_\lambda(t) = \sum_{k=-\infty}^{+\infty} \lambda k\, P_X[\{x\,|\,\lambda k < h(x) \le \lambda(k+1)\}\,|\,t].$$

If $E\{h(X)\}$ exists, it can be shown the sum converges, that $s_\lambda(t)$ approaches a limit as $\lambda \to 0$, and that this limit is a determination of $E\{h(X)\,|\,t\}$ as given by the defining equation (4.13). For the details, see Kolmogorov [5].

We shall frequently need to qualify a condition with a phrase such as "$\cdots$ except perhaps for t in a set having P_T measure zero." For convenience we abbreviate this to "$\cdots$ almost everywhere (P_T)" and even further abbreviate to "$\cdots$ a.e. (P_T)."

5. SUFFICIENT STATISTICS

We have been considering only a single probability measure over a space $\mathscr{X}(\mathscr{A})$. However, in applications we shall seldom know the probability measure applicable to an experiment, but we may be able to say that it is one of a class of probability measures. In fact, we can always do this by choosing a sufficiently large class.

Let $\{P_\theta(A)\,|\,\theta \in \Omega\}$ be a class of probability measures over $\mathscr{X}(\mathscr{A})$. θ is called the *parameter* of the class, and it indexes the probability measures. The range of θ is Ω and is called the *parameter space*. In our statistical model the class $\{P_\theta | \theta \in \Omega\}$ will consist of all the probability measures which the statistician on the basis of previously obtained information considers to be possible representations of the random experiment he is investigating.

In general, the statistician's purpose is to make some sort of statement or decision about the probability measure applicable to his experiment: that is, to make a decision about the value of the parameter θ. After choosing the class $\{P_\theta | \theta \in \Omega\}$, the only information he has to guide his decision about θ is the result of the experiment, the random variable X. However, in many cases the outcome X is a complicated set of numbers, and, as mentioned in Section 1 when statistic was introduced, a simplification is desirable. If at all feasible he should choose for his condensation a statistic which loses as little as possible of the information contained in the outcome and relevant to the parameter θ. It is this desire which prompts the definition of *sufficient statistic*.

R. A. Fisher introduced the concept of a sufficient statistic as one "containing all the relevant information" in an experiment. To illustrate this idea, consider the class of probability measures over R^n obtained from $(X_1, \cdots, X_n)$ where the X_i are independent and each is normally distributed with mean ξ and variance 1, ξ taking any value from $-\infty$ to $+\infty$. Here $\theta = \xi$ and $\Omega = R^1$. It can be easily shown, and will be later in this section, that the conditional distribution of $(x_1 - \bar{x}, x_2 - \bar{x}, \cdots, x_n - \bar{x})$, given the sample mean $\bar{x}$, is independent of the parameter ξ. Consequently, to examine the values of $x_1 - \bar{x}, \cdots, x_n - \bar{x}$, after examining the value of $\bar{x}$, is equivalent to taking an outcome from a given fixed distribution having nothing to do with ξ. It is in this sense then that we say the statistic $y = \bar{x}$ contains "all the relevant information."

Fisher gave a more formal definition of a sufficient statistic $y = t(x)$: For any other statistic $t'(x)$, the conditional distribution of $t'(x)$, given $t(x)$, is independent of θ. Halmos and Savage [6] give a definition of sufficient statistic to fit the framework of our probability model. In our notation, it is:

A statistic $y = t(x)$ is a sufficient statistic for the family of probability measures $\{P_\theta | \theta \in \Omega\}$ over $\mathscr{X}(\mathscr{A})$ if there exists a function $P(A|t)$ such that

$$(5.1) \qquad P_\theta(A \cap t^{-1}(B)) = \int_B P(A|t)\, dP_\theta^T(t)$$

for all $A \in \mathscr{A}$, $B \in \mathscr{B}$; that is, if there exists a determination of the conditional distribution, given $t(x)$, which is independent of θ. P_θ^T is the measure for $t(x)$ induced from the measure P_θ over $\mathscr{X}$.

A sufficient statistic is important in problems both of estimation and of hypothesis testing. In the next chapter we shall have a general result and results particular to the two fields; estimation and hypothesis testing. However, the description of Fisher's approach should indicate that we have justification for ignoring the outcome in an experiment if a sufficient statistic is available. Of course the outcome itself forms a sufficient statistic, but we shall usually be interested in a statistic that makes a reduction in the problem.

We give now two examples of sufficient statistics.

EXAMPLE 5.1. Consider the class of probability measures over R^n mentioned earlier in this section. $\mathbf{X} = (X_1, \cdots, X_n)$, where the X_i are independent, each has the normal distribution with mean ξ and variance 1, and $\xi \in]-\infty, +\infty[$. We wish to show that $\bar{x} = n^{-1} \sum_{i=1}^{n} x_i$ is a sufficient statistic or equivalently that $t(x) = n^{1/2}\bar{x}$ is sufficient.

For convenience we introduce a new random variable $\mathbf{Y} = (Y_1, \cdots, Y_n)$ by means of the transformation† $\mathbf{y}' = M\mathbf{x}'$ where M is an orthogonal $n \times n$ matrix. Giving M the first row $(n^{-1/2}, \cdots, n^{-1/2})$, we find that $y_1 = n^{1/2}\bar{x} = t(\mathbf{x})$. The $\mathbf{X}$ distribution over R^n is

$$(5.2) \qquad P_\xi^\mathbf{X}(A) = c^n \int_A \exp\left[-\frac{1}{2} \sum_1^n (x_i - \xi)^2 \right] \prod_{i=1}^n dx_i,$$

where $c = (2\pi)^{-1/2}$. The transformation from $\mathbf{x}$ to $\mathbf{y}$ has Jacobian 1, and

$$\sum_{i=1}^n (x_i - \xi)^2 = (y_1 - n^{1/2}\xi)^2 + \sum_{i=2}^n y_i^2;$$

therefore

$$(5.3) \quad P_\xi^\mathbf{Y}(A^*) = c^n \int_{A^*} \exp\left[-\frac{1}{2}(y_1 - n^{1/2}\xi)^2 - \frac{1}{2} \sum_{i=2}^n y_i^2 \right] \prod_{i=1}^n dy_i$$

To exhibit $y_1 = t(\mathbf{x})$ as a sufficient statistic, we need to show that the probability measure $P_\xi^\mathbf{X}$ can be used in formula (5.1). We have the relation

$$P_\xi^\mathbf{X}(A \cap t^{-1}(B)) = P_\xi^\mathbf{Y}(MA \cap Mt^{-1}(B)),$$

where MA for example is the set obtained by applying the transformation M to the points in A. $t^{-1}(B)$ is the set of points having $t(x)$ in B; therefore,

† $\mathbf{y} = (y_1, \cdots, y_n)$ is a row vector and the matrix transpose $\mathbf{y}'$ is a column vector. The transformation then is given by the ordinary matrix multiplication $M\mathbf{x}'$.

since $y_1 = t(x)$, $Mt^{-1}(B)$ is the set of points having the first coordinate y_1 in B, and we can write

$$Mt^{-1}(B) = B \times R^{n-1},$$

Then we have

(5.4) $P_\xi^X(A \cap t^{-1}(B))$

$$= P_\xi^Y(MA \cap B \times R^{n-1})$$

$$= c^n \int_B \left[\int_{R^{n-1}} \phi_{MA}(y_1, \cdots, y_n) \exp\left(-\frac{1}{2} \sum_2^n y_i^2 \right) \prod_2^n dy_i^2 \right]$$

$$\exp\left[-\frac{1}{2}(y_1 - n^{1/2}\xi)^2 \right] dy_1$$

$$= c \int_B P(MA|y_1) \exp\left[-\frac{1}{2}(y_1 - n^{1/2}\xi)^2 \right] dy_1.$$

$P(MA|y_1)$, defined by the bracket in the previous expression, is the probability measure of MA for fixed y_1. It is seen that formula (5.4) is in the form (5.1) and hence that $t(\mathbf{x}) = n^{1/2}\bar{x}$ is a sufficient statistic.

EXAMPLE 5.2. Let X_1, X_2 be independent, and let $X_i = 1, 0$ with probability, respectively, p, $q = 1 - p$. Consider the probability measures of (X_1, X_2) over R^2 for $p \in]0, 1[$. By using the first and simpler definition of conditional probability it is quite easy to show that $t(\mathbf{x}) = x_1 + x_2$ is a sufficient statistic.

It is seen directly from the definition of a sufficient statistic that the following theorem is obvious.

THEOREM 5.1. If $t(x)$ is a sufficient statistic for $\{P_\theta | \theta \in \Omega\}$, then $t(x)$ is sufficient for $\{P_\theta | \theta \in \omega\}$ where ω is a subset of Ω.

In most statistical problems the class of probability measures can be represented by means of a class of density functions. Such is the case if the class of measures is dominated.

A class of measures $\{P_\theta | \theta \in \Omega\}$ is dominated if there exists a measure μ such that $P_\theta \ll \mu$ for all $\theta \in \Omega$.

In other words all the measures in P_θ are absolutely continuous with respect to μ. Applying the Radon–Nikodym theorem, we have the existence of a function $p_\theta(x)$ such that

$$P_\theta(A) = \int_A p_\theta(x) \, d\mu(x)$$

for all $A \in \mathscr{A}$, $\theta \in \Omega$. The function $p_\theta(x)$ is called a *probability density function* with respect to μ and is uniquely determined except on a set having

μ measure zero.   Thus a dominated set of probability measures $\{P_\theta | \theta \in \Omega\}$ can equivalently be given by a class of probability densities $\{p_\theta(x) | \theta \in \Omega\}$ with respect to a measure μ.   The usual discrete and continuous distributions in R^n are of this type.

In 1935 Neyman formalized a criterion for a sufficient statistic when the distributions are given by probability density functions.   Under restrictive conditions it was that the density function should factor into two parts, one depending only on x and the other only on θ and the statistic.   In 1949 Halmos and Savage [6] generalized this criterion in the following theorem.

THEOREM 5.2.   (HALMOS and SAVAGE).   A necessary and sufficient condition that $t(x)$ be a sufficient statistic for the class of densities $\{p_\theta^{(x)}\}$ re the measure μ is that there exist measurable functions $h(x)$, $g_\theta(t)$ such that

(5.5) $$p_\theta(x) = h(x)\, g_\theta(t(x))$$

almost everywhere (μ) where $h(x) \geq 0$ and is integrable with respect to μ.

Proof.   See Halmos and Savage [6].   This condition for a sufficient statistic we shall call the *Neyman criterion.*

As an illustration consider the example involving normal distributions mentioned earlier in the section.   For $\mathbf{X} = (X_1, \cdots, X_n)$, where the X_i are independent and each is normal with mean ξ and variance 1, we have the density function

$$p_\xi(x) = c^n \exp\left[-\frac{1}{2}\sum_{i=1}^n (x_i - \xi)^2\right]$$

$$= c^n \exp\left[-\frac{1}{2}\sum_{i=1}^n (x_i - \bar{x})^2\right] \exp\left[-\frac{1}{2}n(\bar{x} - \xi)^2\right].$$

Letting

$$h(x) = \exp -\frac{1}{2}\sum_{i=1}^n (x_i - \bar{x})^2,$$

$$g_\theta(x) = c^n \exp\left[-\frac{1}{2}n(\bar{x} - \xi)^2\right],$$

we see that $p_\xi(x)$ factors as required in the theorem. $h(x)$ is positive but unfortunately is not integrable as required.   However, if we slightly alter our definitions,

$$h'(x) = \exp\left[-\frac{1}{2}\sum_{i=1}^n (x_1 - \bar{x})^2\right] \exp\left[-\frac{1}{2}n\bar{x}^2\right],$$

$$g'_\theta(x) = c^n \exp\left[-\frac{1}{2}n(\bar{x} - \xi)^2\right] \exp\left[+\frac{1}{2}n\bar{x}^2\right],$$

it is seen that the conditions of the theorem are fulfilled.   Hence $\bar{x}$ is a sufficient statistic.

▶ Other conditions for a sufficient statistic with respect to densities have been given by Koopman [7]. For these we first describe a homogeneous set of probability measures. $\{P_\theta \mid \theta \in \Omega\}$ *is a homogeneous set of measures if, for every* $\theta, \theta' \in \Omega, P_\theta \ll P_{\theta'}$. For a homogeneous set we have $P_\theta \ll P_{\theta'}$ and $P_{\theta'} \ll P_\theta$. We designate the combination of these statements by $P_\theta \equiv P_{\theta'}$ and say the measures are equivalent. If we interpret the condition of homogeneity for the corresponding class of densities, we find that the region S_θ of positive density,

$$S_\theta = \{x \mid p_\theta(x) > 0\},$$

must be independent of θ a.e. (μ); that is, $\mu(S_\theta - S_{\theta'}) = 0$ for all $\theta, \theta' \in \Omega$.

Koopman [7] proves that, if a homogeneous set of densities over R^n was obtained from n independent and identically distributed random variables and satisfied certain regularity conditions, then the density function for the component random variable must factor into terms of an exponential form:

$$(5.6) \qquad p_\theta(x) = c(\theta) \exp\left[\sum_{s=1}^{p} a_s(\theta)\, h_s(x) + r(x) \right].$$

If the region of positive density S_θ is not independent of θ, it is possible in some cases to obtain a sufficient statistic as a combination of a statistic designed to detect the variation of S_θ and of a sufficient statistic for a related class of densities for which the region of positive probability is independent of θ. The method is described in [8] where a constructive procedure is given for obtaining a sufficient statistic when all the dependence on θ is through the set S_θ: that is, if the density is of the form

$$p_\theta(x) = c(\theta)\phi_{S_\theta}(x)\, g(x)$$

where $\phi_{S_\theta}(x)$ is the characteristic function of the set S_θ, and $g(x)$ is independent of θ. Subject to some regularity conditions, the sufficient statistic is given by

$$t(x) = \bigcap_{x \in S_\theta} S_\theta,$$

and its values are subsets of $\mathscr{X}$.

It often happens that two independent random variables are considered simultaneously. If each random variable has a class of probability measures and a sufficient statistic, then the following theorem gives a sufficient statistic for the combined experiment.

THEOREM 5.3.   If X_i has distributions $\{P_{\theta_i}^{X_i} \mid \theta_i \in \Omega_i\}$ over $\mathscr{X}_i(\mathscr{A}_i)$ $(i = 1, 2)$ and if $t_i(x_i)$ is sufficient for $\theta_i \in \Omega_i$, then $(t_1(x_1), t_2(x_2))$ is sufficient for the class of product measures given by $(\theta_1, \theta_2) \in \Omega_1 \times \Omega_2$ (under the assumption that the conditional probabilities are measures).

Proof. From the assumption that $t_1(x_1)$, $t_2(x_2)$ are sufficient we have, for all A_1, A_2, B_1, B_2,

$$P_{\theta_1}^{X_1}(A_1 \cap t_1^{-1}(B_1)) = \int_{B_1} P_1(A_1 \mid t_1) \, dP_{\theta_1}^{T_1}(t_1)$$

$$P_{\theta_2}^{X_2}(A_2 \cap t_2^{-1}(B_2)) = \int_{B_2} P_2(A_2 \mid t_2) \, d_{\theta_2}^{T_2}P(t_2).$$

By assumption $P_1(A_1|t_1)$, $P_2(A_2|t_2)$ are measures over $\mathcal{X}_1$, $\mathcal{X}_2$; let $P(A|(t_1, t_2))$ be the product measure over $\mathcal{X}_1 \times \mathcal{X}_2$. Then, if $\mathcal{X} = \mathcal{X}_1 \times \mathcal{X}_2$, $t = (t_1, t_2)$, $\theta = (\theta_1, \theta_2)$, $X = (X_1, X_2)$, we have

(5.7) $$P_\theta^X(A \cap t^{-1}(B)) = \int_B P(A|t) \, dP_\theta^T(t)$$

for all $A = A_1 \times A_2$ and $B = B_1 \times B_2$. But both sides of the above equation define, by means of A, a product measure on $\mathcal{X}$. The measures are identical for all product sets $A = A_1 \times A_2$; therefore they agree for any A in the product space σ-algebra. This implies that (5.7) holds for all $A \in (\mathcal{A}_1, \mathcal{A}_2)$ and for all $B = B_1 \times B_2$. A similar argument gives equality for all $B \in (\mathcal{B}_1, \mathcal{B}_2)$ and establishes that (t_1, t_2) is sufficient for $(\theta_1, \theta_2) \in \Omega_1 \times \Omega_2$.

EXAMPLE 5.3. Let $\mathbf{X} = (X_1, \cdots, X_n)$ where the X_i are independent and each is normally distributed with mean ξ and variance σ^2. Similarly let $\mathbf{Y} = (Y_1, \cdots, Y_m)$ where the Y_i are independent and each is normally distributed with mean η and variance τ^2. By Problem 33 $(\bar{x}, (n-1)^{-1} \Sigma(x_i - \bar{x})^2)$ is a sufficient statistic for (ξ, σ^2) and $(\bar{y}, (m-1)^{-1} \Sigma(y_i - \bar{y})^2)$ is a sufficient statistic for (η, τ^2). Then by the above theorem $[\bar{x}, \bar{y}, (n-1)^{-1} \Sigma(x_i - \bar{x})^2, (m-1)^{-1} \Sigma(y_i - \bar{y})^2]$ is a sufficient statistic for the combined experiment with ξ, $\eta \in]-\infty, +\infty[$ and σ^2, $\tau^2 \in]0, \infty[$.

In problems of estimation and hypothesis testing it often happens that one parameter in particular is being considered while other "nuisance" parameters are present. For some of these problems a generalized definition of sufficiency can be applied. If X has the measures $\{P_{\theta,\eta}^X \mid (\theta, \eta) \in \Theta \times H\}$ over $\mathcal{X}(\mathcal{A})$, then we define: *$t(x)$ is a sufficient statistic (θ) for the family of measures $\{P_{\theta,\eta}^X \mid (\theta, \eta) \in \Theta \times H\}$ if there exists a function $P_\eta(A \mid t)$ such that*

$$P_{\theta,\eta}^X(A \cap t^{-1}(B)) = \int_B P_\eta(A \mid t) \, dP_\theta^T(t)$$

for all $A \in \mathcal{A}$, $B \in \mathcal{B}$. The induced measure of $t(x)$, $P_\theta^T(B)$ is independent of η. The meaning of this definition is straightforward. The statistic $t(x)$ has a distribution depending only on θ, the parameter of interest, while the conditional distribution, given $t(x)$, depends only on the nuisance parameter η. ◀

6. COMPLETENESS

We have just investigated a property that a statistic may have relative to a class of probability measures. That property was sufficiency. We now consider another such property: *completeness*. Although we shall use the term completeness for a statistic, actually it is a property of a class of measures and when applied to a statistic will be in reference to the induced measures of the statistic.

A family of measures $\{P_\theta^T | \theta \in \Omega\}$ *is complete if the fulfillment of*

$$(6.1) \qquad E_\theta\{h(T)\} = \int h(t) \, dP_\theta^T(t) = 0$$

for all $\theta \in \Omega$ *and any real statistic* $h(t)$ *implies that* $h(t) = 0$ *almost everywhere with respect to each of the measures* P_θ^T.

In general, the expectation of a statistic will depend on the measure used in taking the expectation; that is,

$$(6.2) \qquad E_\theta\{h(T)\} = g(\theta),$$

a function of θ. We say for this equation that $h(t)$ is an *unbiased estimate* of $g(\theta)$, but leave until the next chapter a justification for the term unbiased estimate. Then it is possible to interpret the completeness of the measures of a random variable by saying that there does not exist an unbiased estimate $h(t)$ of zero other than the trivial unbiased estimate which is zero almost everywhere.

We shall say a *statistic* $t(x)$ *is complete relative to the measures* $\{P_\theta^X | \theta \in \Omega\}$ *over* $\mathscr{X}(\mathscr{A})$ *if the induced class of measures* $\{P_\theta^T | \theta \in \Omega\}$ *over* $\mathscr{T} = t(\mathscr{X})$ *is complete.*

EXAMPLE 6.1. Consider the random variable $\mathbf{X} = (X_1, \cdots, X_n)$ where the X_i are independent and each has the normal distribution with mean μ and variance 1, and let the class of measures over R^n be those obtained from all values of μ in $]-\infty, +\infty[$. We demonstrate that the statistic $\bar{x} = n^{-1} \sum_{i=1}^{n} x_i$ is complete. $\bar{x}$ takes its values in R^1 and has an induced distribution which is normal with mean μ and variance $1/n$. Thus we wish to show that the class of densities

$$\left\{ \left(\frac{n}{2\pi}\right)^{1/2} \exp\left[-\frac{n}{2}(y - \mu)^2\right] \,\middle|\, \mu \in]-\infty, +\infty[\right\}$$

is complete. To do this we consider a statistic which has expectation zero for all μ.

$$\int_{-\infty}^{\infty} h(y) \left(\frac{n}{2\pi}\right)^{1/2} \exp\left[-\frac{n}{2}(y-\mu)^2\right] dy = 0,$$

or, by removing the nonzero constant factor,

$$\int_{-\infty}^{\infty} h(y) \exp\left[-\frac{n}{2}y^2\right] \exp\left[ny\mu\right] dy = 0.$$

By letting $n\mu = v$, we have

$$\int_{-\infty}^{\infty} h(y) \exp\left[-\frac{n}{2}y^2\right] \exp\left[vy\right] dy = 0,$$

and this equation states that the LaPlace transform of the function

$$h(y) \exp\left(-\frac{n}{2}y^2\right)$$

is zero identically. But the function 0 also has the transform which is zero identically. Hence, by the uniqueness property of LaPlace transforms, it follows that

$$h(y) \exp\left(-\frac{n}{2}y^2\right) = 0,$$

and hence $h(y) = 0$, almost everywhere (Lebesgue). We have proved that our statistic with zero expectation is zero almost everywhere. This establishes the completeness of the class of densities for $\bar{x}$, and we say that $\bar{x}$ is a complete statistic.

In the theory of hypothesis testing a modification of the above definition is useful.

A class of measures $\{P_\theta^T | \theta \in \Omega\}$ *is boundedly complete if*

$$E_\theta\{h(T)\} = \int_{\mathcal{T}} h(t) \, dP_\theta^T(t) = 0$$

for all $\theta \in \Omega$, *and any real statistic* $h(t)$ *satisfying*

$$|h(t)| < M$$

implies that $h(t) = 0$ *almost everywhere with respect to each measure* P_θ^T.
In words the condition is the nonexistence of a bounded real statistic having zero expectation other than the trivial statistic which is zero almost everywhere.

We now have a simple theorem concerning completeness and bounded completeness.

THEOREM 6.1.   If a class of measures is complete, then it is boundedly complete.

Proof.   Given completeness, (6.1) is sufficient to prove $h(t) = 0$ almost everywhere (P_θ^T).   Then certainly (6.1) plus a condition of boundedness will prove the same.

However, the converse to this Lemma is not necessarily true.   This is illustrated by the following example given by Girshick, Mosteller and Savage [9].

EXAMPLE 6.2.   Let T be a random variable standing for the measure which assigns probability $q, p^2, p^2q, \cdots, p^2q^i, \cdots$ respectively to the integers $0, 1, 2, \cdots, i + 1, \cdots$, where $q = 1 - p$, and consider the class of measures obtained by letting p range over $]0, 1[$.   We show that this class is boundedly complete but not complete.

A statistic with zero expectation for all the measures in the class will satisfy

$$f(0)q + f(1)p^2 + f(2)p^2q + \cdots = 0$$

for all $p \in]0, 1[$.   Now by rearrangement we obtain

$$f(1) + f(2)q + f(3)q^2 \cdots$$
$$= -f(0)qp^{-2}$$
$$= -f(0)q(1 - q)^{-2}$$
$$= -f(0)(q + 2q^2 + 3q^3 + \cdots).$$

Thus we have two power series which are identical for $q \in]0, 1[$.   It follows then that the corresponding coefficients must be equal.

$$f(1) = 0,$$
$$f(2) = -f(0),$$
$$f(i) = -(i - 1)f(0).$$

This determines the form of any unbiased estimate of zero.   If $f(0) = 0$, then $f(t) = 0$ at all non-negative integers; otherwise the function $f(t)$ is unbounded.   Thus there are nondegenerate unbiased estimates of zero, but there are none that are bounded.   We conclude that the class of measures is boundedly complete but not complete.

In the last section we found that, if a statistic was sufficient for a class of measures, then it was sufficient for any subclass of those measures.   The property of completeness works somewhat in the opposite direction: if we have completeness for a class of measures we can sometimes infer completeness for a larger class.

THEOREM 6.2. The completeness of $\{P_\theta^T \mid \theta \in \Omega\}$ implies the completeness of $\{P_\theta^T \mid \theta \in \mathscr{C}\}$ if Ω is a subset of $\mathscr{C}$ and if none of the added measures assign positive probability to sets having zero probability for each measure of Ω. This second condition implies that almost everywhere $\{P_\theta^T \mid \theta \in \Omega\}$ is equivalent to almost everywhere $\{P_\theta^T \mid \theta \in \mathscr{C}\}$.

Proof. We first prove the last statement in the theorem. The condition obviously implies that any set, having zero measure for each P_θ^T, $\theta \in \Omega$, also has zero measure for each P_θ^T, $\theta \in \Omega$; the converse is trivial. But this is just another way of stating the equivalence in the last sentence of the theorem.

By examining the definition of completeness we see that it is necessary to show that a function $h(t)$ which satisfies certain conditions is zero almost everywhere with respect to a class of distributions. Introducing more distributions imposes more conditions. The original conditions (Ω) were sufficient to prove (*ht*) zero almost everywhere $\{P_\theta^T \mid \theta \in \Omega\}$. But, since almost everywhere $\{P_\theta^T \mid \theta \in \Omega\}$ is equivalent to almost everywhere $\{P_\theta^T \mid \theta \in \mathscr{C}\}$, we have completeness for the larger class, and hence the theorem is proved.

▶ Completeness of a class of product measures over a product space can sometimes be obtained from completeness over the component spaces. For this we need a modification of the concept of completeness:

The measures $\{P_\eta^T \mid \eta \in H\}$ are strongly complete with respect to a measure m on H if, for any subset H* of H for which $m(H - H^*) = 0$, the condition

(6.3) $$E_\eta\{h(T)\} = 0$$

for all $\eta \in H^*$, and any real statistic $h(t)$ implies that $h(t) = 0$ almost everywhere $\{P_\eta^T \mid \eta \in H\}$.

This is a stronger property than completeness; it requires that any unbiased estimate of zero for a subclass of the measures is necessarily zero almost everywhere with respect to the full class, provided the measures omitted form a set having *m* measure zero.

THEOREM 6.3. If the random variable T is complete re $\{P_\theta^T \mid \theta \in \Omega\}$ over $\mathscr{T}(\mathscr{B})$, and the random variable T' is strongly complete re $\{P_\eta^{T'} \mid \eta \in H\}$ over $\mathscr{T}'(\mathscr{B}')$, then (T, T') is complete re the class of product measures $\{P_\theta^T \times P_\eta^{T'} \mid (\theta, \eta) \in \Omega \times H\}$ over $\mathscr{T} \times \mathscr{T}'$.

Proof. It is necessary to prove that the condition

(6.4) $$\int_{\mathscr{T} \times \mathscr{T}} h(t, t')\, dP_\theta^T(t)\, dP_\eta^{T'}(t') = 0$$

for all (θ, η) implies that $h(t, t') = 0$ almost everywhere $\{P_\theta^T \times P_\eta^{T'} \mid (\theta, \eta) \in \Omega \times H\}$. Defining $g_\eta(t)$ by

$$g_\eta(t) = \int_{\mathscr{T}'} h(t, t')dP_\eta^{T'}(t')$$

and applying Fubini's theorem concerning the interchange of order of integration, we obtain

$$\int g_\eta(t) \, dP_\theta^T(t) = 0$$

for all $\theta \in \Omega$. But from the completeness of $\{P_\theta^T\}$ we have that for each η, $g_\eta(t) = 0$ almost everywhere $\{P_\theta^T\}$. Now, if we treat $g_\eta(t)$ as a function of η and t over the product space $H \times \mathscr{T}$, then it follows that, for almost all $\{P_\theta^T\}$ values of t, $g_\eta(t) = 0$ for almost all (m) values of η. But, using the form of $g_\eta(t)$ and the strong completeness of $\{P_\eta^{T'}\}$, we obtain that, for almost all $\{P_\theta^T\}$ values of t and for almost all $\{P_\eta^{T'}\}$ values of t', $h(t, t') = 0$. This is what we set out to prove. ◀

7. TWO EXAMPLES OF COMPLETENESS

In Problem 29 a statistic of particular interest in nonparametric theory is introduced. In that problem the sample space is R^n, and an outcome is a point $\mathbf{x} = (x_1, \cdots, x_n)$ in R^n. The statistic is $t(\mathbf{x}) = (x_{(1)}, \cdots, x_{(n)})$, where $x_{(1)}, \cdots, x_{(n)}$ are the numbers $x_1, \cdots, x_n$ arranged in order of magnitude from smallest to largest: $x_{(1)} \leq x_{(2)} \leq \cdots \leq x_{(n)}$. Thus the statistic gives the magnitude of the numbers $x_1, \cdots, x_n$ but not the order in which they occur. This statistic has been called in the literature the "order statistics"; we shall call it the *order statistic* in accordance with the general definition of statistic.

If we consider this statistic in terms of a partition of the sample space, we can let $t(\mathbf{x})$ stand for the set of points formed by $(x_1, \cdots, x_n)$ and all the points obtained by permuting the coordinates $x_1, \cdots, x_n$. It is easily seen that the set $t(\mathbf{x})$ contains at most $n!$ points. Alternatively the order statistic can be given as a mapping from the point $(x_1, \cdots, x_n)$ to the set whose elements are $x_1, \cdots, x_n$ that is, the set $\{x_1, \cdots, x_n\}$. It is easily seen that this is equivalent to the above definitions by examining what points are mapped into a given set $\{x_1, \cdots, x_n\}$: Obviously the points are those obtained by permuting the numbers $x_1, \cdots, x_n$ and using the resulting permutation as a set of coordinates for a point.

In some nonparametric problems the probability measures under a hypothesis are symmetric in the coordinates $x_1, \cdots, x_n$. Each permutation of $(x_1, \cdots, x_n)$ thus bears the same relation to the problem as any other permutation. Under an alternative hypothesis there may be asymmetry.

In such a situation the original ordering of the numbers $x_1, \cdots, x_n$ before it was lost in calculating the statistic $t(\mathbf{x})$ is all important. Here the statistic does not extract all the important information contained in the outcome, but nevertheless the statistic is useful because for some of these problems as we shall find in a later chapter, the statistician constructs his test in the subspace given $t(\mathbf{x})$ as if it were the sample space for the problem.

Let $X_1, \cdots, X_n$ be independent, and let each X_i have the same distribution function $F(x)$ on the real line. Problems 29 and 30 are to prove that the order statistic $t(\mathbf{x})$ forms a sufficient statistic for the class obtained by considering all absolutely continuous distributions $F(x)$. In a later chapter we shall show that $t(\mathbf{x})$ is sufficient for the class obtained by considering all distributions $F(x)$ on the real line. By Theorem 5.1 $t(\mathbf{x})$ is then sufficient corresponding to any class of distributions on the real line. The order statistic also has the property of completeness provided the class of distributions is not too small. In this section we prove the order statistic complete corresponding to the absolutely continuous distributions on R^1 and corresponding to the discrete distributions on R^1. For this we need a lemma on homogeneous polynomials.

LEMMA 7.1 (HALMOS). If $Q(p_1, \cdots, p_n)$ is a homogeneous polynomial of degree greater than 0 and satisfying $Q(p_1, \cdots, p_n) = 0$ whenever $0 \leq p_i \leq 1$ $(i = 1, \cdots, n)$ and $\sum_1^n p_i = 1$, then $Q(p_1, \cdots, p_n)$ is zero identically.

Proof. When $n = 1$, the lemma is trivial. The proof follows by induction, assuming that it holds for $n - 1$ and proving for n.

If we replace each p_i by cp_i, then from homogeneity a power of c will factor out leaving the original polynomial. Therefore the restrictions $0 \leq p_i \leq 1$ and $\Sigma p_i = 1$ may be replaced by the restrictions $0 \leq p_i$ $(i = 1, \cdots, n)$.

If we write $Q(p_1, \cdots, p_n)$ as a polynomial in p_n, we have for given $p_1, \cdots, p_{n-1}$ that it is identically zero for all $p_n \geq 0$. Hence the coefficients of the different powers of p_n must be zero. But, since these coefficients are homogeneous functions of $n - 1$ variables, the lemma follows by induction.

Let $F(x)$ define a distribution which assigns probability $p_1, p_2, \cdots, p_n$, respectively, to the disjoint intervals $I_1, I_2, \cdots, I_n$ on the real line $(\Sigma p_i = 1)$. Within each we assume that the distribution is uniform; that is, we assume that the distribution has a density function which is constant-valued within each interval. We call such a distribution *uniform within intervals*.

THEOREM 7.1. The order statistic $t(\mathbf{x})$ is complete for the class of distributions over R^n corresponding to each coordinate having the same distribution function $F(x)$ which is any distribution uniform within intervals.

Proof. We need to show that any real function $h(t(\mathbf{x}))$ of the order statistic satisfying

(7.1) $E\{h(t(\mathbf{X}))\} = 0$

for all the given distributions is necessary zero almost everywhere with respect to Lebesgue measure. First we find a convenient way of expressing a function of the order statistic $t(\mathbf{x})$. Obviously, any function of $t(\mathbf{x})$ is a symmetric function of the $x_1, \cdots, x_n$. Conversely, any symmetric function is a function of the x_i's which does not depend on the order in which they are inserted into the function and hence is a function of the set $\{x_1, \cdots, x_n\}$: that is, is a function of $t(\mathbf{x})$. We therefore consider any symmetric function $h(x_1, \cdots, x_n)$ having zero expectation, and prove that it is zero almost everywhere. We have

(7.2) $0 = E\{h(X_1, \cdots, X_n)\}$

$$= \sum_{i_1=1}^{n} \cdots \sum_{i_n=1}^{n} p_{i_1} \cdots p_{i_n} J(i_1, \cdots, i_n)$$

where

(7.3) $J(i_1, \cdots, i_n) = \dfrac{1}{1(i_1) \cdots 1(i_n)} \displaystyle\int_{I_{i_1}} \cdots \int_{I_{i_n}} h(x_1, \cdots, x_n) \prod_{1}^{n} dx_i$

and $1(1), \cdots, 1(n)$ are the lengths, respectively, of the intervals $I_1, \cdots, I_n$. Since $h(x_1, \cdots, x_n)$ is symmetric, so also is $J(i_1, \cdots, i_n)$. Therefore (7.2) can be written

(7.4) $0 = \Sigma p_1^{a_1} \cdots p_n^{a_n} c(a_1, \cdots, a_n)$

where the summation is over all non-negative integers $a_1, \cdots, a_n$ satisfying $\Sigma a_i = n$ and where $c(a_1, \cdots, a_n)$ is an integral multiple of the $J(i_1, \cdots, i_n)$ having a_1 of the i_α's equal 1, a_2 of the i_α's equal 2, and so on.

The expression on the right-hand side of (7.4) satisfies the conditions of Lemma 7.1. Therefore,

$$c(a_1, \cdots, a_n) = 0,$$

and hence

$$J(i_1, \cdots, i_n) = 0.$$

It follows then that

(7.5) $\displaystyle\int_{I_{i_1}} \cdots \int_{I_{i_n}} h(x_1, \cdots, x_n) \prod_{1}^{n} dx_i = 0$

for all $i_1, \cdots, i_n = 1, \cdots, n$ and all disjoint intervals $I_1, \cdots, I_n$.

The expression (7.5) determines a measure for all product sets $I_{i_1} \cdots I_{i_n}$, and this measure is zero.   An extension of the measure (7.5) to all Borel sets is given by

$$\int \cdots \int_A h(x_1, \cdots, x_n) \prod_1^n dx_i$$

as determined by the left-hand side and by

$$\int \cdots \int_A o \prod_1^n dx_i$$

as determined by the right-hand side.   But, since the two extensions of the measure must be identical, we have by the Radon–Nikodym Theorem 4.1 that $h(x_1, \cdots, x_n) = 0$ almost everywhere.   This completes the proof. Heretofore we have extended measures and used the Radon–Nikodym theorem only for positive measures.   Actually we need the theory for measures which may take positive and negative values.   For references on this account see Halmos [2].

COROLLARY.   The order statistic $t(\mathbf{x})$ is complete for the class of distributions over R^n corresponding to each coordinate having the same distribution function $F(x)$ which is any absolutely continuous distribution.

Proof.   By Theorem 6.2 we have completeness for any class of absolutely continuous distributions for $F(x)$, provided these contain the distributions uniform within intervals.

▶ The theorem we have just proved is a particular case of a theorem which we shall give below without proof.   The proof may be found in [10], together with a more general version covering the combination of a number of order statistics from separate experiments.

We first define some necessary concepts.   Let $\mathscr{X}(\mathscr{A})$ be a measurable space. *A class $\mathscr{T}$ of subsets of $\mathscr{X}$ is a ring if the conditions*
(1)   *If $A_1, A_2 \in \mathscr{T}$, then $A_1 \cup A_2 \in \mathscr{T}$;*
(2)   *If $A_1, A_2 \in \mathscr{T}$, then $A_1 - A_2 \in \mathscr{T}$;*
are satisfied.   If (1) is replaced by

(1)′   *If $A_1, A_2, \cdots \in \mathscr{T}$, then $\bigcup_{i=1}^{\infty} A_i \in \mathscr{T}$,*

then of course the ring is a σ ring.   We shall say that a ring $\mathscr{T}$ is a basis for the σ-algebra $\mathscr{A}$ and write $\mathscr{T} = \mathrm{Bas}\,(\mathscr{A})$ if the smallest σ ring containing $\mathscr{T}$ is the σ-algebra $\mathscr{A}$.   Thus $\mathscr{T}$ generates $\mathscr{A}$ under the operations of taking countable union and difference.

THEOREM 7.2.   If $\mu(A)$ is a given nonatomic measure over $\mathscr{X}(\mathscr{A})$, if P_B is the measure of a uniform distribution over the set B with respect to the measure

μ, and if $\{P_B^n \mid B \in \text{Bas}(\mathscr{A})\}$ is the class of power-product measures P_B^n over $\mathscr{X}^n$ for the sets B of a basis, then $t(x_1, \cdots, x_n) = \{x_1, \cdots, x_n\}$ is a complete statistic.

We interpret some of the statements in the theorem. P_B will have the form

$$P_B(A) = \int_A \phi_B(x)\, d\mu(x),$$

where

$$\phi_B(x) = c \qquad x \in B$$
$$= 0 \qquad x \in \bar{B}.$$

If P_B is a probability measure, $c = \mu(B)$. A measure $\mu(x)$ is nonatomic if there does not exist a set A having $\mu(A) \neq 0$ and such that, for any $C \subset A$, either $\mu(C) = 0$ or $\mu(C) = \mu(A)$. If such a set existed, it would be called an atom. The power-product measure P_B^n is the measure over $\mathscr{X}^n$ obtained from the measures P_B for each coordinate combined according to "independence" as given in Section 3.

The order statistic is also complete for sampling from suitable classes of discrete distributions. We have an analog of Theorem 7.1.

THEOREM 7.3. (HALMOS). The order statistic $t(\mathbf{x})$ is complete for the class of distributions over R^n corresponding to each coordinate having the same distribution function $F(x)$ which is any discrete distribution on the points of any set B.

Proof. There are no restrictions on the set B. Of course, any discrete distribution can have probability on at most a countable number of the points of B. The proof follows in the pattern of that for Theorem 7.1 with the intervals replaced by points. If it should happen that B contain fewer than n points, the argument remains valid since the only restriction in Lemma 7.1 is that the degree of the polynomial be greater than zero. ◀

8. PROBLEMS FOR SOLUTION

1. If $\mathscr{A}$ is a σ-algebra, show that, if $A_1, A_2, \cdots \in \mathscr{A}$, then $\bigcap_{i=1}^{n} A_i \in \mathscr{A}$.

2. If $\mathscr{A}$ is a σ-algebra, show that $\mathscr{X} \in \mathscr{A}$.

3. If $\mathscr{A}_\alpha$ is any group of σ-algebras on the space $\mathscr{X}$, show that $\bigcap_\alpha \mathscr{A}_\alpha$ is also a σ-algebra on $\mathscr{X}$. Of course, $\bigcap_\alpha \mathscr{A}_\alpha$ consists of sets A which belong to each of the σ-algebras $\mathscr{A}_\alpha$. Hence $\bigcap_\alpha \mathscr{A}_\alpha \subset \mathscr{A}_\alpha$ for each α, and we say that $\bigcap_\alpha \mathscr{A}_\alpha$ is a smaller σ-algebra than $\mathscr{A}_\alpha$.

4. On the product space $\mathscr{X}_1 \times \cdots \times \mathscr{X}_n$, is there necessarily any σ-algebra containing all the product sets $A_1 \times \cdots \times A_n$ where $A_i \in \mathscr{A}_i$? For this show that the class of all subsets of a space $\mathscr{X}$ is a σ-algebra.

5. Use Problems 3 and 4 to prove the existence of the *natural* σ-algebra on a product space $\mathscr{X}_1 \times \cdots \times \mathscr{X}_n$.

6. Prove that relations (2.3) and (2.4) hold for α ranging over *any* index set I.

7. Prove that $\mathscr{B}^*$ defined by (2.2) is a σ-algebra on $\mathscr{T}$.

8. Prove that $\mathscr{B}^*$ defined by (2.2) is the largest σ-algebra for which $t(x)$ is measurable.

9. Show that $\mathscr{B} \subset \mathscr{B}^*$ defined by (2.2) is a necessary and sufficient condition for $t(x)$ to be measurable from $\mathscr{X}(\mathscr{A})$ to $\mathscr{T}(\mathscr{B})$.

10. Define the partition of $\mathscr{X}$ induced by a statistic $t(x)$ from $\mathscr{X}(\mathscr{A})$ to $\mathscr{T}(\mathscr{B})$.

11. Prove that the four axioms for a probability measure hold exactly for the frequency ratio.

12. Prove that the function $F(x_1, \cdots, x_n)$ defined in Section 3 satisfies the three conditions, (i)*, (ii)*, (iii)*, for a distribution function.

13. In the notation of Section 3 prove that

$$P(]a_1, b_1] \times \cdots \times]a_n, b_n]) = \Delta_{x_1}(a_1, b_1) \cdots \Delta_{x_n}(a_n, b_n)F(x_1, \cdots, x_n).$$

14. Show that the induced "measure" $Q(B)$ defined by (3.3) satisfies the four condition for a probability measure.

15. For the definition of the integral show that the limit (3.1) exists.

16. If $f(x)$, $g(x)$ are real-valued measurable function over $\mathscr{X}(\mathscr{A})$, prove that $f(x) + g(x)$ and $f(x) g(x)$ are also measurable.

17. Prove that

$$\int_A \alpha f(x)\, d\mu(x) = \alpha \int_A f(x)\, d\mu(x).$$

18. Prove that

$$\int_A [f(x) + g(x)]\, d\mu(x) = \int_A f(x)\, d\mu(x) + \int_A g(x)\, d\mu(x).$$

19. Prove that, if $f(x) \geq 0$,

$$\int_A f(x)\, d\mu(x) \geq 0.$$

20. Prove that, if $f(x) \geq g(x)$,

$$\int_A f(x)\, d\mu(x) \geq \int_A g(x)\, d\mu(x).$$

21. Prove that

$$\int_A |f(x) + g(x)|\, d\mu(x) \leq \int_A |f(x)|\, d\mu(x) + \int_A |g(x)|\, d\mu(x).$$

22. Prove that, if $a \leq f(x) \leq b$ on the set A,

$$a\mu(A) \leq \int_A f(x)\, d\mu(x) \leq b\mu(A).$$

23. If $g(x)$ is a statistic from $\mathscr{X}(\mathscr{A})$ to $\mathscr{Y}(\mathscr{B})$ and $f(y)$ is a real-valued statistic over $\mathscr{Y}(\mathscr{B})$, show that
$$E\{f(Y)\} = E\{f(g(X))\},$$

where $Y = g(X)$ and X stands for the measure $P(A)$ over $\mathscr{X}(\mathscr{A})$. Hence establish the uniqueness of the definition in formula (3.4).

24. Prove that the binomial distribution has a probability measure which is absolutely continuous with respect to the Poisson distribution; which is not absolutely continuous

with respect to the normal. Show that the function $N(A) =$ number of non-negative integers in A is a measure. Express the binomial distribution by means of a density with respect to $N(A)$. Express the binomial by means of a density with respect to the Poisson measure.

25. Prove that all probability measures given by a simple density function

$$P(A) = \int_A f(x)\, dx$$

are absolutely continuous with respect to Lebesgue measure.

26. Let $X_i = 1, 0$ with probabilities, respectively, $p, q = 1 - p$, and let $X_1, \cdots, X_n$ be independent. Find the conditional probability measure, given $t(\mathbf{x}) = \sum_{i=1}^{n} x_i = t$.

27. Is the class of all probability measures on R^1 dominated?

28. Prove that, if $P_X(A \mid t)$ is a determination of conditional probability, given $t(x) = t$, then (i) $P_X(\mathcal{X} \mid y) = 1$ a.e. (P_T); (ii) $0 \le P_X(A \mid t) \le 1$ a.e. (P_T). (iii) for $A_1, A_2 \cdots$ disjoint $\sum_{i=1}^{\infty} P_X(A_i \mid t) = P_X \left(\bigcup_{i=1}^{\infty} A_i \mid t \right)$ a.e. (P_T).

29. Let X be a random variable with the distribution function $F(x) = \int_{-\infty}^{x} f(x)\, dx$.

$f(x)$ is called the probability density function with respect to Lebesgue measure, and by the Radon–Nikodym theorem the probability measure of X is absolutely continuous re Lebesgue measure. If $(X_1, \cdots, X_n)$ has the distribution function $\prod_{i=1}^{n} F(x_i)$ and density function $\prod_{i=1}^{n} f(x_i)$ over R^n, then prove that $(X_1, \cdots, X_n)$ has the product measure of the measure of X for each coordinate—the power-product measure. Consider a statistic $t(\mathbf{x}) = (x_{(1)}, \cdots, x_{(n)})$, called the *order statistic*, where $x_{(1)}, \cdots, x_{(n)}$ are the values $x_1, \cdots, x_n$ arranged in order of magnitude: $x_{(1)} \le \cdots \le x_{(n)}$. Show that a determination of the conditional distribution is

$$P_X(A \mid t) = \frac{i(A, t)}{n!}$$

$$= \frac{\sum_{P} \phi_A(t_p)}{n!}$$

where $i(A, t)$ is the number of permutations of $(x_{(1)}, \cdots, x_{(n)})$ that belong to A, and $\phi_A(\mathbf{x})$ is the characteristic function of $A \subset R^n$, P denotes summation over all the $n!$ permutations t_p, and t_p is a typical permutation of $(x_{(1)}, \cdots, x_{(n)})$.

30. For the class of distributions of the form given in Problem 29, use the Neyman criterion to prove that the order statistic is a sufficient statistic.

31. Let $X_i = 1, 0$ with probability $p, q = 1 - p$, and let $X_1, \cdots, X_n$ be independent. Find the conditional measure given $t(\mathbf{x}) = \sum_{i=1}^{n} x_i = t$.

32. Show that $t(\mathbf{x})$ in Problem 31 is sufficient for $p \in]0, 1[$.

33. Let $X_1, \cdots, X_n$ be independent, and let each be normally distributed with mean ξ, and variance σ^2. Use the Neyman criterion to show that $\left(\bar{x}, \sum_{i=1}^{n} (x_i - \bar{x})^2 \right)$ is a sufficient statistic for $\xi \in]-\infty, +\infty[$ and $\sigma^2 \in]0, \infty[$.

34. For the distributions in Problem 33 with $\xi = 0$ and $\sigma^2 \in]0, \infty[$, show that Σx_i^2 is a sufficient statistic.

35. If $X_1, \cdots, X_n$ are independent, and each has the Poisson distribution with mean m, show that $\sum_1^n x_i$ is a sufficient statistic for $m \in]0, \infty[$.

36. If $X = (X_1, \cdots, X_N)$ are independent, and each has the binomial distribution with parameters n, p, show that Σx_i is a sufficient statistic for given n and $p \in [0, 1]$.

37. If $X = (X_1, X_2)$ has a multivariate normal distribution over R^2 with zero means and covariance matrix

$$\left\| \begin{matrix} \sigma^2 + \tau^2 & \sigma^2 - \tau^2 \\ \sigma^2 - \tau^2 & \sigma^2 + \tau^2 \end{matrix} \right\|,$$

show that $t(x) = x_1 + x_2$ is a sufficient statistic (σ^2) for the family of distributions $(\sigma^2, \tau^2) \in]0, \infty[^2$.

38. If $X_1, \cdots, X_n$ are independent, and each is normally distributed with mean ξ and variance σ^2, show that $t(\mathbf{x}) = \Sigma x^2$ is a complete statistic relative to the class of distributions corresponding to $\xi = 0$ and $\sigma^2 \in]0, \infty[$.

39. For Problem 38 show that $t(\mathbf{x}) = (\bar{x}, \Sigma(x_i - \bar{x})^2)$ is complete corresponding to $(\xi, \sigma^2) \in R^1 \times]0, \infty[$.

40. Show that the Poisson distributions $m \in]0, \infty[$ form a complete class. Hence show that Σx_i is a complete statistic corresponding to the distributions in Problem 35 with $m \in]0, \infty[$.

41. Show that the binomial distributions form a complete class, n fixed and $p \in]0, 1[$. Show that Σx_i is a complete statistic corresponding to the distributions in Problem 36 with $p \in]0, 1[$.

42. The hypergeometric distribution arises in acceptance sampling. Consider N objects, D with a certain property and $N - D$ without that property. If each selection of n from the N objects has the same probability $\binom{N}{n}^{-1}$ of being chosen in a sampling procedure, then the probability distribution for the number Y of objects with the property in the sample is given by

$$\Pr(Y = y) = \frac{\binom{D}{y}\binom{N - D}{n - y}}{\binom{N}{n}}$$

if y is an integer between 0 and min $\{D, n\}$, inclusive. Show that the probability measures corresponding to $D = 0, 1, \cdots, N$ form a complete class.

43. Consider the class of absolutely continuous distributions over $]-\infty, 0[\times]0, \infty[$ (the second quadrant in R^2). If $(X_1, Y_1), \cdots, (X_n, Y_n)$ are independent, and each has the same distribution in the class above, then show that $t(\mathbf{x}, \mathbf{y}) = \{(x_1, y_1), \cdots, (x_n, y_n)\}$ is a sufficient statistic. Use Theorem 7.2 to show that $t(\mathbf{x}, \mathbf{y})$ is complete corresponding to the class of absolutely continuous distributions.

44. Prove Theorem 7.3.

REFERENCES AND BIBLIOGRAPHY

1. M. E. Monroe, *Introduction to Measure and Integration*, Addison and Wesley, 1953.
2. P. R. Halmos, *Measure Theory*, D. Van Nostrand Co., 1950.
3. H. Cramér, *Mathematical Methods of Statistics*, Princeton University Press, 1950.
4. J. Doob, "Asymptotic properties of Markov transition probabilities," *Trans. Am. Math. Soc.*, Vol. 63 (1949), p. 393.
5. A. Kolmogorov, *Foundations of Probability*, Chelsea, 1950.
6. P. R. Halmos and L. J. Savage, "Applications of the Radon–Nikodym theorem to the theory of sufficient statistics," *Ann. Math. Stat.*, Vol. 20 (1949), p. 225.
7. B. O. Koopman, "On distributions admitting a sufficient statistic," *Trans. Am. Math. Soc.*, Vol. 39 (1939), p. 399.
8. D. A. S. Fraser, "Sufficient statistics and selection depending on the parameter," *Ann. Math. Stat.*, Vol. 22 (1952), p. 417.
9. M. Girshick, F. Mosteller, and L. J. Savage, "Unbiased estimates for certain binomial sampling problems with applications," *Ann. Math. Stat.*, Vol. 17 (1946), p. 13.
10. D. A. S. Fraser, "Completeness of the order statistics," *Can. J. Math.*, Vol. 6 (1953), p. 42.
11. E. L. Lehmann and H. Scheffé, "Completeness, similar regions, and unbiased estimation," *Sankhyā*, Vol. 10 (1950), p. 305.

CHAPTER 2

Statistical Inference

1. THE DECISION PROBLEM

In Chapter 1 we introduced the concept of probability and considered the recording of the outcome of an experiment in a sample space, the frequency interpretation of probability in a sequence of repetitions of an experiment, and the summarizing of the outcome by means of a statistic. Also we considered two properties, sufficiency and completeness, which a statistic may possess in relation to a class of probability measures. These two properties will find considerable application in the later sections.

In this section we shall sketch the model of decision theory. The different branches of statistical inference, estimation, hypothesis testing, confidence regions and tolerance regions, can all be considered as examples of decision theory. The present developments in nonparametric theory are rather special to the branches in which they occur, and seemingly the general theory has less to offer here than is the case for other parts of statistics. Consequently, we shall spend only a few pages formulating the general model and then in the later sections of the chapter develop the four branches as much in the style of the general theory as is possible.

Suppose the statistician has chosen the sample space and the class of probability measures $\{P_\theta \,|\, \theta \in \Omega\}$ suitable to the experiment. By examining the experimental arrangement and the purposes for which the experiment was designed, he can consider the different decisions he may wish to make upon the completion of the experiment. This aggregation of decisions we call the *decision space* and designate it by $\mathscr{D}$; a particular *decision* we designate by d. The decision space $\mathscr{D}$ will usually bear some simple relation to the space of probability measures Ω; for the purpose of a decision is to try to say something about the unknown situation confronting the statistician, and as far as the model is concerned this situation is given by the parameter θ. Thus in effect the statistician wishes to say something about the probability measure which produces the outcome he observes.

36

If the statistician has a plan which tells him what decision to make for each possible outcome of the experiment, he has what we call a *decision function* $d(x)$ which for each outcome x of the experiment prescribes a decision $d(x)$ in $\mathscr{D}$. A decision function is thus a statistic with values in $\mathscr{D}$. Once he has decided on a decision function, he has a definite plan of action to follow as soon as the outcome of the experiment is observed. The statistician's objective in any experiment is to find a decision function $d(x)$ which is in some sense good or best.

The full aggregation of decision functions would be obtained by considering all possible statistics from $\mathscr{X}$ into $\mathscr{D}$. However, in many cases the statistician is willing to restrict his attention to some subclass of all decision functions. He may do this for various reasons—the mathematical complexity of the full class, the physical difficulty of applying a very abstract procedure, or practical expediency. The *class of decision functions* to which the statistician restricts his attention we designate by $\mathscr{D}_f$.

In some situations it is to the statistician's advantage to take the outcome of an experiment and randomly choose a decision from $\mathscr{D}$, the probabilities for the different decisions being dependent on the outcome x. We now formulate this notion and then later in the section indicate the advantages by a simple example. In order to apply probabilities to $\mathscr{D}$, we need a σ-algebra of subsets, say $\mathscr{F}$ over $\mathscr{D}$; then $\mathscr{D}(\mathscr{F})$ is a measurable space. We now consider the *class of probability measures over* $\mathscr{D}(\mathscr{F})$, designating it by $\mathscr{M}$ and *a typical measure* by $m(\mathscr{D})$. A *randomized decision function* m_x is a function from $\mathscr{X}$ to $\mathscr{M}$, that is, a statistic with values in $\mathscr{M}$. To use a decision function m_x the statistician obtains the outcome x from his experiment, chooses the probability measure $m_x(D)$ given by the decision function, and constructs a random experiment which applies probability to $\mathscr{D}$ in accord with $m_x(D)$. From this constructed experiment he chooses an outcome, and this outcome, an element of $\mathscr{D}$, is his final decision. We designate by $\mathscr{M}_f$ the *class of randomized decision functions* to which the statistician restricts his attention.

Once the statistician has set up a model for his experiment, his main problem is to choose a decision function that is in some sense good or best. However, before he can judge decision functions, he must have some idea of the relative merits of the different decisions d for each situation θ in which he might find himself. Accordingly, we suppose the statistician can measure the loss, perhaps economic, that he suffers in making a decision d in the situation θ. He thus obtains a *loss function* $W(d, \theta)$, and we require that $W(d, \theta) \geq 0$. Naturally, if d were the "correct" decision for some situation θ, we would expect the statistician not to suffer any loss; i.e. $W(d, \theta) = 0$.

The statistician can now examine the effect of a decision function $d(x)$ in the various situations θ.   Unfortunately the loss he will suffer depends not only on θ and the particular function he uses but also on the value of the outcome x, a random variable.   A standard procedure is to examine the expected or average loss, called the *risk*, and given by

(1.1) $$\mathbf{R}_{d(x)}(\theta) = E_\theta\{W(d(X), \theta)\}.$$

$$= \int_{\mathscr{X}} W(d(x), \theta)\, dP_\theta(x),$$

or in the randomized case

(1.2) $$\mathbf{R}_{m_x}(\theta) = \int_{\mathscr{X}}\int_{\mathscr{D}} W(d, \theta)\, dm_x(d)\, dP_\theta(x).$$

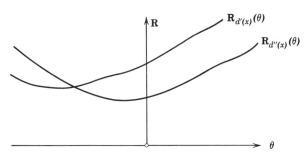

Figure 2. The risk functions for two decision functions $d(x)$, $d'(x)$.

By relating probabilities to frequency ratios this represents the average loss in a series of repetitions of the experiment.   The subscript on $\mathbf{R}_{d(x)}(\theta)$ denotes dependence on the *function* $d(x)$ and not on particular values of the function.   In some situations it may be quite unrealistic to use expected loss to judge a decision function.   A very high loss with a small probability of occurrence may have higher or lower real value to the statistician than the expectation.   Nevertheless much of the theory is based on *average loss* or *risk*.

The statistician has a class of decision functions available, either $\mathscr{D}_f$ or $\mathscr{M}_f$, and for each decision function has a risk function $\mathbf{R}_d(\theta)$ which describes its behavior for the different values of θ.   Ideally he would like a decision function that gave a minimum value to $\mathbf{R}_d(\theta)$ for each θ, a *minimum-risk decision function*:   that is, in terms of Fig. 2, a decision function having risk function beneath all other risk functions.   However, it only occurs in a few special problems that the $d(x)$ for which $\mathbf{R}_d(\theta)$ is minimized for one θ is the $d(x)$ producing a minimum for other values of θ. The theory of games provides us with a partial answer as to how to choose a decision function in other than these exceptional circumstances.

The situation of the statistician faced with the choice of a decision function can be viewed as a two-person game. The statistician is faced with an unknown situation described by $\theta \in \Omega$. For the purposes of the model it is convenient to think of this as having resulted from a *first player*, whom we shall call Nature, making a move θ from a class of moves Ω. The statistician as the second player can make a move, the choice of a decision function $d(x) \in \mathcal{D}_f$. The "pay-off" is the economic loss $\mathbf{R}_d(\theta)$ to the statistician.

The solution proposed in the theory of games is based on the following type of argument. For a choice of decision function $d(x)$, the loss will be $\mathbf{R}_d(\theta)$ in situation θ. The maximum loss that can occur using $d(x)$ is $\max\limits_{\theta} \mathbf{R}_d(\theta)$ [or $\sup\limits_{\theta} \mathbf{R}_d(\theta)$]. The statistician chooses a *minimax decision function* if his choice, say $d^*(x)$, minimizes $\max\limits_{\theta} \mathbf{R}_d(\theta)$:

$$(1.3) \qquad \max_{\theta} \mathbf{R}_{d^*(x)}(\theta) \leq \max_{\theta} \mathbf{R}_{d(x)}(\theta)$$

for any other decision function $d(x)$. Thus the statistician for each decision function observes what is the worst average loss he can suffer using that decision function, and then he chooses the decision function for which this maximum risk is least. Such a choice of decision function can be said to give protection against the most adverse situation that might arise.

Sometimes on the basis of the risk function we are able to state that one decision function $d_1(x)$ is to be preferred over another $d_2(x)$,

If

$$\mathbf{R}_{d_1}(\theta) \leq \mathbf{R}_{d_2}(\theta)$$

for all θ in Ω and

$$\mathbf{R}_{d_1}(\theta) < \mathbf{R}_{d_2}(\theta)$$

for at least one θ in Ω, then we say $d_1(x)$ is better than $d_2(x)$.
So long as we accept the principle of judging a decision function by means of average loss or risk, then, if $d_1(x)$ is *better* than $d_2(x)$, we would always choose d_1 in preference to d_2. The risk is never greater and in some situations is actually less. See Fig. 3.

A decision function is said to be *admissible if there is no decision function that is better.* Thus $d(x)$ is admissible if there does not exist a decision function $d'(x)$ for which

$$\mathbf{R}_{d'(x)}(\theta) \leq \mathbf{R}_{d(x)}(\theta)$$

for all θ with strict inequality for at least one θ. A decision function $d(x)$ is *inadmissible* if there exists a *better* decision function.

A class C of decision functions is said to be *complete if for every decision function not in the class C there is a decision function in C that is better.* If in a problem we can find a complete class, obviously we can restrict our attention to the decision functions in that class, because for any decision function outside the class we can always do better within.

It is easily seen that an admissible decision function must be contained in any complete class. For, if $d(x)$ is admissible and is outside the complete class, then the "complete class" definition says there is a better decision function in the class whereas the "admissible decision function" definition says there just is not a better decision function. This is a contradiction.

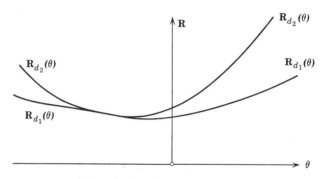

Figure 3. $d_1(x)$ is better than $d_2(x)$.

EXAMPLE 1.1. Suppose a statistician is put in a very difficult position. He is given a weighted coin with the information that the probability p for a head is either $1/4$ or $3/4$, and he must decide on the basis of two tosses of the coin the value of the probability. The penalty for an incorrect decision is severe, say death. We have

$$\mathscr{X} = \{2H, 1H, 0H\},$$

where 1H for example indicates the result of exactly one head in the two tosses. The probability measure $P_p(x)$ is given by

$$\{p^2, 2pq, q^2\},$$

where the three values in the brace give the probability measure of the corresponding points in the previous brace $(q = 1 - p)$. Also

$$\Omega = \left\{\frac{1}{4}, \frac{3}{4}\right\}.$$

The decisions available are $p = 1/4$ and $p = 3/4$. We designate these decisions by 1/4 and 3/4, respectively;

$$\mathscr{D} = \left\{ \frac{1}{4}, \frac{3}{4} \right\}.$$

We shall consider two nonrandomized decision functions, say $d_0(x)$ and $d_1(x)$ and a class of randomized decision functions $\{m_x^\alpha \mid \alpha \in \,]0, 1[\}$. These are given in Tables 1 and 2. It is easily seen that m_x^α is a compromise

Table 1. Decisions using $d_0(x)$ and $d_1(x)$

Decision Function	$x = $ 2H	1H	0H
$d_0(x)$	$\dfrac{3}{4}$	$\dfrac{1}{4}$	$\dfrac{1}{4}$
$d_1(x)$	$\dfrac{3}{4}$	$\dfrac{3}{4}$	$\dfrac{1}{4}$

Table 2. Probabilities for the randomized decision function m_x^α

Randomized Decision Function	$x = $ 2H	1H	0H
$m_x\left(\dfrac{3}{4}\right)$	1	α	0
$m_x\left(\dfrac{1}{4}\right)$	0	$1 - \alpha$	1

between the two nonrandomized decision functions in the sense that it can be described as choosing $d_1(x)$ with probability α and $d_0(x)$ with probability $1 - \alpha$. For example $m_{1H}^\alpha(3/4) = \alpha$ means that, when the outcome is 1H, the statistician chooses the decision 3/4 with probability α and of course the remaining decision 1/4 with probability $1 - \alpha$.

For each of these decision functions we could quite easily calculate the probabilities for each decision when $p = 1/4$ and for each decision when $p = 3/4$. Such a set of probabilities would be called the *operating characteristic* of the decision function. However, we shall introduce a loss function and directly calculate the risk. Consider the loss function

$$\begin{aligned} W(d, p) &= 1 \quad \text{if} \quad d \neq p \\ &= 0 \qquad\quad = p. \end{aligned}$$

The loss is one unit, in this case one statistician, for an incorrect decision and no loss for a correct decision.

By using the probabilities, the loss function, and the table of decision functions, we can straightforwardly calculate the risk. For instance:

$$\mathbf{R}_{d_0}\left(\frac{1}{4}\right) = 1 \cdot \left(\frac{1}{4}\right)^2 + 0 \cdot 2 \cdot \left(\frac{1}{4}\right)\left(\frac{3}{4}\right) + 0 \cdot \left(\frac{3}{4}\right)^2$$

$$\mathbf{R}_{m^\alpha}\left(\frac{3}{4}\right) = [1 \cdot 0 + 0 \cdot 1]\left(\frac{3}{4}\right)^2$$
$$+ [\alpha \cdot 0 + (1-\alpha) \cdot 1] \, 2 \left(\frac{1}{4}\right)\left(\frac{3}{4}\right)$$
$$+ [0 \cdot 0 + 1 \cdot 1]\left(\frac{1}{4}\right)^2$$
$$= \frac{7 - 6\alpha}{16}.$$

Making a table of the risk for $d_0(x)$, $d_1(x)$, m_x^α and the particular case $m_x^{0.5}$, we obtain Table 3. With either of the nonrandomized decision functions

Table 3

	$\mathbf{R}\left(\dfrac{1}{4}\right)$	$\mathbf{R}\left(\dfrac{3}{4}\right)$	$\max_p \mathbf{R}(p)$
d_0	$\dfrac{1}{16}$	$\dfrac{7}{16}$	$\dfrac{7}{16}$
d_1	$\dfrac{7}{16}$	$\dfrac{1}{16}$	$\dfrac{7}{16}$
m^α	$\dfrac{1 + 6\alpha}{16}$	$\dfrac{7 - 6\alpha}{16}$	
$m^{0.5}$	$\dfrac{4}{16}$	$\dfrac{4}{16}$	$\dfrac{4}{16}$

the risk can be as high as 7/16; that is, 7/16 chance of losing the statistician. However, using the randomized "strategy" with $\alpha = 1/2$, the maximum risk has been reduced to 1/4; and it is easily seen that among the decision functions exhibited above this is as small as the maximum risk can be made. Therefore we say that $m_x^{0.5}$ is a minimax decision function. The choice of such a decision function represents the conservative attitude of guarding against adverse situations. It is to be noted that the introduction of a randomized decision function reduced the maximum risk from 7/16 to 4/16.

EXAMPLE 1.2. We consider a simple problem of sampling from a normal distribution. Let $\mathscr{X} = R^9$ and an outcome be a sequence of nine real numbers. Also let the probability distributions be those corresponding to sampling from a normal distribution with mean μ and variance 1. The parameter space is $\Omega = \{\mu\} = R^1$. We have

$$(1.4) \qquad P_\mu(A) = \int_A \left(\frac{1}{2\pi}\right)^{9/2} \exp\left[-\frac{1}{2}\sum_1^9 (x_i - \mu)^2\right] \prod_1^9 dx_i.$$

Suppose the statistician is interested in only two decisions: the decision $\mu \leq 0$ designated by d_1 and the decision $\mu > 0$ designated by d_2.

Very often in problems of this sort d_1 represents the sort of standard situation present in similar problems in the past—the status quo—whereas d_2 represents a change from the past which might exist in the present problem. A familiar practice among statisticians is to restrict the class of decision functions to those that give a certain level of protection in the standard situation. The usual restriction is that the decision function $d(x)$ must have

$$\Pr_\mu \{d(X) = d_2\} \leq \alpha$$

when $\mu \leq 0$. Then the probability of an incorrect decision is bounded by α (say 0.05) if the standard situation exists in the problem.

A decision function satisfying this restriction is

$$(1.5) \qquad\qquad d^*(x) = d_2 \quad \text{if} \quad \frac{\Sigma x_i}{9} \geq \frac{1.64}{3}$$

$$= d_1 \qquad\qquad < \frac{1.64}{3}.$$

We can easily check to see if the restriction is satisfied. The induced distribution of the statistic is normal with mean μ and variance $1/3$. Therefore

$$\Pr\{d^*(X) = d_2\} = \Pr\left\{\frac{\Sigma X_i}{9} \geq \frac{1.64}{3}\right\}$$

$$= \Pr\left\{\frac{\Sigma X_i}{9} - \mu \geq \frac{1.64 - 3\mu}{3}\right\}$$

$$= \Pr\{Z \geq 1.64 - 3\mu\},$$

where Z stands for a random variable with the normal distribution, mean zero, and variance 1. From tables of the normal distribution, the above probability is 0.05 when $\mu = 0$ and is less than 0.05 when $\mu < 0$.

In problems such as this the operating characteristic of a decision function has a particularly simple form. Since there are only two decisions, and a decision must be made at the completion of the experiment, it suffices to give the probability for one of them which by tradition is d_2.

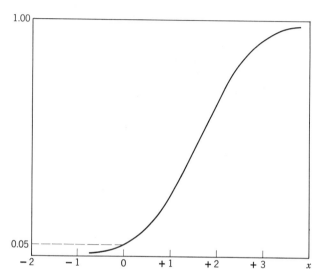

Figure 4. The power function for the decision function given by (1.5).

This probability of a decision d_2 is given a special name, the *power function*, and is designated by $\mathbf{P}_d(\mu)$:

$$\mathbf{P}_d(\mu) = \mathrm{Pr}_\mu \{d(X) = d_2\}.$$

For the decision function defined above,

$$(1.6) \qquad \mathbf{P}_{d*}(\mu) = \mathrm{Pr} \left\{ \frac{\Sigma X_i}{9} \geq \frac{1.64}{3} \right\}$$

$$= \mathrm{Pr} \{Z \geq 1.64 - 3\mu\}.$$

This is plotted in Fig. 4. The restriction on the decision functions is that the power $\mathbf{P}_d(\mu)$ should be less than 0.05 when $\mu \leq 0$; that is, the power function curve should remain beneath the sketched line segment at height 0.05.

Consider a simple loss function such as

$$W(d_2, \mu) = 1 \quad \text{if} \quad \mu \leq 0$$
$$= 0 \qquad\qquad > 0$$
$$W(d_1, \mu) = 0 \quad \text{if} \quad \mu \leq 0$$
$$= a \qquad\qquad > 0.$$

The loss for an incorrect decision is 1 when $\mu \leq 0$ and is a when $\mu > 0$.

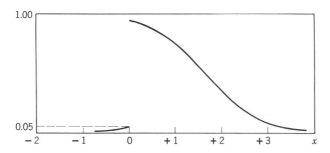

Figure 5. The risk function for $d^*(x)$ when $a = 1/2$.

The risk can be given simply in terms of the power:

$$\mathbf{R}_d(\mu) = \mathbf{P}_d(\mu) \qquad\qquad \text{if} \quad \mu \leq 0$$
$$= a[1 - \mathbf{P}_a(\mu)] \qquad\qquad > 0.$$

For all values of $\mu \leq 0$ the restriction has given the protection that the probability of a wrong decision is kept below 0.05. Therefore it seems reasonable to examine the risk function only for values of $\mu > 0$. If we do this, then it can be shown, and will be in Section 3, that $d^*(x)$ is *uniformly better* than any other decision function satisfying the restriction.

▶ To complete this section on decision theory we give a theorem which says that in any problem the statistician need consider only those decision functions that are based on a sufficient statistic.

THEOREM 1.1. If $t(x)$ is a sufficient statistic for $\{P_\theta | \theta \in \Omega\}$, then, for any decision function $d(x)$, there is a randomized decision function based on $t(x)$ which has the same risk function (assuming that the conditional probability is a measure).

Proof. We define a randomized decision function based on the statistic $t(x)$. Consider the conditional probability measure $P(A|t)$ over $\mathscr{X}$ and the statistic

$d(x)$; take the randomized decision function $m_t(D)$ to be the probability measure over $\mathscr{D}$ induced from $P(A \mid t)$ by the statistic $d(x)$. Then we have

$$\mathbf{R}_{m_t}(\theta) = \int_{\mathscr{T}} \int_{\mathscr{D}} W(d, \theta) \, dm_t(d) \, dP_\theta^T(t)$$

$$= \int_{\mathscr{T}} \int_{\mathscr{X}} W(d(x), \theta) \, dP(x \mid t) \, dP_\theta^T(t)$$

$$= \int_{\mathscr{X}} W(d(x), \theta) \, dP_\theta(x)$$

$$= \mathbf{R}_{d(x)}(\theta).$$

For further reading on decision theory see Wald [1], and on the two-person game see Von Neumann and Morgenstern [2].   ◀

2. THE ESTIMATION OF REAL PARAMETERS

2.1. Introduction. In Chapter 1 we used the term parameter for a symbol which indexed a class of probability measures. It has, however, a more general interpretation as a quantity calculated from a probability measure and therefore characteristic of the measure. We define a *parameter* to be a *function $g^*(P_\theta)$ defined over a class of probability measures* or equivalently to be a *function $g(\theta)$ defined over the parameter space Ω*. A real parameter $g(\theta)$ is a real-valued function over Ω. A vector parameter $\mathbf{g}(\theta) = (g_1(\theta), \cdots, g_k(\theta))$ is a vector-valued function over Ω, taking its values in a real space of k dimensions, R^k. Thus a vector parameter has coordinates which are real parameters.

For the class of normal distributions on the real line with mean μ and variance σ^2, we have $\theta = (\mu, \sigma^2)$ which is an element of $\Omega = R \times \,]0, \infty[$. As examples of real parameters consider μ, σ^2, $E_{\mu,\sigma^2}\{X^2\}$. As examples of vector parameters consider (μ, σ), $[E_{\mu,\sigma^2}\{X\}, E_{\mu,\sigma^2}\{X^2\}, E_{\mu,\sigma^2}\{X^3\}]$, where the latter can be more simply written $[\mu, \mu^2 + \sigma^2, \mu^3 + 3\mu\sigma^2]$.

We confine the theory of estimation to a consideration of real or vector parameters. Now for applications the statistician wants a statistic that will produce from the outcome a real- or vector-valued quantity as an "estimate" of the parameter being considered. He wishes the value of the statistic to be close to the value of the parameter or as close as is possible considering the randomness in the experiment. These ideas we now make precise by imposing restrictions on the general model introduced in the previous section.

Let the parameter of interest be $\mathbf{g}(\theta) = (g_1(\theta), \cdots, g_k(\theta))$. If the statistician obtains an outcome from an experiment characterized by θ, then

he wishes to calculate from the outcome a possible value for the parameter
g and he hopes that this "estimate" is close to the true value $\mathbf{g}(\theta)$.
Accordingly the space of decisions must be a real space of k dimensions,
$\mathscr{D} = R^k$. Also a decision function must have the form, $\mathbf{d}(x) = (d_1(x),$
$\cdots, d_k(x))$, where $d_1(x), \cdots, d_k(x)$ are real statistics. The loss function is
then used to formalize the requirement that the estimate be close to the
parameter. We require that

(2.1) $$W(\mathbf{d}, \theta) \leq W(\mathbf{d} + \epsilon^2(\mathbf{d} - \mathbf{g}(\theta)), \theta)$$

where **d** is a vector and by $\mathbf{d} - \mathbf{g}$ we mean the vector difference,
$(d_1 - g_1, \cdots, d_k - g_k)$. The above inequality means that the loss for the
decision **d** must be less than or equal the loss for the decision $\mathbf{d} + \epsilon^2 (\mathbf{d} - \mathbf{g})$
which is a proportion ϵ^2 farther away from the parameter value **g**. We
shall also use the term *estimator* for a decision function in an estimation
problem.

From the decision theory it follows then that a randomized estimator
must be a statistic taking its values in the space of probability measures
over R^k. As yet, randomized estimators have found little application in
the standard problems, and we shall have a theorem later in the section
which supports this result. As a practice, however, we should be prepared
to examine the larger class consisting of randomized estimators in the hope
of perhaps finding a better estimator there. Theorem 1.1 in the preceding
section says that, if we restrict attention to estimators based on a sufficient
statistic, then in general we must examine the randomized estimators if we
wish to cover all the possibilities of the nonrandomized estimators based
on the original outcome. See Problem 3.

The general theory suggests that, in looking for an estimator $\mathbf{d}(x)$, we
try to find one for which the risk

(2.2) $$\mathbf{R}_\mathbf{d}(\theta) = \int_{\mathscr{X}} W(\mathbf{d}(x), \mathbf{g}(\theta))\, dP_\theta(x)$$

is as small as possible simultaneously for each θ. We give a simple
example to indicate that this only occurs in the most trivial problems.

EXAMPLE 2.1. Let the parameter $g(\theta)$ be real-valued, and assume that
the loss function $W(d, \theta)$ has a single minimum value for each θ, say for
example $W(d, \theta) = (d - g(\theta))^2$. Then the trivial estimator, $d(x) = d_0$,
which ignores the value of the outcome, has minimum risk for all the θ's
having $g(\theta) = d_0$:

$$R_{d_0}(\theta) = \int_{\mathscr{X}} (d_0 - g(\theta))^2\, dP_\theta(x)$$

$$= (d_0 - g(\theta))^2.$$

For the θ's for which $g(\theta) = d_0$, we have $R_{d_0}(\theta) = 0$; and for other θ's the risk is greater than zero. A short analysis will also show that this is the only estimator having minimum risk at the θ's with $g(\theta) = d_0$. Thus we can minimize the risk for certain θ's but not for all simultaneously. An estimator having uniformly minimum risk does not exist.

We are thus faced with the quite general nonexistence of uniformly minimum risk estimators, at least within the full class of estimators.

The minimax principle offers an alternative criterion on which to base our choice of estimator. The desirability of an estimator is measured by the maximum risk it encounters: $\sup_{\theta} R_{d(x)}(\theta)$. A minimax estimator is then one for which $\sup_{\theta} R_{d(x)}(\theta)$ has its minimum value. With the simple loss functions such as squared error, $W(d, \theta) = (d - g(\theta))^2$, used in the standard problems, it can happen that the maximum risk is $+\infty$ for all estimates. Then any estimate is minimax. However, simple modifications in the loss function often produce better-behaved risk functions, and consequently make the application of the minimax criterion more sensible. The minimax criterion has been successfully applied to some of the simple parametric problems involving normal distributions. For an interesting paper on this field of estimation, see Hodges and Lehmann [3]. However, it has not had extensive application in parametric problems, and there are few indications of extensive application in the nonparametric field.

Another approach is to place moderate and reasonable restrictions on the estimators under consideration, and thus reduce the class of estimates $\mathcal{D}_f$ in the hope of finding a minimum risk estimator in the smaller class. One such restriction is to require that an estimator be unbiased.

An estimator $\mathbf{d}(x)$ *is an unbiased estimator of* $\mathbf{g}(\theta)$ *if*

$$(2.3) \qquad E_\theta\{\mathbf{d}(X)\} = (E_\theta\{d_1(X)\}, \cdots, E_\theta\{d_k(X)\})$$

$$= (g_1(\theta), \cdots, g_k(\theta))$$

$$= \mathbf{g}(\theta)$$

for all $\theta \in \Omega$.

It is to be noted that the expectation of a vector is obtained by taking the expectation of each coordinate.

Unbiasedness has an experimental interpretation which supports the statement that it is a reasonable requirement to place on an estimator. In a long series of repetitions of an experiment, the average of the different values assumed by $\mathbf{d}(x)$ will be close to the value of $\mathbf{g}(\theta)$ with high probability. This follows from Khintchine's theorem to be given in Chapter 6. In the present notation the theorem says that, if $E_\theta\{\mathbf{d}(X)\}$ exists as is implicitly assumed in formula (2.3), then the probability that the average is in any small neighborhood of $g(\theta)$ can be made arbitrarily close to one by taking a large enough number of repetitions. A stronger version of Khintchine's theorem states that, with probability one, the sequence of averages obtained by taking more and more repetitions will converge to $E_\theta\{\mathbf{d}(X)\}$.

There is another definition of unbiasedness which from some points of view is as reasonable as or more reasonable than that above. However it applies only to real estimators.

An estimator $d(x)$ is a median unbiased estimator of $g(\theta)$ if

$$\xi_{0.5}^\theta\,(d(X)) = g(\theta)$$

where $\xi_{0.5}^\theta\,(d(X))$ is the median value of the distribution of $d(x)$ obtained from the measure θ.

The symbol ξ_p can also be defined for all values of p between zero and one. Roughly speaking, it is the point in the distribution of a real-valued random variable that has probability p to the left of it and $1 - p$ to the right of it. Precisely, *$\xi_p(Y)$ for a real-valued random Y with distribution function $F(x)$ is the real number satisfying*

(2.4)
$$\int_{-\infty}^{\xi_p} dF(y) = F(\xi_p) = p.$$

If the solution to the equation is not unique, ξ_p is taken to be any one of the possible values; in any of our applications the ambiguity will be unimportant. *If the equation does not have a solution, ξ_p is chosen to satisfy*

$$F(\xi_p - 0) \le p \le F(\xi_p).$$

Median unbiasedness has found little application in estimation theory primarily because it does not seem to lend itself to the mathematical analysis needed to find minimum risk estimates.

In Section 2.3 we shall consider briefly another reasonable restriction to place on the class of estimators. It is the restriction to estimators satisfying a property of *invariance*.

2.2 Unbiased Estimation.   In this section we consider some theory and methods concerned with estimators that satisfy the restriction of unbiasedness as given by formula (2.3).

First we give some examples of loss functions which are frequently used with the property of unbiasedness. If $g(\theta)$ is a real parameter, consider

(2.5)
$$W_1(d, \theta) = [d - g(\theta)]^2$$
$$W_2(d, \theta) = |d - g(\theta)|^p \qquad \text{if } p \ge 1$$
$$W_3(d, \theta) = W_0(d)$$

where $W_\theta(d)$ is a convex function of d for each value of θ. For this we define

$W(\mathbf{d})$ is a convex function of $\mathbf{d}$ over R^k if, for each $\mathbf{d}$, $\mathbf{d}'$, and $\alpha \in \,]0, 1[$,

(2.6) $\alpha W(\mathbf{d}) + (1 - \alpha)W(\mathbf{d}') \geq W(\alpha\mathbf{d} + (1 - \alpha)\mathbf{d}').$

The function is strictly convex if the inequality is always strict.

For an illustration of the definition see Fig. 6. It is easily seen that $W_1(d, \theta)$ and $W_2(d, \theta)$ are strictly convex functions of d and hence that they are particular cases of $W_3(d, \theta)$.

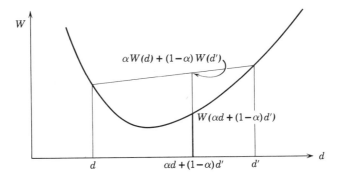

Figure 6. Illustration of a convex function.

For unbiased estimators the risk functions corresponding to W_1 and W_2 have a familiar form. With W_1 we obtain

$$\mathbf{R}_d(\theta) = \int_{\mathscr{X}} [d(x) - g(\theta)]^2 \, dP_\theta(x)$$
$$= \int_{\mathscr{X}} [d(x) - E\,(d(X))]^2 \, dP_\theta(x)$$
$$= \sigma^2_{d(X)}(\theta),$$

which is the variance of $d(X)$ corresponding to the probability distribution θ. With W_2, the risk function becomes the pth absolute moment of $d(X)$ about its mean.

For vector parameters we give the following two examples of loss functions:

(2.7) $W_1(\mathbf{d}, \theta) = \displaystyle\sum_{i=1}^{k} [d_i - g_i(\theta)]^2$

$W_2(\mathbf{d}, \theta) = W_\theta(\mathbf{d})$

where $W_\theta(\mathbf{d})$ is a convex function of the vector $\mathbf{d}$. For the first of these loss functions the risk function takes a particularly simple form. We have

$$\mathbf{R_d}(\theta) = E_\theta \left\{ \sum_{i=1}^{k} (d_i - g_i(\theta))^2 \right\}$$

$$= \sum_{i=1}^{k} \sigma^2_{d_i(X)}(\theta),$$

where $\sigma^2_{d_i(X)}(\theta)$ is the variance of the coordinate $d_i(X)$ when the distribution is given by θ.

There is a property not based directly on the idea of risk which can sometimes be attained by unbiased vector estimators. It was introduced by Cramér [4], p. 300 and p. 491. Let $\sigma_{ij}(\theta)$ be the covariance matrix for the coordinates of $\mathbf{d}(X) = (d_1(X), \cdots, d_k(X))$ when the probability measure is given by θ:

(2.8) $$\sigma_{ij}(\theta) = E_\theta\{[d_i(X) - g_i(\theta)][d_j(X) - g_j(\theta)]\}.$$

Also, assuming that the matrix $\| \sigma_{ij}(\theta) \|$ is nonsingular, we let $\| \sigma^{ij}(\theta) \|$ be the inverse matrix. Then Cramér defined the *ellipsoid of concentration* for $\mathbf{d}(X)$ to be

(2.9) $$\sum_{i,j=1}^{k} \sigma^{ij}(\theta) y_i y_j = k + 2$$

where, for convenience, we have let $y_i = d_i - g_i(\theta)$. This ellipsoid has a rather simple interpretation. For, if we consider the multivariate normal distribution in R^k having the same mean and covariance matrix as $\mathbf{d}(x)$, then the quadratic form on the left-hand side of equation (2.9) is, except for a factor $-\frac{1}{2}$ the exponent in the multivariate probability density. The ellipsoid given by the equation is then a surface of constant probability density which in a certain sense outlines or displays the probability distribution. Also, if we consider a probability distribution that is uniform within the ellipsoid, then it will have the same means, variances, covariances as the given distribution; this is the justification for the constant $k + 2$ on the right-hand side of (2.9). Following Cramér we say that an unbiased estimator $\mathbf{d}(x)$ has *minimum concentration ellipsoid if* (2.9) *is contained in the ellipsoid of concentration for any other unbiased estimator.*

The remainder of the theory using risk functions will depend on the use of convex loss functions. Convex loss functions are open to some criticism. Frequently in application the statistician wants his estimate to be close to the parameter, but, if it is far from the parameter, then a little farther does not matter much. The convex loss does not exhibit this property. For consider a single real parameter $g(\theta)$, and assume that the loss function $W_\theta(d)$ is not asymptotic to the d axis in either direction.   Then it follows easily from the convexity that, for any decision d far from the value $g(\theta)$, the additional loss in going to the value $d + \epsilon$ (or $d - \epsilon$) farther from $g(\theta)$ will be at least as large (larger if strict convexity) as the additional loss when d is closer to $g(\theta)$.

Before commencing the theory itself for unbiased estimation, we develop a few results concerning convex functions and ellipsoids of concentration.

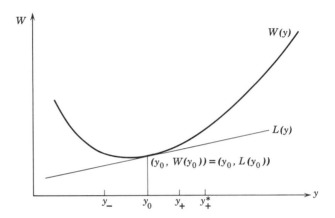

Figure 7. A strictly convex curve and a line of support.

THEOREM 2.1.   A convex function defined over the real line is a continuous function.

Proof.   This is given as Problem 4 at the end of the Chapter.

THEOREM 2.2.   Through any point on a convex curve defined over the real line there passes a straight line which stays beneath the curve or at most touches it.   Such a line is called a line of support.   If the curve is strictly convex, then the line of support is strictly beneath the curve except at the one point of contact.

Proof.   See Fig. 7.   Let $(y_0, W(y_0))$ be an arbitrary point on a convex curve $W(y)$.   Also let y_-, y_+, y_+^* be three points satisfying $y_- < y_0 < y_+ < y_+^*$. We consider the slopes of the lines joining the points above y_+^*, y_+, y_- to the point $(y_0, W(y_0))$.   It is easily seen that the line joining the points on the curve above y_+^* and y_0 has slope

$$\frac{W(y_+^*) - W(y_0)}{y_+^* - y_0},$$

which is greater than or equal the slope

$$\frac{W(y_+) - W(y_0)}{y_+ - y_0}$$

for the line joining the points above y_+ and y_0. For, if not, then the slope inequality could be rearranged and would violate the convexity property applied to the points y_0, y_+^* with intermediate point y_+. Similarly, the slope of the line for y_+ and y_0 is greater than or equal the slope of the line for y_0 and to y.

From the above argument it follows that the slope

$$\frac{W(y) - W(y_0)}{y - y_0}$$

is decreasing (or at least nonincreasing) as y decreases towards y_0. Also the values of the slope for $y > y_0$ are bounded below by

$$\frac{W(y_-) - W(y_0)}{y_- - y_0}.$$

Therefore the derivative to the right, say D_R, exists at y_0:

(2.10)
$$D_R = \lim_{y \downarrow y_0} \frac{W(y) - W(y_0)}{y - y_0},$$

where $y \downarrow y_0$ means that y approaches y_0 from the right. Similarly the derivative from the left exists,

(2.11)
$$D_L = \lim_{y \uparrow y_0} \frac{W(y) - W(y_0)}{y - y_0}.$$

These two derivatives satisfy $D_L \leq D_R$ because we have proved that each element for the right-hand side of (2.10) is greater than or equal to each element of the right-hand side of (2.11).

Take D_0 to be any number satisfying $D_L \leq D_0 \leq D_R$. We now prove that the straight line $L(y) = D_0(y - y_0) + W(y_0)$ is a line of support at $(y_0, W(y_0))$. First; the line obviously passes through $(y_0, W(y_0))$. Second we prove $W(y) \geq L(y)$. For any point y_+, the inequality $D_R \geq D_0$ gives

$$\frac{W(y_+) - W(y_0)}{y_+ - y_0} \geq D_0.$$

By rearrangement

$$W(y_+) \geq D_0 (y_+ - y_0) + W(y_0)$$
$$\geq L(y_+).$$

Similarly the inequality holds for any point y_- to the left of y_0.

The last statement in the theorem concerns strict convexity, and it follows easily by checking a few of the details in the above argument.

By an extension of the above proof, we obtain

THEOREM 2.3. Through any point y_0 on a convex function $W(y)$ defined over R^k, there passes a hyperplane $L(y) = \sum_{i=1}^{k} l_i y_i + l_0$ which satisfies

$$(2.12) \qquad\qquad W(y) \geq L(y).$$

If the function is strictly convex, then (2.12) is strict unless $y = y_0$.

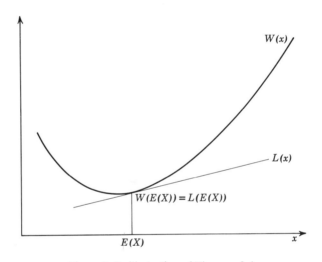

Figure 8. In illustration of Theorem 2.4.

The next theorem proves as special cases a number of familiar inequalities on expectations.

THEOREM 2.4. If $W(x)$ is a convex function and X is a real random variable, then

$$(2.13) \qquad\qquad E\{W(X)\} \geq W(E(X));$$

and, if $W(x)$ is strictly convex, the inequality is strict

$$(2.14) \qquad\qquad E\{W(X)\} > W(E(X))$$

unless X has all its probability at one point.

Proof. See Fig. 8. Let $L(x)$ be a line of support to $W(x)$ at $[E\{X\}, W(E\{X\})]$. Then $W(x) \geq L(x)$ and $E\{W(X)\} \geq E\{L(X)\}$. But the expectation of a linear function is the linear function of the expected value; therefore

$$E\{W(X)\} \geq E\{L(X)\}$$
$$= L(E(X))$$
$$= W(E(X)).$$

If $W(x)$ is strictly convex, then, from Theorem 2.2, $L(x) < W(x)$ unless x is the common point which in our case is $E(X)$. We have

$$E\{W(X) - L(X)\} > 0,$$

unless $W(X) = L(X)$ with probability one. The theorem follows by noting that $W(x) = L(x)$ implies $x = E\{X\}$.

A familiar example of this lemma is the following inequality for a real-valued *nondegenerate* random variable

$$E(X^2) > (E(X))^2.$$

Also we have

$$E\{|X - EX|^r\} > |E\{X - EX\}|^r$$

if $r > 1$. For the theorem these two examples use, respectively, the convex function x^2 and $|x^r|$ with $r > 1$.

The next theorem will be of use when we consider estimators having minimum concentration ellipsoids.

THEOREM 2.5. If $\|\sigma_{ij}\|$, $\|\sigma_{ij}^*\|$ are positive definite matrices and if $\|\sigma^{ij}\|$, $\|\sigma_*^{ij}\|$ are the corresponding inverse matrices, then

$$(2.15) \qquad \sum_{i,j=1}^{k} \sigma_{ij} l_i l_j \geq \sum_{i,j=1}^{k} \sigma_{ij}^* l_i l_j$$

for all $l_1, \cdots, l_k$ implies

$$(2.16) \qquad \sum_{i,j=1}^{k} \sigma^{ij} l_i l_j \leq \sum_{i,j=1}^{k} \sigma_*^{ij} l_i l_j$$

for all $l_1, \cdots, l_k$. Also identical equality in (2.15) implies the same in (2.16).

Proof. From the theory of matrices we know there exists a nonsingular matrix A such that

$$A' \|\sigma_{ij}^*\| A = I,$$

where A' is the transpose of A and I is the identity matrix. Also for any matrix there exists an orthogonal matrix which will diagonalize. Let O diagonalize $A' \| \sigma_{ij} \| A$; then

$$O'A' \| \sigma_{ij} \| AO = D$$

$$= \begin{Vmatrix} d_1 & & & O \\ & \cdot & & \\ & & \cdot & \\ & & & \cdot \\ O & & & d_k \end{Vmatrix}$$

Letting $AO = B$ and noting that $O'IO = I$, we obtain

(2.17) $$B' \| \sigma_{ij}^* \| B = I,$$
$$B' \| \sigma_{ij} \| B = D.$$

If $\mathbf{l} = (l_1, \cdots, l_k)$, the assumed inequality in the theorem may be written.

$$\mathbf{l}' \| \sigma_{ij} \| \mathbf{l} \geq \mathbf{l}' \| \sigma_{ij}^* \| \mathbf{l}.$$

Substituting $\mathbf{l} = B\mathbf{t}$ and using (2.17), we obtain

$$\mathbf{t}' D \mathbf{t} \geq \mathbf{t}' I \mathbf{t},$$

which may be rewritten

(2.18) $$\Sigma d_i t_i^2 \geq \Sigma t_i^2.$$

Since (2.18) holds for all $t_1, \cdots, t_k$, we have $d_i \geq 1$ $(i = 1, \cdots, k)$. Therefore we can write, for all $\mathbf{t}$,

$$\Sigma d_i^{-1} t_i^2 \leq \Sigma t_i^2$$

or

$$\mathbf{t}' D^{-1} \mathbf{t} \leq \mathbf{t}' I \mathbf{t}.$$

Now, if we make the substitution $\mathbf{t} = B'\mathbf{l}$ (which is not the inverse of the one above!), we obtain

$$\mathbf{l}' B D^{-1} B' \mathbf{l} \leq \mathbf{l}' B B' \mathbf{l}.$$

Then, since

$$\| \sigma^{ij} \| = [B'^{-1} D B^{-1}]^{-1}$$
$$= B D^{-1} B',$$

and

$$\| \sigma_*^{ij} \| = [B'^{-1} I B^{-1}]^{-1}$$
$$= B B',$$

we have the required inequality

$$\mathbf{l}' \| \sigma^{ij} \| \mathbf{l} \leq \mathbf{l}' \| \sigma_*^{ij} \| \mathbf{l}$$

or in summation form

$$\Sigma l_i l_j \sigma^{ij} \leq \Sigma l_i l_j \sigma_*^{ij}.$$

The last statement in the theorem is obtained by noting that equality is equivalent to $\geq$ and $\leq$ holding simultaneously and then applying the first part of the theorem for each direction of inequality.

We now develop some theorems which provide a constructive procedure for improving estimators and under certain conditions a method for obtaining minimum-risk unbiased estimators.

THEOREM 2.6. (RAO–BLACKWELL). If $t(x)$ is a sufficient statistic for $\{P_\theta \mid \theta \in \Omega\}$ over $\mathcal{X}(\mathcal{A})$ and if $f(x)$ is an unbiased estimator of $g(\theta)$, then $h(t) = E\{f(X) \mid t\}$ is an unbiased estimator based on $t(x)$. The inequality $\sigma_f^2(\theta) > \sigma_h^2(\theta)$ holds unless $f(x) = h(t(x))$ almost everywhere (P_θ). With a strictly convex loss function the inequality $\mathbf{R}_f(\theta) > \mathbf{R}_h(\theta)$ holds unless $f(x) = h(t(x))$ almost everywhere (P_θ), in which case $\mathbf{R}_f(\theta) = \mathbf{R}_h(\theta)$.

Proof. The part of the theorem concerning the variance inequality follows as a particular case of the next part by using the strictly convex loss function $W(d, \theta) = (d - g(\theta))^2$.

$t(x)$ is a sufficient statistic. Therefore the conditional probability is independent of θ and $h(t)$ which is the conditional expectation of $f(x)$, given $t(x) = t$, does not depend on θ. This proves that $h(t)$ is a statistic defined over the space of $t(x)$, say $\mathcal{T}$. We now show that it, also, is an unbiased estimator of $g(\theta)$.

$$
\begin{aligned}
E_\theta\{h(T)\} &= \int_{\mathcal{T}} h(t) \, dP_\theta^T(t) \\
&= \int_{\mathcal{T}} \int_{\mathcal{X}} f(x) \, dP(x \mid t) \, dP_\theta^T(t) \\
&= \int_{\mathcal{X}} f(x) \, dP_\theta(x) \\
&= E_\theta\{f(X)\}.
\end{aligned}
$$

In short, $h(t)$ is the conditional expectation of $f(x)$, and therefore the expectation of $h(t)$ is just the over-all expectation of $f(x)$. The above equations assume that the conditional probability is a measure, but, if we use directly the definition of conditional expectation, the result remains valid in general.

We now consider the *conditional* expectation of the loss, *given the sufficient statistic* $t(x)$. For $f(x)$ we have

$$E\{W(f(X), \theta) \mid t\},$$

and for $h(t)$ we have

$$W(h(t), \theta).$$

Now, applying Theorem 2.4 and remembering that $h(t) = E\{f(X)|t\}$, we obtain

$$E\{W(f(X), \theta)|t\} \geq W(h(t), \theta)$$

with equality only if $f(X)$ is equal $h(t)$ with conditional probability one. Now, taking the marginal expectation with respect to the distribution for t, we have

$$E_\theta\{W(f(X), \theta)\} \geq E_\theta\{W(h(T), \theta)\}$$

or equivalently

$$\mathbf{R}_f(\theta) \geq \mathbf{R}_h(\theta),$$

with equality only if $f(X) = h(t(X))$ with probability one. This completes the proof under the assumption that the conditional probability is a measure. However, by combining the proof of Theorem 2.4 with the sort of argument above, the theorem can be proved without this assumption.

COROLLARY 1. If the loss function is convex, $\mathbf{R}_f(\theta) \geq \mathbf{R}_h(\theta)$ for all θ.

Proof. The proof is a minor alteration of the second part of the proof above.

COROLLARY 2. If the loss function is strictly convex, then the estimators based on the sufficient statistic form a complete class of decision functions for the estimation of $g(\theta)$.

Proof. The proof follows directly from the definition of complete class and from the statement of the theorem, provided we call $f(x)$ a function of $t(x)$ if it can be written $f(x) = h(t(x))$ almost everywhere $\{P_\theta|\theta \in \Omega\}$.

COROLLARY 3. If the loss function is convex, then for any randomized unbiased estimator, there is a nonrandomized unbiased estimator with smaller or equal risk.

Proof. The proof follows by replacing the random choice of estimate by its conditional expectation, given the outcome and following the pattern of proof for the theorem.

EXAMPLE 2.2. Let $X_1, \cdots, X_n$ be independent and each have the same absolutely continuous distribution on R^1, and let the class of probability measures correspond to all the absolutely continuous distributions on R^1. Then, freely speaking, we have a sample of n from some absolutely continuous distribution on R^1. Problems 29 and 30 in Chapter 1 are to prove that $t(\mathbf{x}) = (x_{(1)}, \cdots, x_{(n)})$, the order statistic, is sufficient. Consider now the estimation of $E(X)$, the mean of the absolutely continuous distribution. Obviously $f(\mathbf{x}) = x_1$ is an unbiased estimator, but, since it ignores $x_2, \cdots, x_n$, we should expect to be able to find a better estimator. We apply the Rao–Blackwell theorem and calculate $h(t)$, the conditional expectation of x_1. The conditional probability, given the order statistic, assigns equal probability to each of the $n!$ permutations of $(x_{(1)}, \cdots, x_{(n)})$; therefore

$$\Pr\{X_1 = x_{(i)}\,|\,t(x)\} = \frac{(n-1)!}{n!}$$

$$= \frac{1}{n},$$

and

(2.19) $$h(t) = x_{(1)} \cdot \frac{1}{n} + \cdots + x_{(n)} \cdot \frac{1}{n}$$

$$= \frac{\Sigma x_{(i)}}{n}$$

$$= \frac{\Sigma x_i}{n}$$

$$= \bar{x}.$$

The Rao–Blackwell theorem then says that $\bar{x}$ is unbiased and that it has smaller variance and smaller risk (strictly convex loss) than x_1.

Similarly for the estimation of $E(X^2)$ the Rao–Blackwell theorem says that $\Sigma x_i^2/n$ is unbiased and has smaller variance than the statistic x_1^2.

There is one detail we have overlooked. The parameters $E(X)$ and $E(X_2)$ do not exist for all the probability measures of this example. This frequently happens in nonparametric problems, and we shall consider it further in Chapter 4. For our example here, the results obtained are valid.

EXAMPLE 2.3. Let $X_1, \cdots, X_n$ be independent and each have the normal distribution with μ and variance one, and let the class of probability measures correspond to all $\mu \in R^1$. Consider the estimation of $E(X^2) = \mu^2 + 1$. By example 5.1 in Chapter 1, we know that $t(\mathbf{x}) = n^{-1}\Sigma x_i = \bar{x}$ is a sufficient statistic. Also from the previous example we know that $n^{-1}\Sigma x_i^2$ is an unbiased estimator for all absolutely continuous distributions on R^1 and so certainly for the normal distributions here. We apply the Rao–Blackwell theorem, noting that $\Sigma x_i^2 = \Sigma(x_i - \bar{x})^2 + n\bar{x}^2$ and that the distribution of $\bar{X}$ is independent of the distribution of $\Sigma(X_i - \bar{X})^2$:

$$E_\mu\left\{\frac{\Sigma X_i^2}{n}\,\Big|\,\bar{x}\right\} = E_\mu\left\{\frac{\Sigma(X_i - \bar{X})^2}{n} + \bar{X}^2\,\Big|\,\bar{x}\right\}$$

$$= E_\mu\left\{\frac{\Sigma(X_i - \bar{X})^2}{n}\right\} + \bar{x}^2$$

$$= \frac{n-1}{n} + \bar{x}^2.$$

This is then unbiased for the distributions of this example and has smaller variance that $n^{-1}\Sigma x_i^2$.

We have now for vector estimation an analog of the Rao–Blackwell theorem.

THEOREM 2.7.   (BLACKWELL–LEHMANN–SCHEFFÉ).   If $t(x)$ is a sufficient statistic for $\{P_\theta | \theta \in \Omega\}$ and if $\mathbf{f}(x)$ is an unbiased estimator of $\mathbf{g}(\theta)$, then $\mathbf{h}(t) = E\{\mathbf{f}(X) | t\}$ is an unbiased estimator based on $t(x)$.   With a strictly convex loss function, the inequality $\mathbf{R}_f(\theta) > \mathbf{R}_h(\theta)$ holds unless $\mathbf{f}(x) = \mathbf{h}(t(x))$ almost everywhere (P_θ), in which case $\mathbf{R}_f(\theta) = \mathbf{R}_h(\theta)$.   The ellipsoid of concentration for $\mathbf{h}$ is contained in the ellipsoid of concentration for $\mathbf{f}$ with equality of ellipsoids only if $\mathbf{f}(x) = \mathbf{h}(t(x))$ almost everywhere P_θ).

Proof.   Most of the proof duplicates that for the previous theorem but uses vectors instead of real numbers for $\mathbf{f}$ and $\mathbf{h}$.   The part needing special proof concerns the ellipsoids of concentration.

Since $\mathbf{f}(x)$ is an unbiased estimator of $g(\theta)$, any linear combination of the coordinates of $\mathbf{f}(x)$, say $\Sigma l_i f_i$, is an unbiased estimator of the same linear combination of the coordinates of $g(\theta)$.   By Theorem 2.6 we have that

$$E\{\Sigma l_i f_i(X) | t\} = \Sigma l_i E\{f_i(X) | t\}$$
$$= \Sigma l_i h_i(t),$$

is an unbiased estimator of $\Sigma l_i g_i(\theta)$ and has smaller variance unless $\Sigma l_i f_i(X) = \Sigma l_i h_i(t(X))$ with probability one, in which case the variances are equal.

Let $\mathbf{f}(x)$ and $\mathbf{h}(t)$ have, respectively, the covariance matrices $\|\sigma_{ij}(\theta)\|$ and $\|\sigma_{ij}^*(\theta)\|$.   Now, since the variance of $\Sigma l_i f_i(x)$ is $\Sigma l_i l_j \sigma_{ij}(\theta)$ and of $\Sigma l_i h_i(t)$ is $\Sigma l_i l_j \sigma_{ij}^*(\theta)$, we can write the variance inequality

$$\Sigma l_i l_j \sigma_{ij}(\theta) \geq \Sigma l_i l_j \sigma_{ij}^*(\theta).$$

This inequality holds for all $l_1, \cdots, l_k$.   Then, assuming that the matrices are positive definite and applying Theorem 2.5, we obtain

$$\Sigma l_i l_j \sigma^{ij}(\theta) \leq \Sigma l_i l_j \sigma_*^{ij}(\theta)$$

for all $l_i, \cdots, l_k$.   Now, for the $l_1, \cdots, l_k$ for which

(2.20) $\Sigma l_i l_j \sigma^{ij}(\theta) = k + 2$

we need $\delta \leqslant 1$ in order that

$$\Sigma \delta l_i \delta l_j \sigma_*^{ij}(\theta) = k + 2.$$

This obviously implies that the ellipsoid (2.20) contains the ellipsoid

$$\Sigma l_i l_j \, \sigma_*^{ij}(\theta) = 2k + 2.$$

The equality of ellipsoids means that the inequalities above should all be identities, and this means that $\mathbf{f}(X) = \mathbf{h}(t(X))$ with probability one.

If the matrices are singular, then certain of the linear combinations will have zero variance, and this implies that all probability is in a linear subspace. The preceding argument can be applied in such a subspace. The constant $k + 2$ gives the proper relationship between ellipsoids in one space and the related ellipsoids in a subspace. The details of this argument are quite straightforward.

The next theorem we consider helps us to avoid for many problems the sometimes tedious calculation of conditional expectations, and it produces unbiased estimators with minimum risk (convex loss). First, a definition:

A parameter $\mathbf{g}(\theta)$ for $\{P_\theta \,|\, \theta \in \Omega\}$ over $\mathscr{X}(\mathscr{A})$ is estimable if there exists a statistic $\mathbf{f}(x)$ such that $E_\theta\{\mathbf{f}(X)\} = \mathbf{g}(\theta)$ for $\theta \in \Omega$; that is, if there exists an unbiased estimator for it.

THEOREM 2.8. (LEHMANN–SCHEFFÉ). If there is a complete and sufficient statistic $t(x)$ for $\{P_\theta \,|\, \theta \in \Omega\}$, then every estimable real parameter $g(\theta)$ has a unique unbiased estimator with minimum variance and minimum risk (strictly convex loss); this estimator is the only unbiased estimator which is a function of $t(x)$.

Proof. From the assumptions of the theorem we know there is at least one unbiased estimator of $g(\theta)$. By the Rao–Blackwell Theorem 2.6 we know that, for any unbiased estimator $f(x)$, there is an unbiased estimator $h(t)$ based on $t(x)$ such that $\mathbf{R}_f(\theta) \geq \mathbf{R}_h(\theta)$ with strict inequality for at least one θ unless $h(x)$ can be written as a function of $t(x)$ almost everywhere for each θ. Therefore, in looking for minimum-risk estimators, we can restrict our attention to the unbiased estimators based on $t(x)$.

If there are two such estimators, say $h_1(t)$ and $h_2(t)$, then

$$E_\theta\{h_1(T)\} = g(\theta),$$

$$E_\theta\{h_2(t)\} = g(\theta),$$

and therefore

$$E_\theta\{h_1(T) - h_2(T)\} = g(\theta) - g(\theta) = 0.$$

But, from the completeness of the statistic $t(x)$, we have $h_1(t) - h_2(t) = 0$ almost everywhere with respect to each of the measures P_θ^T. Thus the unbiased estimator based on $t(x)$ is essentially unique and has smaller variance and risk than any other unbiased estimator.

EXAMPLE 2.4.   Let $X_1, \cdots, X_n$ be independent, let each have the normal distribution with mean μ and variance 1, and let $\mu \in R^1$.   From Chapter 1 we know that $\bar{x}$ is a complete sufficient statistic.

Consider the problem of estimating the real parameters: μ, μ^2, $E(X^2) = \mu^2 + 1$.   All we need is to find an unbiased estimator based on $\bar{x}$, and it will have uniformly minimum variance and uniformly minimum risk for any strictly convex loss function.

For μ, $\bar{x}$ itself is the obvious estimator and, of course, the only one that is a function of $\bar{x}$.

For μ^2, let us calculate the expectation of $\bar{x}^2$.

$$E_\mu\{\bar{X}^2\} = [E_\mu(\bar{X})]^2 + \sigma_\mu^2\{\bar{X}\}$$

$$= \mu^2 + \frac{1}{n} \, ;$$

therefore

$$E_\mu\left\{\bar{X}^2 - \frac{1}{n}\right\} = \mu^2,$$

and $\bar{x}^2 - 1/n$ is the unique minimum variance estimator.

For $E(X^2) = \mu^2 + 1$, we obviously take $\bar{x}^2 + (n-1)/n$ as the minimum-risk estimator.

For vector parameters we have the following extension of the Lehmann–Scheffé Theorem 2.8.

THEOREM 2.9.   (LEHMANN–SCHEFFÉ).   If there is a complete and sufficient statistic $t(x)$ for $\{P_\theta \,|\, \theta \in \Omega\}$, then every estimable vector parameter has a unique unbiased estimator with minimum concentration ellipsoid and minimum risk (strictly convex loss); this estimator is the only unbiased estimator that is a function of $t(x)$.

Proof.   The proof is a vector analog of that for the previous theorem.

EXAMPLE 2.5.   Let $X_1, \cdots, X_n$ be independent, and let each X_i have the normal distribution with mean μ and variance σ^2.   We consider all distributions corresponding to $\mu \in R^1$ and $\sigma^2 \in]0, \infty[$.   By Problems 33 and 39 in Chapter 1 we know that $(\bar{x}, \Sigma(x_i - \bar{x})^2)$ is a complete sufficient statistic.

For the estimation of the parameter (μ, σ^2) it is easily seen that the statistic $(\bar{x}, \frac{1}{n-1}\sum(x_i - \bar{x})^2$ is unbiased.   Also it is a function of the complete sufficient statistic.   By the Lehmann–Scheffé Theorem 2.9 it is the unbiased estimator with minimum risk for any strictly convex loss function.   Also by Theorem 2.9 it is the unbiased estimate with minimum ellipsoid of concentration.

For the parameter $(\mu, \mu^2 + \sigma^2)$ we look for an unbiased estimator based on the sufficient statistic.   By examining the expectation of $\bar{x}^2$ we find that the required statistic is $\left((\bar{x}, \bar{x}^2 + \dfrac{n-1}{n} \left(\dfrac{1}{n-1} \sum (x_i - \bar{x})^2 \right) \right)$. This estimator has minimum ellipsoid of concentration and minimum risk (strictly convex loss) among the unbiased estimators.

▶ The Lehmann–Scheffé theorem proves under rather special assumptions that, if there is an unbiased estimator with uniformly smallest risk, then it is essentially unique. However this is true in general on the one assumption that the loss function is strictly convex.

THEOREM 2.10.   If $f_1(x)$ and $f_2(x)$ are unbiased estimators of $g(\theta)$ having uniformly minimum risk (strictly convex loss), then $f_1(x) = f_2(x)$ almost everywhere $\{P_\theta\}$.

Proof. Let $R(\theta)$ be the minimum value of the risk at θ.   Then

$$R(\theta) = E_\theta \{ W(f_1(X), \theta) \}$$
$$= E_\theta \{ W(f_2(X), \theta) \}.$$

Since $f_1(x), f_2(x)$ are unbiased, $\alpha\, f_1(x) + (1 - \alpha)\, f_2(x)$ is also an unbiased estimator of $g(\theta)$, and it must have of course risk at least as large as $R(\theta)$; that is,

(2.21) $E_\theta \{ W(\alpha\, f_1(X) + (1 - \alpha)\, f_2(X), \theta) \} \geq R(\theta).$

However, with $\alpha \in\,]0, 1[$ the strict convexity of W gives

(2.22) $E_\theta \{ W(\alpha\, f_1(X) + (1 - \alpha)\, f_2(X), \theta) \}$

$$\leq E_\theta \{ \alpha\, W(f_1(X), \theta) + (1 - \alpha)\, W(f_2(X), \theta) \}$$
$$\leq \alpha\, R(\theta) + (1 - \alpha)\, R(\theta)$$
$$\leq R(\theta),$$

but with equality if and only if

$$W(\alpha\, f_1(x) + (1 - \alpha) f_2(x), \theta) = \alpha\, W(f_1(x), \theta) + (1 - \alpha)\, W(f_2(x), \theta)$$

with probability (P_θ) one.   Again, by the strict convexity, this last condition can only hold if $f_1(x) = f_2(x)$ with probability (P_θ) one.

The two inequalities (2.21) and (2.22) together imply that

$$E_\theta \{ W(\alpha\, f_1(X) + (1 - \alpha) f_2(X), \theta) \} = R(\theta),$$

and this inequality by the last remark in the paragraph above implies that $f_1(x) = f_2(x)$ with probability (P_θ) one. Thus any two minimum risk estimators must be essentially equivalent.

If a problem has a complete sufficient statistic, the Lehmann–Scheffé theorem provides a constructive procedure for obtaining minimum-variance, minimum-risk unbiased estimators so long as the parameter in question has an unbiased estimator. Even in cases where a sufficient statistic that is complete cannot be found, the Rao–Blackwell theorem shows how any unbiased estimator can be improved upon by making it depend directly on a sufficient statistic. If the statistician is willing to accept squared error for the loss and variance for the risk then it remains possible under weaker assumptions to describe those statistics that are minimum-variance unbiased estimators of real parameters. For this we need to define a class of unbiased estimators of zero.

The class of unbiased estimators of zero for $\{P_\theta \mid \theta \in \Omega\}$ based on a sufficient statistic $t(x)$ is the class ν_0 of statistics:

$$\nu_0 = \{f(t) \mid E_\theta\{f(T)\} = 0 (\theta \in \Omega)\}.$$

A related class which is sometimes the class of statistics that are minimum-variance unbiased estimators is

$$\nu_1 = \left\{ h(t) \left| \begin{matrix} E_\theta\{h(T)\} \text{ exists} & \text{for } \theta \in \Omega \\ E_\theta\{h(T)f(T)\} = 0 & \text{for } f(t) \in \nu_0, \text{ and each } \theta \text{ for which } \sigma^2_{h(T)} < \infty. \end{matrix} \right. \right.$$

ν_1 consists of all those statistics having finite expectation and, when their variance is finite, zero covariance with all statistics in ν_0. The following is an extension of a theorem by Lehmann and Scheffé.

THEOREM 2.11. If all the statistics in ν_0 have finite variance, then a statistic is a minimum-variance estimator of its expected value if and only if it belongs to ν_1.

Proof. By the Rao–Blackwell theorem we restrict attention to estimators based on the sufficient statistic $t(x)$.

Let $h(t)$ be a minimum-variance unbiased estimator of $g(\theta)$. If $f(t)$ belongs to ν_0, then $h(t) + \lambda f(t)$ is also an unbiased estimator of $g(\theta)$,

$$E_\theta\{h(T) + \lambda f(T)\} = E_\theta\{h(T)\} + \lambda E_\theta\{f(T)\}$$
$$= g(\theta) + \lambda \cdot 0$$
$$= g(\theta),$$

and must have variance no smaller than that of the minimum-variance estimator $h(t)$. Therefore

$$\sigma^2_{h(T)+\lambda f(T)}(\theta) = \sigma^2_{h(T)}(\theta) + \lambda^2 \sigma^2_{f(T)}(\theta) + 2\lambda E\{h(T)f(T)\}$$
$$\geqslant \sigma^2_{h(T)}(\theta).$$

If $\sigma^2_{h(T)}(\theta)$ is finite, then the above inequality becomes

$$\lambda^2 \sigma^2_{f(T)} + 2\lambda E\{h(T)f(T)\} \geq 0,$$

and holds for all λ. By taking λ small, the first term becomes negligible with respect to the second, and, by then changing the sign of λ, the inequality would be reversed producing a contradiction—unless as must be the case the second term is zero. Thus $E_\theta\{h(T)f(T)\} = 0$ whenever $\sigma^2_{h(T)}(\theta)$ is finite, and therefore $h(t)$ belongs to ν_1.

Now suppose $h(t)$ belongs to ν_1. Let $h'(t)$ be any other unbiased estimator of $g(\theta) = E_\theta\{h(T)\}$. Then by subtraction $h'(t) - h(t)$ is an unbiased estimator of zero, say $f(t)$, and belongs to ν_0. Then, using the definition of ν_1, we have

$$\sigma^2_{h'(T)}(\theta) = \sigma^2_{h(T)+f(T)}(\theta)$$

$$= \sigma^2_{h(T)}(\theta) \qquad \text{if} \quad \sigma^2_{h(T)} = \infty$$

$$= \sigma^2_{h(T)}(\theta) + \sigma^2_{f(T)}(\theta) \qquad \text{if} \quad \sigma^2_{h(T)} < \infty.$$

In either case we have $\sigma^2_{h'(T)} \geq \sigma^2_{h(T)}$, which means that $h(t)$ is a minimum-variance unbiased estimator of its expected value.　　　◀

2.3. Invariant Estimation. In the previous section the requirement of unbiasedness was used to restrict the class of estimators in the hope of finding a good estimator, say with minimum risk, in the smaller class. Another property that can be used is invariance, and we discuss it briefly in this section.

In general terms the method of invariance is based on the following ideas. Suppose for an experiment that a statistician knows the probability measure is in the class $\{P_\theta \mid \theta \in \Omega\}$ of measures over $\mathscr{X}(\mathscr{A})$ and that he is interested in estimating the parameter $g(\theta)$. Also suppose that he knows of a transformation sx which maps $\mathscr{X}$ into $\mathscr{X}$ in such a way that the class of induced measures for sX is exactly the class $\{P_\theta \mid \theta \in \Omega\}$. Then the transformation s is called *invariant* in the sense that it leaves the probability structure of the problem unchanged. Of course, if the transformation s is applied to the outcome of the experiment, the new probability measure in general will not be the same as the original measure. If the statistician has decided on an estimator for the problem, then there are two courses open to him. He can use his estimator with the outcome of the experiment and obtain an estimate of the parameter $g(\theta)$. Or he can apply the transformation to the outcome, and then, since the new problem is essentially the same as the old, he can use his estimator to obtain an estimate of the new value of the parameter. His estimate for the original parameter is that value which corresponds to his estimated value of the new parameter. The estimator is called an *invariant estimator* if these two estimates are equal. The restriction to estimators having this property is called the *invariance principle*.

We give these ideas concisely by means of a simple example. Assume that a length is being measured. If an estimate is obtained from the measurements expressed in inches and if an estimate is obtained for the measurements expressed in centimeters, then the two estimates should correspond.

We now formalize these ideas. Let the class of probability measures be $\{P_\theta | \theta \in \Omega\}$ over $\mathscr{X}(\mathscr{A})$, and suppose that we have a class $\mathscr{G}$ of transformations sx which map $\mathscr{X}$ into itself $\mathscr{X}$. We shall call $\mathscr{G}$ an *invariant class of transformations* if it satisfies the following modest restrictions:

(1) $\mathscr{G}$ is a group; that is, it satisfies:
   (a) If $s_1, s_2 \in \mathscr{G}$, then the product transformation $s_1 s_2 \in \mathscr{G}$,
   (b) If $s \in \mathscr{G}$, then the inverse transformation $s^{-1} \in \mathscr{G}$.
(2) The class of measures $\{P_\theta | \theta \in \Omega\}$ is closed under $\mathscr{G}$; that is, if X has the probability measure $P_\theta(\theta \in \Omega)$, then sX for $s \in \mathscr{G}$ has the probability measure $P_{\bar{s}\theta}$ where $\bar{s}\theta \in \Omega$.

The second restriction has the following interpretation. If a transformation s is applied to the outcome of an experiment, then the measures that describe the transformed outcome should be ones included in the original class of measures. Thus in a certain sense the application of a transformation in $\mathscr{G}$ does not alter the problem but leaves it "invariant." The first restriction is to insure that the inverse of each transformation is in $\mathscr{G}$ and that, if we apply two transformations successively, then the composite transformation is also in the class $\mathscr{G}$.

It is to be noted that, for each transformation $s \in \mathscr{G}$, there is a corresponding transformation $\bar{s}$ which maps Ω into Ω. Problem 18 is to prove that each $\bar{s}$ maps Ω onto Ω in the form of a one-to-one correspondence. Also it is quite easy to prove that the class $\overline{\mathscr{G}}$ of transformations $\bar{s}$ is a group. See Problem 19.

We have a class $\mathscr{G}$ of transformations which leave the probability model unchanged. Consider now the estimation of a real parameter $g(\theta)$. To apply the methods of invariance it is necessary that the class $\mathscr{G}$ be restricted so that it leaves the structure of the parameter unchanged; we impose the further restriction:

(3) For each $s \in \mathscr{G}$, $g(\theta) = g(\theta')$ implies that $g(\bar{s}\theta) = g(\bar{s}\theta')$ for all $\theta, \theta' \in \Omega$.

This means that, when a transformation s is applied to the outcome, a value of the parameter $g(\theta)$ is also transformed, and the new value does not depend on which θ corresponded to the original value of $g(\theta)$. Thus a transformation s on $\mathscr{X}$ or the corresponding transformation $\bar{s}$ on Ω induces a transformation on the values of the parameter $g(\theta)$. Designating this transformation by $\bar{s}_g$, we have the defining equation

$$\bar{s}_g \, g(\theta) = g(\bar{s}\theta).$$

This means that, if $g(\theta)$ is the parameter value for X, then $\bar{s}_g \, g(\theta)$ is the parameter value for sX.   If condition (3) is fulfilled, we say that the class $\mathscr{G}$ is *invariant for the parameter* $g(\theta)$.

The invariance principle for the estimation of $g(\theta)$ is to confine attention to the invariant estimators:

$f(x)$ *is an invariant estimator for* $g(\theta)$ *if*

$$\bar{s}_g f(x) = f(sx)$$

for all $s \in \mathscr{G}$ *and all* $x \in \mathscr{X}$.

The interpretation is that, if a transformation in $\mathscr{G}$ changes the parameter values, then the values of the estimate should be changed in exactly the same manner.

For the estimation of the parameter $g(\theta)$ we suppose then that the statistician restricts his attention to the estimators which are invariant for $g(\theta)$ and looks for one having some optimum property such as uniformly minimum risk.   If there is a loss function which is natural to a problem, it is usual to impose a further restriction on the class of transformations $\mathscr{G}$; viz., that the loss for a decision in the untransformed problem should be the same as the loss for the corresponding decision in the transformed problem. We therefore introduce one further restriction:

(4)   For each $s \in \mathscr{G}$,

$$W(f, \theta) = W(\bar{s}_g f, \bar{s}\theta)$$

for all $\theta \in \Omega, f \in R^1$.

A loss function satisfying this requirement for a given group is called an *invariant loss function*.

EXAMPLE 2.6.   Let the random variables $Y_1, \cdots, Y_n$ be defined by the equations,

$$Y_1 = \alpha + \beta x_1 + U_1,$$

$$\cdot \quad \cdot \quad \cdot \quad \cdot \quad \cdot \quad \cdot \quad \cdot$$

$$Y_n = \alpha + \beta x_n + U_n.$$

where $U_1, \cdots, U_n$ are independent random variables, each with the uniform distribution over the interval $[-\frac{1}{2}, +\frac{1}{2}]$.   The class of probability distributions corresponds to all values of $(\alpha, \beta) \in R^2$, and the numbers $x_1, \cdots, x_n$ are given constants of the problem.   This is the probability model for the simple regression problem, but with the one change that the "errors" have a uniform distribution with known range rather than the normal distribution.   Consider the estimation of the vector-valued parameter (α, β).

We can assume that $\Sigma x_i = 0$.   For otherwise we write

$$\alpha + \beta x_i = \alpha + \beta \bar{x} + \beta(x_i - \bar{x})$$
$$= \alpha' + \beta'(x_i - \bar{x})$$

and, using the simply transformed parameters α' and β', the vector corresponding to β', $(x_1 - \bar{x}, \cdots, x_n - \bar{x})$, has the sum of its coordinates equal to zero.

Consider the group of transformations

$$\mathscr{G} = \{sy_i = y_i + a_s + b_s x_i \ (i = 1, \cdots, n) \,|\, (a_s, b_s) \in R^2\}.$$

This class of transformations satisfies our requirements.   First, the class is a group (actually a symmetric group).   Second, each probability distribution is transformed by an element of $\mathscr{G}$ into another of the distributions for the problem.   In fact, we have the following induced group of transformations on the parameter space R^2 of (α, β).

$$\bar{\mathscr{G}} = \left\{ \begin{matrix} \bar{s}\,\alpha = \alpha + a_s \\ \bar{s}\,\beta = \beta + b_s \end{matrix} \,\middle|\, (a_s, b_s) \in R^2 \right\}.$$

A statistic for the estimation of the parameter (α, β) will be a pair of real-valued functions, $(f(y_1, \cdots, y_n), g(y_1, \cdots, y_n))$.   We shall consider the application of the invariance method to this estimation problem.   According to the theory above, we want the estimate (f, g) to be transformed by an element of the group $\mathscr{G}$ in exactly the same way as the parameter (α, β) being estimated is transformed.   We therefore have the following conditions on (f, g):

$$f(sy) = \bar{s} f(\mathbf{y}),$$
$$g(sy) = \bar{s}\, g(\mathbf{y}).$$

Substituting a typical transformation s, we obtain the equations

$$f(y_1 + a_s + b_s x_1, \cdots, y_n + a_s + b_s x_n) = f(y_1, \cdots, y_n) + a_s,$$
$$g(y_1 + a_s + b_s x_1, \cdots, y_n + a_s + b_s x_n) = g(y_1, \cdots, y_n) + b_s.$$

The invariance method is to restrict our attention to the estimators satisfying this requirement and make us look for one for which the risk function is a minimum.

A reasonable loss function for this problem might be

$$W(f, g; \alpha, \beta) = p(f - \alpha)^2 + q(g - \beta)^2,$$

where we take $p, q > 0$.   This represents a weighting of the squared error for each of α and β.   The estimator which minimizes the risk corresponding to this loss function is of the following form: For a given outcome $(y_1, \cdots, y_n)$ there are only a certain set of values of (α, β) for which the probability density at $(y_1, \cdots, y_n)$ is positive, not equal to zero; the value of the estimator for this outcome is the center of gravity of this set of "possible" values for (α, β). The derivation of this result is given as Problem 20 at the end of the Chapter. See [9].

It is perhaps interesting to show that the loss function introduced above is an invariant loss function:

$$W(\bar{s}f, \bar{s}g; \bar{s}\alpha, \bar{s}\beta)$$

$$= p(\bar{s}f - \bar{s}\alpha)^2 + q(\bar{s}g - \bar{s}\beta)^2$$

$$= p(f - \alpha)^2 + q(g - \beta)^2$$

$$= W(f, g; \alpha, \beta).$$

3. THE THEORY OF HYPOTHESIS TESTING

3.1. Introduction. Suppose for a given experiment the statistician has decided on the class of distributions $\{P_\theta | \theta \in \Omega\}$ over the space $\mathscr{X}(\mathscr{A})$. Then the statistical problem remaining is what we call a hypothesis testing problem if there are only two decisions which can be made at the completion of the experiment: the decision that the parameter value θ which produced the outcome is in a subset of Ω, or the decision that it is in the complement of that subset. Also, there is often an asymmetry inherent in the problem whereby one of the subsets represents the situation found in similar problems in the past, the status quo, while the complement represents some new situation that may be present. It is for this reason that the usual method of treating these problems is also asymmetric. The object is of course to make the decision appropriate to the situation—to make a correct decision as to which set the underlying probability measure is in. An example of a hypothesis testing problem is in Example 1.2 in Section 1 of this chapter, page 43. There, the asymmetry in the method of treatment is in the restriction to decision functions in the class $\mathscr{D}_f$.

We designate by ω the subset of values in Ω which correspond to the probability measures of the "standard" situation and by $\Omega - \omega$ the complementary set which corresponds to the measures of the new situation. We refer to these as the *hypothesis*: $\theta \in \omega$, and the *alternative hypothesis*: $\theta \in \Omega - \omega$. This latter term will usually be abbreviated to *alternative*. The two decisions, one of which the statistician must make on the completion of the experiment, are d_1, the decision to accept the hypothesis and say that θ belongs to ω, and d_2, the decision to accept the alternative and say that θ belongs to $\Omega - \omega$.

Because there are only two decisions, the loss function has a simplified form. Let

$$W(d_1, \theta) = W_1(\theta)$$

and

$$W(d_2, \theta) = W_2(\theta).$$

If the θ of the underlying probability measure is in ω, then a decision d_1 to accept the hypothesis is correct, and we usually require the loss to be zero:

$$W_1(\theta) = 0$$

for $\theta \in \omega$. Similarly, for θ in $\Omega - \omega$, the decision d_2 to accept the alternative is correct, and we usually have

$$W_2(\theta) = 0$$

for $\theta \in \Omega - \omega$. It follows that we can further simplify the notation and designate by $W(\theta)$ the loss resulting from an incorrect decision; then we have

$$W(\theta) = W_1(\theta) + W_2(\theta).$$

A decision function also has a simplified form. For each outcome $x \in \mathscr{X}$ there will be associated either d_1 or d_2. Consequently a decision function can be represented by a subset of $\mathscr{X}$ which is called the *critical region*, and consists of those points x that result in the decision d_2 to accept the alternative. These are the points for which the statistician makes the decision that the probability measure is one of those representing the "new" situation.

In hypothesis testing the randomized decisions play a very important role. Since there are only two decisions to which a randomized decision can assign probability, it suffices to give the probability for one of them which by tradition is d_2, the decision to accept the alternative. Accordingly, we describe a randomized decision function by means of a real-valued statistic $\phi(x)$, which is called the *test function* and is defined over $\mathscr{X}$. We require $\phi(x)$ to satisfy $0 \leq \phi(x) \leq 1$. For a given outcome x, $\phi(x)$ is taken to be the probability with which the statistician accepts the alternative, and then $1 - \phi(x)$ is the probability with which he accepts the hypothesis. The test function corresponding to a *non*randomized decision takes the value 1 on the critical region and the value 0 elsewhere.

In the examples of Section 1 the term *operating characteristic* was introduced for the function that gave the probability for each decision in each situation. Since there are only two decisions, the operating characteristic of a test function $\phi(x)$ can be described by a single function $\mathbf{P}_\phi(\theta)$, called the *power function*. $\mathbf{P}_\phi(\theta)$ gives the probability of accepting the alternative when the parameter is θ. Since $\phi(x)$ is the conditional probability of accepting the alternative given the value x, then

$$\mathbf{P}_\phi(\theta) = E_\theta\{\phi(X)\}$$

$$= \int_{\mathscr{X}} \phi(x)\, dP_\theta(x).$$

We can obtain the risk function directly from the power function; we have

$$\mathbf{R}_\phi(\theta) = W_2(\theta)\, \mathbf{P}_\phi(\theta) \qquad \text{for } \theta \in \omega$$

$$= W_1(\theta)\, (1 - \mathbf{P}_\phi(\theta)) \qquad \text{for } \theta \in \Omega - \omega.$$

The risk function is just the power function or its complement weighted at each value of θ. Therefore it should not be surprising that much of the theory of hypothesis testing is based directly on the power function, and in fact for many of the standard problems a loss function is not even considered.

In hypothesis testing the class of decision or test functions is restricted to those that give the statistician protection in the "standard" situation represented by the hypothesis. This protection takes the form of a bound on the probability of an incorrect decision. To formulate this we need the definition:

A test function is of size α if

(3.1) $$\mathbf{P}_\phi(\theta) = \int_{\mathscr{X}} \phi(x)\, dP_\theta(x) \leq \alpha$$

for all $\theta \in \omega$.

For θ belonging to ω the power function $\mathbf{P}_\phi(\theta)$ is the probability of an incorrect decision; therefore the definition means that, when the underlying probability measure is represented by the hypothesis, the test makes a wrong decision with probability no more than α. The statistician will examine his experimental situation, and choose a value for α (often 0.10, 0.05, or 0.01) to give the protection he desires should the parameter value in his experiment be one of those of the "standard" situation. *He then restricts his class of test functions $\mathscr{D}_f$ to those of size* α. For some later results in this section it is convenient to have a somewhat more restrictive definition:

A test function is of exact size α if

$$\mathbf{P}_\phi(\theta) = \int_{\mathscr{X}} \phi(x)\, dP_\theta(x) \leq \alpha$$

for all $\theta \in \omega$ and if

$$\mathbf{P}_\phi(\theta) = \int_{\mathscr{X}} \phi(x)\, dP_\theta(x) = \alpha$$

for at least one θ, or more generally if

$$\sup_{\theta \in \omega} \mathbf{P}_\phi(\theta) = \alpha. \cdot$$

In choosing a test function in $\mathscr{D}_f$ the statistician wishes to minimize the risk. For θ belonging to ω, he has already obtained protection by the restriction on the tests in $\mathscr{D}_f$. Therefore he only examines the risk function for those values of θ in $\Omega - \omega$, and for these

$$\mathbf{R}_\phi(\theta) = W(\theta)\,(1 - \mathbf{P}_\phi(\theta)).$$

To find a test with minimum risk is clearly to find a test with maximum power. It is worth pointing out that the function $\mathbf{P}_\phi(\theta)$ is named the power function because, for θ belonging to the alternative, $\mathbf{P}_\phi(\theta)$ is the probability of a correct decision—*power* in the sense of ability *to detect a probability measure belonging to the alternative.*

For some of the simpler problems it happens that the test function having maximum power for one value of θ in $\Omega - \omega$ also has maximum power for every other θ. Such a test function is called a *uniformly most powerful test function of size α*; this is frequently abbreviated to *most powerful test of size α*. Among the tests in $\mathscr{D}_f$ such a test has uniformly smallest risk, regardless of the loss function, provided of course we accept the size condition as giving the protection under the hypothesis and we examine the risk function only for those θ belonging to the alternative. It would seem then that a reasonable first step toward getting most powerful test functions is to find a procedure for obtaining a size α test that has maximum power for a particular θ in the alternative. This we shall do, but first we give a verbal picture of the search for a test. The statistician finds all the test functions of size α and puts them together to form the class $\mathscr{D}_f$. With each test $\phi(x)$ he associates a collection of real numbers $(\mathbf{P}_\phi(\theta'), \mathbf{P}_\phi(\theta''), \mathbf{P}_\phi(\theta'''), \cdots)$ which gives the power or performance of that test for the different situations $\theta', \theta'', \theta'''$ of the alternative. For a particular θ he can examine the class $\mathscr{D}_f$ and pick out the test having the maximum power for that θ (see Problem 21). He could repeat this for another θ, say θ', and he would be surprised and lucky if the same test produced the maximum power at θ'.

3.2. The Fundamental Lemma. If there is only one probability measure in the hypothesis, that is, one θ in ω, we speak of a *simple* hypothesis, and

if there is more than one we speak of a *composite* hypothesis.   Similarly,
$\Omega - \omega$ can be a *simple* or a *composite* alternative hypothesis. The theorem
we now consider produces a most powerful test for any problem having
a simple hypothesis and a simple alternative.

THEOREM 3.1. (NEYMAN–PEARSON). THE FUNDAMENTAL LEMMA. For
testing the

$$\text{Hypothesis:}\quad P(A) = \int_A f(x)\, d\mu(x),$$

against the

$$\text{Alternative:}\quad P'(A) = \int_A g(x)\, d\mu(x),$$

a most powerful size-α test exists and has the form

(3.2)
$$\phi(x) = 1 \qquad \text{if} \quad \frac{g(x)}{f(x)} > c$$
$$= a \qquad\qquad\qquad = c$$
$$= 0 \qquad\qquad\qquad < c$$

where c and a are constants chosen to make the test have exact size α,

(3.3)
$$\int_{\mathscr{X}} \phi(x)\, dP(x) = \alpha.$$

Any two measures, $P(A)$ and $P'(A)$, will satisfy the requirements of the
theorem.   Problem 23 is to show that, for any two measures P, P', there
exists a dominating measure $\mu(A): P_X(A) << \mu(A), P'_X(A) << \mu(A)$.
The Radon–Nikodym theorem then supplies the probability density
functions, $f(x)$ and $g(x)$.

Proof of Theorem 3.1.   We are looking among the test functions that
satisfy

(3.4)
$$\int_{\mathscr{X}} \phi(x)\, f(x)\, d\mu(x) \le \alpha$$

for one that gives

(3.5)
$$\int_{\mathscr{X}} \phi(x)\, g(x)\, d\mu(x)$$

its maximum value.

We first show that a test of the form (3.2) can be found to satisfy the
requirement (3.3). $g(x)/f(x)$ is a function taking real values (or $+\infty$ if
the denominator is zero) and defined over $\mathscr{X}$.   Corresponding to the
measure $P(A)$ of the hypothesis, it has an induced distribution on the real

line, and this distribution is restricted to the positive axis (and possibly $+\infty$). Let c be a number such that

$$\Pr\left\{\frac{g(X)}{f(X)} \geq c\right\} \geq \alpha \geq \Pr\left\{\frac{g(X)}{f(X)} > c\right\}.$$

If we use the symbol ξ_p defined in Section 2.2, then we can write

$$c = \xi_{1-\alpha}\frac{g(X)}{f(X)}$$

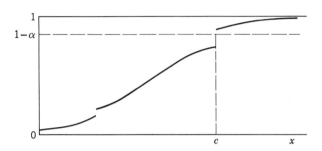

Figure 9. The hypothesis distribution of $g(X)/f(X)$.

Figure 9 illustrates the derivation of this value c. Problem 24 is to prove that, for X having the hypothesis distribution, $g(X)/f(X)$ does not have probability at $+\infty$, and hence that $c < +\infty$. From the definition of c we have

$$\Pr\left\{\frac{g(X)}{f(X)} > c\right\} \leq \alpha$$

and

$$\Pr\left\{\frac{g(X)}{f(X)} > c\right\} + \Pr\left\{\frac{g(X)}{f(X)} = c\right\} \geq \alpha.$$

Consequently there will always exist a number a between 0 and 1 such that

$$\Pr\left\{\frac{g(X)}{f(X)} > c\right\} + a\Pr\left\{\frac{g(X)}{f(X)} = c\right\} = \alpha.$$

But this last equation demonstrates that (3.3) is satisfied:

$$\int_{\mathscr{x}} \phi(x)\, dP(x) = \int_{\mathscr{x}} \phi(x) f(x)\, d\mu(x)$$

$$= 1 \cdot \Pr\left\{\frac{g(X)}{f(X)} > c\right\} + a \cdot \Pr\left\{\frac{g(X)}{f(X)} = c\right\}$$

$$+ 0 \cdot \Pr\left\{\frac{g(X)}{f(X)} < c\right\}$$

$$= \alpha.$$

We now show that the test $\phi(x)$ satisfying (3.2) is at least as powerful as any other test, say $\phi^*(x)$, of size α: We divide $\mathscr{X}$ into three disjoint sets $\mathscr{X}^+, \mathscr{X}^0, \mathscr{X}^-$:

$$\mathscr{X}^+ = \left\{ x \Big| \frac{g(x)}{f(x)} > c \right\},$$

$$\mathscr{X}^0 = \left\{ x \Big| \frac{g(x)}{f(x)} = c \right\},$$

$$\mathscr{X}^- = \left\{ x \Big| \frac{g(x)}{f(x)} < c \right\}.$$

On these sets, respectively, $g(x) > c f(x), = c f(x)$, and $< c f(x)$. We now compare the powers

$$\mathbf{P}_\phi - \mathbf{P}_{\phi^*} = \int_{\mathscr{X}} \phi(x) g(x) \, d\mu(x) - \int_{\mathscr{X}} \phi^*(x) g(x) \, d\mu(x)$$

$$= \int_{\mathscr{X}} (\phi - \phi^*) g(x) \, d\mu(x)$$

$$= \int_{\mathscr{X}^+} (\phi - \phi^*) g(x) \, d\mu(x) + \int_{\mathscr{X}^0} (\phi - \phi^*) g(x) \, d\mu(x)$$

$$+ \int_{\mathscr{X}^-} (\phi - \phi^*) g(x) \, d\mu(x).$$

On $\mathscr{X}^+$, $\phi(x)$ is equal to one; hence $\phi - \phi^*$ is positive or zero. On $\mathscr{X}^-$, $\phi(x)$ is equal to zero; hence $\phi - \phi^*$ is negative or zero. Then, noting the sign of the integrand for each term and using the relative magnitudes of $g(x)$ and $cf(x)$ on the three sets, we obtain

$$\mathbf{P}_\phi - \mathbf{P}_{\phi^*} \geq \int_{\mathscr{X}^+} (\phi - \phi^*) c f(x) \, d\mu(x) + \int_{\mathscr{X}^0} (\phi - \phi^*) c f(x) \, d\mu(x)$$

$$+ \int_{\mathscr{X}^-} (\phi - \phi^*) c f(x) \, d\mu(x)$$

$$= c \int_{\mathscr{X}} (\phi - \phi^*) f(x) \, d\mu(x)$$

$$= c \left[\int_{\mathscr{X}} \phi(x) f(x) \, d\mu(x) - \int_{\mathscr{X}} \phi^* f(x) \, d\mu(x) \right]$$

$$\geq c \left[\alpha - \int_{\mathscr{X}} \phi^* f(x) \, d\mu(x) \right]$$

$$\geq 0,$$

where the last inequality follows from the fact that ϕ^* satisfies 3.4 and the bracket is positive or zero.

EXAMPLE 3.1. Let $X_1, \cdots, X_n$ be independent, and let each have the normal distribution with mean ξ and variance 1. Consider the simple hypothesis and alternative.

$$\text{Hypothesis:} \quad \xi = 0,$$
$$\text{Alternative:} \quad \xi = \xi' \quad (>0).$$

We shall use the fundamental lemma to find a most powerful test of size α; that is, to find among test functions $\phi(x)$ satisfying

(i)
$$\int_{R^n} \phi(\mathbf{x}) \, k \exp\left[-\frac{1}{2}\sum x_i^2\right] \prod_{i=1}^{n} dx_i \leq \alpha$$

one that maximizes

(ii)
$$\int_{R^n} \phi(\mathbf{x}) \, k \exp\left[-\frac{1}{2}\sum (x_i - \xi')^2\right] \prod_{i=1}^{n} dx_i,$$

where $k = (2\pi)^{-n/2}$. By the lemma, the most powerful test is

$$\phi(\mathbf{x}) = 1 \quad \text{if} \quad \frac{k \exp\left[-\frac{1}{2}\Sigma(x_i - \xi')^2\right]}{k \exp\left[-\frac{1}{2}\Sigma x_i^2\right]} > c$$
$$= 0 \qquad\qquad\qquad\qquad\qquad < c,$$

where it is unnecessary to consider the points corresponding to the equality with c, since, as we shall see, they have probability zero. We have

$$\phi(\mathbf{x}) = 1 \quad \text{if} \quad \frac{k \exp\left[-\frac{1}{2}\Sigma(x_i - \xi')^2\right]}{k \exp\left[-\frac{1}{2}\Sigma x_i^2\right]} > c$$
$$= 0 \qquad\qquad\qquad\qquad\qquad < c$$
$$\qquad\quad \text{if} \quad \frac{\exp\left[-\frac{1}{2}\Sigma x_i{}^2 + \xi'\Sigma x_i - \frac{1}{2}n\xi'^2\right]}{\exp\left[-\frac{1}{2}\Sigma x_i^2\right]} > c$$
$$\qquad\qquad\qquad\qquad\qquad\qquad\qquad < c$$
$$\qquad \text{if} \quad \exp \xi'\Sigma x_i > c$$
$$\qquad\qquad\qquad\qquad < c,$$

where c stands for a constant with respect to $x_1, \cdots, x_n$, and it may be different in value from line to line in the relations above. The only restriction on c is that *at some stage* it be chosen to give the test function exact size α under the distribution of the hypothesis.

$$\phi(\mathbf{x}) = 1 \quad \text{if} \quad \xi'\Sigma x_i > c$$
$$= 0 \qquad\qquad\qquad\quad < c$$
$$\qquad \text{if} \quad \Sigma x_i > c$$
$$\qquad\qquad\qquad\quad < c$$
$$\qquad \text{if} \quad \bar{x} > c$$
$$\qquad\qquad\qquad\quad < c.$$

The test procedure is to accept the alternative if $\bar{x} > c$ and to accept the hypothesis if $\bar{x} < c$.   Since $\Pr(\bar{X} = c)$ is equal to zero under both the hypothesis and the alternative, the definition of the test for points having $\bar{x} = c$ is unimportant.   We now choose the value c:

$$\int_{R^n} \phi(\mathbf{x}) \, k \, \exp\left[-\tfrac{1}{2}\Sigma x_i^2\right] \Pi \, dx_i$$
$$= \Pr_{\xi=0}\{\bar{X} > c\}$$
$$= \Pr_{\xi=0}\{n^{1/2}\bar{X} > n^{1/2}c\}$$
$$= \alpha$$

Under the hypothesis distribution $n^{1/2}\bar{X}$ has the normal distribution with mean 0 and variance 1; hence $n^{1/2}c = z_\alpha$ where z_α is the value exceeded with probability α according to the standardized no mal distribution.   It follows then that a size α test having maximum power for the alternative is given by

$$\phi(\mathbf{x}) = 1 \quad \text{if} \quad \bar{x} > n^{-1/2}z_\alpha$$
$$< n^{-1/2}z_\alpha.$$

Now, the nice thing about this test is that it in no way depends on the value ξ', so long as $\xi' > 0$.   Our test is thus a *uniformly most powerful test for*

Hypothesis: $\xi = 0$,

Alternative: $\xi > 0$.

EXAMPLE 3.2.   Let X be a random variable with the Poisson distribution given by

$$P_m(A) = \int_A e^{-m} \frac{m^x}{x!} \, dN(x)$$

where N gives unit measure to each non-negative integer and zero measure to the set of all other points, and consider the hypothesis testing problem

Hypothesis: $m = m_0$,

Alternative: $m = m_1 \quad (>m_0)$.

By the fundamental lemma the most powerful size-α test is given by

$$\phi(x) = 1 \quad \text{if} \quad \frac{e^{-m_1}m_1^x}{x!} \left[\frac{e^{-m_0}m_0^x}{x!}\right]^{-1} > c$$
$$= a \qquad\qquad\qquad\qquad = c$$
$$= 0 \qquad\qquad\qquad\qquad < c,$$

where c is chosen to give the test exact size α by satisfying the equation

$$\Pr_{m_0}\{X > c\} + a \, \Pr_{m_0}\{X = c\} = \alpha.$$

We have

$$\phi(x) = 1 \qquad \text{if} \quad e^{m_0 - m_1} \left(\frac{m_1}{m_0}\right)^x > c$$
$$= a \qquad\qquad\qquad\qquad = c$$
$$= 0 \qquad\qquad\qquad\qquad < c,$$
$$\text{if} \quad \left(\frac{m_1}{m_0}\right)^x \qquad > c$$
$$= c$$
$$< c,$$
$$\text{if} \quad x \qquad\qquad > c$$
$$= c$$
$$< c.$$

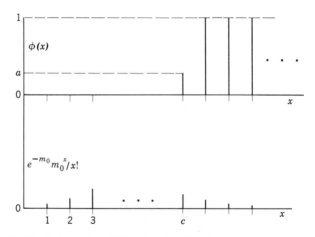

Figure 10. The test function $\phi(x)$ and probability density function $e^{-m_0} m_0^x / x!$.

The test procedure is to accept the alternative if $x > c$, to accept the alternative or the hypothesis, respectively, with probabilities a and $1 - a$ when $x = c$, and to accept the hypothesis when $x < c$.

It is for problems such as this involving discrete distributions that the randomized test functions offer a distinct advantage by allowing the statistician to use an exact size-α test and thereby increase the power.

The test in this example does not depend on m_1 so long as $m_1 > m_0$. It is therefore a *uniformly most powerful size-α test* for

Hypothesis: $m = m_0$,
Alternative: $m > m_0$.

3.3. Composite Hypotheses. If the hypothesis and alternative are simple, the fundamental lemma in the preceding section gives explicitly the test function of size α having maximum power. But, if the hypothesis is composite and the alternative simple, we do not have an analog of that lemma. However, the lemma, in conjunction with a method inherent in Wald's work [1] and developed by E. L. Lehmann, can sometimes be used to obtain size α tests with maximum power.

Consider the hypothesis testing problem

(3.6)
$$\text{Hypothesis:} \quad \theta \in \omega,$$
$$\text{Alternative:} \quad \theta = \theta' \quad (\theta' \notin \omega).$$

The method is to look for a most powerful test not just among tests satisfying

(3.7)
$$\int \phi(x) \, dP_\theta(x) \le \alpha$$

for *each* $\theta \in \omega$, but *among* the larger class of tests satisfying only

(3.8)
$$\int \phi(x) \, dP_{\theta_0}(x) \le \alpha$$

for *some particular* θ_0. In effect, then, we are considering the simple hypothesis, simple alternative problem given by

(3.9)
$$\text{Hypothesis:} \quad \theta = \theta_0,$$
$$\text{Alternative:} \quad \theta = \theta',$$

and this can be handled by the fundamental lemma. If we should be very lucky and find that the most powerful test in the class satisfying (3.8) just happened to be in the smaller class satisfying (3.7), then it is obviously most powerful among those in the smaller class, and hence is the most powerful test for the original problem (3.6). How are we to guide our choice of θ_0? If we consider the various measures in ω and look for one that seems to most resemble the measure of the alternative, θ', or that would seem to be most difficult for the statistician to test against or distinguish from the alternative, then the most powerful test of the simple hypothesis *may* be of the correct size for the original problem; i.e., be in the smaller class satisfying (3.7). Such a choice of θ in ω is called "*least favorable*" to the statistician.

EXAMPLE 3.3. For the probability measures of Example 3.1, consider the hypothesis testing problem:

(3.10)
$$\text{Hypothesis:} \quad \xi \le 0,$$
$$\text{Alternative:} \quad \xi = \xi_1 \quad (\xi_1 > 0).$$

What value of ξ in the hypothesis would be most difficult for the statistician to distinguish from the alternative value ξ_1? The most obvious choice guided by intuition is to choose the ξ closest to ξ_1: i.e., $\xi = 0$. Therefore we first consider the modified hypothesis testing problem with a simple hypothesis:

(3.11)
$$\text{Hypothesis:} \quad \xi = 0,$$
$$\text{Alternative:} \quad \xi = \xi_1.$$

But from Example 3.1 we know that for (3.11) the most powerful test is
$$\phi(\mathbf{x}) = 1 \quad \text{if} \quad \bar{x} > z_\alpha n^{-1/2}$$
$$= 0 \quad \quad < z_\alpha n^{-1/2}.$$

We must now see if our choice of ξ was truly least favorable; that is, if the test $\phi(\mathbf{x})$ is the smaller class of tests that are of the correct size for the original hypothesis. We evaluate, for $\xi \leqslant 0$,
$$E_\xi\{\phi(\mathbf{X})\} = \Pr_\xi \{ \bar{X} > z_\alpha n^{-1/2} \}$$
$$= \Pr \{Z > z_\alpha - \xi n^{1/2} \}$$
$$\leq \Pr \{Z > z_\alpha\}$$
$$= \alpha.$$

Z designates a random variable with the standardized normal distribution, and the inequality is a consequence of ξ being less than or equal zero. Our test is of the correct size, and hence by the argument preceding this example is the most powerful test for the original problem (3.10).

Since this test does not depend on the value ξ_1, we have a most powerful size-α test for

(3.12)
$$\text{Hypothesis:} \quad \xi \leq 0,$$
$$\text{Alternative:} \quad \xi > 0.$$

In Section 1, this example was considered with $n = 9$. We have here the proof that the test examined was a most powerful test in the class $\mathscr{D}_f$ of tests satisfying the size restriction.

In most problems there will not exist a *single* θ in ω which is least favorable. However, sometimes a weighted average of hypothesis measures will be least favorable. Then, instead of examining the tests that satisfy

(3.13)
$$\mathbf{P}_\phi(\theta) = \int_{\mathscr{X}} \phi(x) \, dP_\theta(x) \leq \alpha$$

for all θ, we examine the larger class of tests that satisfy the one condition

(3.14)
$$\int_\omega \left[\int_{\mathscr{X}} \phi(x) \, dP_\theta(x) \right] d\lambda(\theta) \leq \alpha,$$

where λ is the probability measure over ω which gives the "weighted average." Obviously any $\phi(x)$ satisfying all the conditions of (3.13) will produce an integrand $\leq \alpha$ for the final integration in (3.14) and hence will satisfy (3.14). This justifies the statement that the second class of tests is "larger" in that it contains the first class.

If we can interchange the order of integration,† the condition (3.14) can be written

(3.15) $$\int_{\mathcal{X}} \phi(x) \, dP_\lambda(x) \leq \alpha,$$

where

$$P_\lambda(A) = \int_\omega P_\theta(A) \, d\lambda(\theta).$$

Or, if the measures in ω are dominated by a measure μ and have the density function $f_\theta(x)$, then the condition (3.14) can be written

(3.16) $$\int_{\mathcal{X}} \phi(x) f_\lambda(x) \, d\mu(x) \leq \alpha$$

where

$$f_\lambda(x) = \int_\omega f_\theta(x) \, d\lambda(\theta).$$

This last step assumes that $f_\theta(x)$ is measurable as a function of (x, θ) over $\mathcal{X} \times \omega$. We consider this latter form, using the condition (3.16).

The idea again is to try to choose a weighting λ which produces an average of the hypothesis measures that most resembles the alternative, which would be most difficult for the statistician to distinguish from the alternative, which would be *least favorable* to the statistician. The procedure is to replace temporarily the original problem (3.10) by the simple hypothesis modification,

(3.17)
$$\text{Hypothesis:} \quad P_\lambda(A) = \int_A f_\lambda(x) \, d\mu(x),$$
$$\text{Alternative:} \quad P_{\theta'}(A) = \int_A f_{\theta'}(x) \, d\mu(x),$$

and find a most powerful test by means of the fundamental lemma. Then, to see if our choice of $\lambda(\theta)$ was really least favorable, to see if the test is in the smaller class of tests for the original problem, we must check whether it satisfies (3.13) for all $\theta \in \omega$. If it is of correct size, then by the same argument as before it is the most powerful test for the original problem.

EXAMPLE 3.4. Let $X_1, \cdots, X_n$ be independent, and each have the normal distribution with mean ξ and variance σ^2. Consider the hypothesis testing problem:

(3.18)
$$\text{Hypothesis:} \quad \sigma^2 \leq \sigma_0^2, \quad \xi \in R^1$$
$$\text{Alternative:} \quad \sigma^2 = \sigma_1^2, \quad \xi = \xi_1 \quad (\sigma_1^2 > \sigma_0^2).$$

† See Robbins [14].

Of course, in considering this problem we really have in mind the problem of testing the variance alone, namely;

(3.19)
$$\text{Hypothesis:} \quad \sigma^2 \leq \sigma_0^2,$$
$$\text{Alternative:} \quad \sigma^2 > \sigma_0^2.$$

However, as a first step we take a particular measure in the alternative of (3.19) and consider the simpler problem (3.18).

The hypothesis is composite. What weighting $\lambda(\xi, \sigma^2)$ of the hypothesis measures will most resemble the measure of the alternative? First, with ξ free, we would naturally think of setting it equal to ξ_1 and then taking σ^2 as large as possible, $\sigma^2 = \sigma_0^2$. This amounts to putting all $\lambda(\xi, \sigma^2)$ probability at the one parameter point (ξ_1, σ_0^2). However, if for the then modified problem we find the most powerful test, we find that it does not satisfy the size condition for the original problem, and hence that this λ was not least favorable.

Let us examine more carefully our choice of probability measure for ξ, σ^2. First, for σ^2 we naturally want to choose it closest to its alternative value; that is, make it as large as possible, and put all the λ probability at $\sigma^2 = \sigma_0^2$. Second, we consider ξ. ξ controls the distribution of $\bar{x}$ but has no effect on the remainder of the outcome $x_1 - \bar{x}, \cdots, x_n - \bar{x}$. So it is natural to see how, by weighting ξ, we can make the distribution of $\bar{X}$ under the hypothesis most like its distribution under the alternative. Under the hypothesis weighted for σ^2, $\bar{X}$ has the normal distribution with mean ξ and variance σ_0^2/n; under the alternative, the normal distribution with mean ξ_1 and variance σ_1^2/n. We describe the distribution of $\bar{X}$ symbolically:

$$\text{Hypothesis:} \quad \bar{X} = \xi + Y,$$
$$\text{Alternative:} \quad \bar{X} = \xi_1 + Y_1,$$

where Y, Y_1 are normally distributed with means zero and variances, respectively, σ_0^2/n and σ_1^2/n. By giving ξ a normal distribution with mean ξ_1 it is easily seen that the marginal distribution of $\bar{X}$ under both the hypothesis and the alternative is normal with mean ξ_1. Then by appropriately choosing the variance for ξ we can make the two marginal distributions of $\bar{X}$ also have identical variances. The appropriate variance σ_ξ^2 is found by equating the marginal variances of $\bar{X}$:

$$\sigma_\xi^2 + \frac{\sigma_0^2}{n} = \frac{\sigma_1^2}{n},$$

whence $\sigma_\xi^2 = n^{-1}[\sigma_1^2 - \sigma_0^2]$. Our $\lambda(\xi, \sigma^2)$ measure thus chooses $\sigma^2 = \sigma_0^2$ with probability one and gives ξ the normal distribution with mean ξ_1 and variance $n^{-1}[\sigma_1^2 - \sigma_0^2]$.

The original probability density function can be written as a product of the density function for $\bar{X}$ and a factor for the remainder of the outcome;

$$(3.20) \quad f_{\xi,\sigma^2}(\mathbf{x}) = k \exp\left[-\frac{n}{2\sigma^2}(\bar{x} - \xi)^2\right] \exp\left[-\frac{1}{2\sigma^2}\Sigma(x_i - \bar{x})^2\right],$$

where k depends only on the parameters and is irrelevant for the ratio of probability densities used in the fundamental lemma. Under the $\lambda(\xi, \sigma^2)$ weighting of the hypothesis, σ^2 is set equal to σ_0^2, and an integration is performed for the distribution of ξ. But ξ occurs only in the $\bar{x}$-density factor of (3.20), and we know from our argument above what marginal density must result for $\bar{X}$ when its conditional density, given ξ, is integrated with respect to the normal distribution of ξ. Obviously we have

$$f_\lambda(\mathbf{x}) = k \exp\left[-\frac{n}{2\sigma_1^2}(\bar{x} - \xi_1)^2\right] \exp\left[-\frac{1}{2\sigma_0^2}\Sigma(x_i - \bar{x})^2\right].$$

And, for the alternative, we have

$$f_{\xi_1\sigma_1^2}(\mathbf{x}) = k \exp\left[-\frac{n}{2\sigma_1^2}(\bar{x} - \xi_1)^2\right] \exp\left[-\frac{1}{2\sigma_1^2}\Sigma(x_i - \bar{x})^2\right].$$

We apply the fundamental lemma to this problem and obtain

$$\phi(\mathbf{x}) = 1 \quad \text{if} \quad \frac{f_{\xi_1\sigma^2}(\mathbf{x})}{f_\lambda(\mathbf{x})} > c$$

$$= 0 \quad\quad\quad\quad < c.$$

Now each succeeding expression below is a monotone-increasing function of the preceding expression:

$$\frac{f_{\xi_1\sigma^2}(\mathbf{x})}{f_\lambda(\mathbf{x})},$$

$$\frac{\exp\left[-\dfrac{1}{2\sigma_1^2}\Sigma(x_i - \bar{x})^2\right]}{\exp\left[-\dfrac{1}{2\sigma_0^2}\Sigma(x_i - \bar{x})^2\right]},$$

$$\exp\left[\left(\frac{1}{2\sigma_0^2} - \frac{1}{2\sigma_1^2}\right)\Sigma(x_i - \bar{x})^2\right],$$

$$\left(\frac{1}{2\sigma_0^2} - \frac{1}{2\sigma_1^2}\right)\Sigma(x_i - \bar{x})^2,$$

$$\Sigma(x_i - \bar{x})^2.$$

Hence the test function can be written

(3.21) $\phi(\mathbf{x}) = 1$ if $\Sigma(x_i - \bar{x})^2 > c$

                           $= 0$ $< c.$

Under the modified hypothesis, $\sigma^2 = \sigma_0^2$, and hence the induced distribution of $\Sigma(x_i - \bar{x})^2$ is that of $\sigma_0^2 \chi^2$ where χ^2 stands here for a random variable having the χ^2 distribution with $n - 1$ degrees of freedom. Let χ_α^2 be the point exceeded with probability α by χ^2. Then, to give our test exact size α, our choice of c is $\sigma_0^2 \chi_\alpha^2$, and the test is

$$\phi(\mathbf{x}) = 1 \quad \text{if} \quad \Sigma(x_i - \bar{x})^2 > \sigma_0^2 \chi_\alpha^2$$
$$= 0 \quad\quad\quad\quad\quad < \sigma_0^2 \chi_\alpha^2.$$

We now check to see if this test is of size α for the original hypothesis. When the parameter is (ξ, σ^2), the induced distribution of $\Sigma(x_i - \bar{x})^2$ is that of $\sigma^2 \chi^2$; therefore

$$E_{\xi\sigma^2}\{\phi(\mathbf{X})\} = \Pr_{\xi\sigma^2}\{\Sigma(X_i - \bar{X})^2 > \sigma_0^2 \chi_\alpha^2\}$$
$$= \Pr\{\sigma^2 \chi^2 > \sigma_0^2 \chi_\alpha^2\}$$
$$= \Pr\left\{\chi^2 > \frac{\sigma_0^2}{\sigma^2} \chi_\alpha^2\right\}$$
$$\leq \Pr\{\chi^2 > \chi_\alpha^2\}$$
$$= \alpha,$$

where the inequality results from $\sigma_0^2/\sigma^2 \geq 1$. The test is of correct size and hence is the most powerful size-α test for the original problem (3.18).

The test does not depend on ξ_1 or on σ_1^2 provided $\sigma_1^2 > \sigma_0^2$. Therefore it is a uniformly most powerful test for

Hypothesis: $\sigma^2 \leq \sigma_0^2$, $\xi \in R^1$,

Alternative: $\sigma^2 > \sigma_0^2$, $\xi \in R^1$,

which is the more general problem (3.19) mentioned at the beginning of the example.

3.4. The use of a Sufficient Statistic. In Section 1 we had a general theorem concerning the use of a sufficient statistic. We have now a closely related result concerning the use in hypothesis testing.

THEOREM 3.2. *If $\phi(x)$ is a test function for a hypothesis testing problem involving $\{P_\theta | \theta \in \Omega\}$, and if $t(x)$ is a sufficient statistic, then $E\{\phi(x) | t\}$ is a test function having the same power function as $\phi(x)$.*

Proof. The power function of $\phi(x)$ is

$$\mathbf{P}_\phi(\theta) = E_\theta^X\{\phi(X)\}.$$

But, from the definition of conditional expectation, we have

$$\mathbf{P}_\phi(\theta) = E_\theta^T\{E^X\{\phi(X)|T\}\},$$

and hence $E\{\phi(X)|t\}$ has the same expectation ("power function") as does $\phi(x)$. All we need prove, then, is that $E\{\phi(X)|t\}$ is a test function, that is, $E\{\phi(X)|t\}$ satisfies

$$0 \le E\{\phi(X)|t\} \le 1$$

for almost all t. But that this occurs follows easily from the representation of conditional expectation as an average with respect to conditional probability. See formula (4.14) in Section 4 of the preceding chapter.

▶ A generalized definition of sufficient statistic was introduced at the end of Section 5, Chapter 1. Let $\{P_{\theta\eta}|(\theta, \eta) \in \Theta \times H\}$ be a class of probability measures over $\mathscr{X}(\mathscr{A})$. A statistic $t(x)$ is *sufficient* for θ if the marginal distribution of $t(X)$ depends only on θ, that is, has the form $\{P_\theta^T|\theta \in \Theta\}$, and if the conditional distribution, given t, depends only on η (the "nuisance" parameter), that is, has the form $\{P_\eta^X(A|t)|\eta \in H\}$. Consider a hypothesis testing problem involving only θ:

(3.22)   Hypothesis: $\theta \in \omega$, $\eta \in H$,

        Alternative: $\theta \in \Theta - \omega$, $\eta \in H$.

For this we have a generalization of Theorem 3.2.

THEOREM 3.3. If $\phi(x)$ is a size-α test function for the problem (3.22) and if $t(x)$ is sufficient (θ), then there is a size-α test function $\psi(t)$ for the problem, its power function depends only on θ, and for each θ has power at least as large as

(3.23) $$\inf_{\eta \in H} \mathbf{P}_\phi(\theta, \eta),$$

the minimum power of $\phi(x)$ for that θ.

Proof. Take any η, say η_0, and define

(3.24) $$\psi(t) = E_{\eta_0}\{\phi(X)|t\}.$$

By the argument in Theorem 3.2 we have $0 \le \psi(t) \le 1$ for almost all t, and hence $\psi(t)$ is a test function.

The power function of $\psi(t)$ is given by

(3.25) $$\mathbf{P}_\psi(\theta, \eta) = E_{\theta\eta}\{\psi(t(X))\}$$
$$= E_\theta^T\{\psi(T)\}.$$

It depends only on θ. Now, using (3.24) we obtain

$$
\begin{aligned}
\mathbf{P}_\psi(\theta) &= E_\theta^T \{\psi(T)\} \\
&= E_\theta^T \{E_{\eta_0} \{\phi(X) \,|\, T\}\} \\
&= E_{\theta\eta_0} \{\phi(X)\} \\
&= \mathbf{P}_\phi(\theta, \eta_0),
\end{aligned}
$$

and then it easily follows that

$$
(3.26) \qquad \inf_\eta \mathbf{P}_\phi(\theta, \eta) \le \mathbf{P}_\psi(\theta) \le \sup_\eta \mathbf{P}_\phi(\theta, \eta).
$$

By taking θ through the values in ω, (3.26) proves that $\psi(t)$ has size α. By taking any θ in $\Theta - \omega$, (3.26) proves (3.23).

A closely related theorem is the following:

THEOREM 3.4. If $t(x)$ is sufficient (θ) for the class of measures $\{P_{\theta\eta} \,|\, (\theta, \eta) \in \Theta \times H\}$, then there is a uniformly most powerful test for the hypothesis testing problem

$$
(3.27) \qquad
\begin{aligned}
&\text{Hypothesis:} \quad \theta = \theta_0, \quad \eta \in H, \\
&\text{Alternative:} \quad \theta = \theta_1, \quad \eta \in H;
\end{aligned}
$$

it can be chosen to have power independent of η.

Proof. Consider the related problem having a simple alternative:

$$
(3.28) \qquad
\begin{aligned}
&\text{Hypothesis:} \quad \theta = \theta_0, \quad \eta \in H, \\
&\text{Alternative:} \quad \theta = \theta_1, \quad \eta = \eta_1.
\end{aligned}
$$

For this composite hypothesis problem we apply the results in the previous section. For the probability measure over the hypothesis $\lambda(\eta)$ it seems natural to put all probability at η_1 in order to get a measure most like the alternative. We have then the modified problem:

$$
(3.29) \qquad
\begin{aligned}
&\text{Hypothesis:} \quad P_{\theta_0\eta_1}(A) = \int P_{\eta_1}(A \,|\, t) \, dP_{\theta_0}(t), \\
&\text{Alternative:} \quad P_{\theta_1\eta_1}(A) = \int P_{\eta_1}(A \,|\, t) \, dP_{\theta_1}(t).
\end{aligned}
$$

Let $\psi(t)$ be the size-α test obtained by applying the fundamental lemma to the hypothesis testing problem on the space $\mathscr{T}$ having hypothesis measure $P_{\theta_0}(B)$ and alternative measure $P_{\theta_1}(B)$. Let $\phi(x)$ be any size-α test for (3.29). Then it is straightforward to show that the power of $\phi(x)$ cannot exceed the power of $\psi(t(x))$, and hence that $\psi(t(x))$ is the most powerful test for (3.29).

Since
$$E_{\theta_0 \eta}\{\psi(t(X))\} = E_{\theta_0}\{\psi(T)\}$$
$$= \alpha,$$

it follows that $\psi(t)$ is a size-α test for (3.28) and hence is the most powerful size-α test for (3.28). The test $\psi(t)$ is obviously independent of η_1. It is therefore a uniformly most powerful test for (3.27).   ◀

3.5. Similar Tests. When in the theory of estimation we could not obtain a best decision function in the full class available, we placed some moderate and reasonable restrictions on the decision functions in the hope of finding a best one in the smaller class. We do this now for hypothesis testing, and the first restriction we consider is that of similarity.

A test function $\phi(x)$ is similar of size α for testing the hypothesis $\theta \in \omega$ if

$$\mathbf{P}_{\phi}(\theta) = \int_{\mathscr{X}} \phi(x) \, dP_{\theta}(x) = \alpha$$

for all $\theta \in \omega$.

For such a test the power function has the constant value α for all values of the parameter in the hypothesis. If the statistician restricts himself to similar tests of size α, he is requiring that the test make incorrect decisions at the full allowable rate for all measures in the hypothesis. It is for this reason that similar tests are open to serious criticism. However, there are two things that can be said in their favor. For some problems the mathematical form of a similar test can be described quite easily. Second, the theory of similar tests is of use in deriving a best test under the restriction we shall consider in the next section.

If a problem possesses a statistic which for the distributions of the hypothesis is sufficient and boundedly complete, then a similar test function has a very simple form. Under the hypothesis the average or expected value of the test function, given the statistic, must be a constant value α for almost all values of the statistic. The test can then be treated as a conditional test, and be constructed in each subspace of values of x having $t(x) = t$. Its size, given the statistic, must be α for the hypothesis; its power can be maximized for any simple alternative by maximizing the conditional power, given the statistic. The problem is then reduced to one which, for each value of the statistic, can be treated by the fundamental lemma.

THEOREM 3.5. LEHMANN–SCHEFFÉ. If $t(x)$ is a sufficient and boundedly complete statistic for $\{P_{\theta} | \theta \in \omega\}$, then any similar size-$\alpha$ test $\phi(x)$ has conditional size α, given t, for almost all $\{P_{\theta} | \theta \in \omega\}$ values of t, that is

(3.30) $E\{\phi(X) | t\} = \alpha$

for almost all values of t.

If a test satisfies (3.30) it is said to have *Neyman structure*.

Proof. Let $\phi(x)$ be a similar size-α test; then

$$E_\theta\{\phi(X)\} = \alpha \qquad \text{for} \quad \theta \in \omega,$$

(3.31)
$$E_\theta\{E(\phi(X)|T)\} = \alpha \qquad \text{for} \quad \theta \in \omega,$$

$$E_\theta\{E(\phi(X)|T) - \alpha\} = 0 \quad \text{for} \quad \theta \in \omega.$$

The conditional expectation does not depend on θ because $t(x)$ is a sufficient statistic. In (3.31), $E\{\phi(X)|t\} - \alpha$ is a function only of t, has zero expectation for each θ, and is bounded. Therefore the bounded completeness of $t(x)$ implies that $E\{\phi(X)|t\} - \alpha = 0$ for almost all $\{P_\theta^T | \theta \in \omega\}$ values of t. This is equivalent to (3.30), and proves the theorem.

Let $t(x)$ be a sufficient and boundedly complete statistic for the *hypothesis* measures $\{P_\theta | \theta \in \omega\}$, and consider the hypothesis testing problem

(3.32)
$$\text{Hypothesis:} \quad \theta \in \omega,$$
$$\text{Alternative:} \quad \theta = \theta_1.$$

We outline the procedure for obtaining a most powerful similar test. We want to examine the test functions $\phi(x)$ that satisfy

(3.33)
$$E_\theta\{\phi(X)\} = \alpha$$

for all $\theta \in \omega$ and choose one that maximizes

(3.34)
$$E_{\theta_1}\{\phi(X)\}.$$

But the theorem above says it is equivalent to examine the test functions $\phi(x)$ which satisfy

(3.35)
$$E_\omega\{\phi(X)|t\} = \alpha$$

for almost all $(\omega)t$. The subscript ω indicates that this is the conditional expectation for any $\theta \in \omega$; the conditional expectation may depend on θ as soon as θ leaves the set ω. Also the expression to be minimized may be written

$$E_{\theta_1}\{E_{\theta_1}\{\phi(X)|T\}\},$$

and it is clearly equivalent to maximize

(3.36)
$$E_{\theta_1}\{\phi(X)|t\}$$

for each t, provided we do not violate the restrictions on $\phi(x)$. However, to maximize (3.36) fits very neatly with the size restriction (3.35) in condition form. Our problem has thus been reduced to the following conditional problem. It is to find a test function $\phi(x)$ which for almost all (ω) values of t satisfies

$$E_\omega\{\phi(X)|t\} = \alpha$$

under the hypothesis and maximizes

$$E_{\theta_1}\{\phi(X)|t\}$$

for all t. Thus the finding of a best similar test over $\mathscr{X}$ is equivalent to finding the best test on the subspace of points having $t(x) = t$, and this is accomplished by applying the fundamental lemma to the conditional measures, given t (assuming the conditional probabilities are measures).

EXAMPLE 3.5. Let $X_1, \cdots, X_n$ be independent and each have the normal distribution with mean μ and variance σ^2. Consider the problem of finding a most powerful similar test of size α for

(3.37)
$$\text{Hypothesis:} \quad \mu = 0, \quad \sigma^2 \in \,]0, \infty[,$$
$$\text{Alternative:} \quad \mu > 0, \quad \sigma^2 \in \,]0, \infty[.$$

$U(\mathbf{x}) = (y_1, y_2) = (\bar{x}, \Sigma(x_i - \bar{x})^2)$ is a sufficient statistic for the class of measure for the problem as a whole. By Theorem 3.2 it suffices to consider tests based on (y_1, y_2), because for any other test there is one based on this statistic that has an identical power function. In terms of the new variables y_1, y_2, our problem has the following form: Y_1 is normally distributed with mean μ and variance σ^2/n; Y_2 is independent of Y_1 and has the $\sigma^2\chi^2$ distribution with $n-1$ degrees of freedom. The hypothesis and alternative, of course, remain the same.

Under the measures of the hypothesis, the statistic $t(x) = \Sigma x_i^2$ is a complete sufficient statistic. It follows, then, that $ny_1^2 + y_2 = n\bar{x}^2 + \Sigma(x_i - \bar{x})^2 = \Sigma x_i^2$ is a complete sufficient statistic for the hypothesis of the problem in terms of y_1 and y_2. In order to apply the argument preceding this example, we need to know the form of the conditional distribution of y_1 and y_2, given the statistic $t(x)$. This we now obtain. For a set A in the space R^2 of y_1 and y_2 ($y_2 \geqslant 0$), we have

$$P_{\mu,\sigma}(A) = \int\int_A \frac{n^{1/2}}{(2\pi)^{1/2}\sigma} \exp\left[-\frac{n(y_1 - \mu)^2}{2\sigma^2}\right] \times$$

$$\frac{1}{2^{\frac{n-1}{2}} \Gamma\left(\frac{n-1}{2}\right) \sigma^{n-1}} y_2^{(n-1)/2-1} \exp\left[-\frac{y_2}{2\sigma^2}\right] dy_2\, dy_1.$$

On this integral we make the transformation

$$t = ny_1^2 + y_2,$$
$$y_1 = y_1,$$

which has the Jacobian equal to 1, and obtain

$$P_{\mu,\sigma}^*(B) = \int\int_B \frac{n^{1/2}}{2^{n/2}\pi^{1/2}\Gamma\left(\dfrac{n-1}{2}\right)\sigma^n}$$

$$\exp\left(-\frac{t}{2\sigma^2} + \frac{n\mu y_1}{\sigma^2} - \frac{n\mu^2}{2\sigma^2}\right)(t - ny_1^2)^{(n-3)/2}\, dt\, dy_1.$$

The joint probability density function for t and y_1 is the integrand of the above expression. To obtain the conditional probability density of y_1, given t, we incorporate into the differential dy_1 a function of y_1 sufficient to make it the differential of the *distribution function* of y_1. Then by analogy with (4.12) in Chapter 1 the integrand is the conditional probability element we want; it is

(3.38) $$\frac{k}{f(t)}\exp\left(-\frac{t}{2\sigma^2} + \frac{n\mu y_1}{\sigma^2}\right)(t - ny_1^2)^{(n-3)/2}$$

This expression only applies to the space of "possible" values for y_1: namely those y_1 for which $(t - ny_1^2)$ is non-negative. Elsewhere the probability density is zero. $f(t)$ is the function that was incorporated into the differential element, and k is a constant. $k/f(t)$ can be found directly from this density function by merely requiring that the density integrate to 1 with respect to y_1.

Let $f_{\mu\sigma}(y_1 \mid t)$ stand for the conditional density function of y_1, given t; its functional form is given by (3.38) above. We have in effect the conditional distribution of y_1 and y_2, given t, because, for a given t and y_1, the value of y_2 is determined by the formula $y_2 = t - ny_1^2$. Hence any conditional test, given t, can be based directly on y_1.

To solve our problem we first substitute a simple alternative and consider

(3.39)
Hypothesis: $\mu = 0,$ $\sigma^2 \in\,]0, \infty[,$

Alternative: $\mu = \mu_1\ (>0),\quad \sigma^2 = \sigma_1^2,$

and then apply the argument preceding this example to find a most powerful similar test. In conditional form we wish to obtain a test function $\phi(y_1 \mid t)$ which has size α with respect to the density $f_{0\sigma}(y_1 \mid t)$ and maximum power with respect to $f_{\mu_1\sigma_1}(y_1|t)$. By the fundamental lemma, we obtain

$$\phi(y_1|t) = 1 \quad \text{if} \quad \frac{f_{\mu_1\sigma_1}(y_1|t)}{f_{0\sigma}(y_1|t)} > c$$
$$= 0 \qquad\qquad < c,$$

where, of course, the denominator of the probability ratio does not actually depend on σ^2 because $\mu = 0$ and t is a sufficient statistic for the hypothesis. Now each succeeding expression below when viewed in terms of y_1 is a monotone-increasing function of the preceding expression:

$$\frac{f_{\mu_1\sigma_1}(y_1|t)}{f_{0\sigma}(y_1|t)},$$

$$\frac{\exp\left(-\dfrac{t}{2\sigma_1^2} + \dfrac{n\mu_1 y_1}{\sigma_1^2} - \dfrac{n\mu_1^2}{2\sigma_1^2}\right)(t - ny_1^2)^{(n-3)/2}}{\exp\left(-\dfrac{t}{2\sigma^2}\right)(t - ny_1^2)^{(n-3)/2}},$$

$$\frac{n\mu_1 y_1}{\sigma_1^2},$$

$$y_1.$$

Therefore the test can be written

$$\phi(y_1|t) = 1 \quad \text{if} \quad y_1 > c(t)$$
$$= 0 \qquad\qquad < c(t),$$

where $c(t)$ is chosen to satisfy the size condition

(3.40) $$\int_{c(t)}^{\infty} f_{0\sigma}(y_1|t)\, dy_1 = \alpha.$$

But $f_{0\sigma}(y_1|t)$ has the form

$$h(t)(t - ny_1^2)^{(n-3)/2}$$

in the range of y_1 for which $t - ny_1^2$ is non-negative and is zero elsewhere. From this it is easily seen that the distribution of $z = (n/t)^{1/2} y_1$ has the conditional density function of the form

$$h'(t)\,(1 - z^2)^{(n-3)/2}.$$

Since this must integrate to 1, $h'(t)$ is a constant and $z = (n/t)^{1/2} y_1$ has a conditional distribution independent of t. Let b_α be the point exceeded with probability α according to this distribution. Then $b_\alpha = (n/t)^{1/2}c(t)$, and the test can be written

$$\phi(y_1|t) = 1 \qquad \text{if} \quad y_1 > (t/n)^{1/2}b_\alpha$$
$$= 0 \qquad \qquad \quad < (t/n)^{1/2}b_\alpha.$$

The following relations on y_1 and t and on y_1 and y_2 are equivalent:

$$y_1 > (t/n)^{1/2}b_\alpha,$$

$$y_1 > \frac{(ny_1^2 + y_2)^{1/2}}{n^{1/2}} b_\alpha,$$

$$y_1 y_2^{-1/2} > \frac{[n(y_1 y_2^{-1/2})^2 + 1]^{1/2}}{n^{1/2}} b_\alpha,$$

$$y_1 y_2^{-1/2} > c_\alpha.$$

The last step follows from the monotonicity of the function $x(1 + x^2)^{-1/2}$. c_α is a constant and depends on b_α and n. From these relations it follows that the test can be written

$$\phi(y_1|t) = 1 \qquad \text{if} \quad \frac{y_1}{y_2^{1/2}} > c_\alpha$$
$$= 0 \qquad \qquad \qquad < c_\alpha,$$

or in terms of the original variables

$$\phi(\mathbf{x}) = 1 \qquad \text{if} \quad \frac{\bar{x}}{[\Sigma(x_i - \bar{x})^2]^{1/2}} > c_\alpha$$
$$= 0 \qquad \qquad \qquad \qquad < c_\alpha,$$

or equivalently

$$(3.41) \qquad \phi(\mathbf{x}) = 1 \qquad \text{if} \quad \frac{n^{1/2}\bar{x}}{\left[\dfrac{1}{n-1}\Sigma(x_i - \bar{x})^2\right]^{1/2}} > d_\alpha$$
$$= 0 \qquad \qquad \qquad \qquad \qquad < d_\alpha.$$

But this is just the ordinary Student's t test. Since it does not depend on $\mu_1\,(>0)$ or on σ_1^2, it is a uniformly most powerful similar size-α test for

$$\text{Hypothesis:} \quad \mu = 0, \quad \sigma^2 \in \,]0, \infty[$$
$$\text{Alternative:} \quad \mu > 0, \quad \sigma^2 \in \,]0, \infty[.$$

3.6. Unbiased Tests. As a second restriction on the class of test functions we consider *unbiasedness*.

A test $\phi(x)$ *of the hypothesis:* $\theta \in \omega$ *against the alternative:* $\theta \in \Omega - \omega$ *is unbiased of size* α *if*

$$E_\theta\{\phi(X)\} \le \alpha$$

for $\theta \in \omega$ *and*

$$E_\theta\{\phi(X)\} \ge \alpha$$

for $\theta \in \Omega - \omega$.

In restricting ourselves to unbiased tests we are requiring that a test should accept the alternative more frequently when to accept is the correct decision than when it is incorrect. Unlike similarity which was primarily a device for obtaining tests, unbiasedness is a very reasonable property for the practicing statistician to require of his test.

The condition of unbiasedness being based on inequalities is not as easy to handle mathematically as similarity. However, in some problems it is possible to make use of our theory on similar tests to obtain a most powerful unbiased test.

THEOREM 3.6. (LEHMANN). If Λ is the common boundary of ω and $\Omega - \omega$ and if the power $P_\phi(\theta)$ is a continuous function of θ for any test ϕ, then an unbiased size-α test of ω against $\Omega - \omega$ is similar of size α for the measures of Λ.

The theorem assumes a topology on Ω with respect to which the continuity and common boundary are defined.

Proof. The common boundary is the set of points that are limit points both of sequences in ω and in $\Omega - \omega$. Since $P_\phi(\theta) \le \alpha$ for $\theta \in \omega$, $P_\phi(\theta) \le \alpha$ for $\theta \in \Lambda$ by the continuity. Similarly, since $P_\phi(\theta) \ge \alpha$ for $\theta \in \Omega - \omega$, then $P_\phi(\theta) \ge \alpha$ for $\theta \in \Lambda$. However, the two inequalities give $P_\phi(\theta) = \alpha$ for $\theta \in \Lambda$.

By this theorem the class of unbiased tests of ω against $\Omega - \omega$ is contained in the class of tests similar on Λ. If we can find a most powerful similar test of Λ against $\Omega - \omega$, and if this test is unbiased, of size α, then necessarily it is the most powerful test in the smaller class of unbiased tests.

EXAMPLE 3.6. Let $X_1, \cdots, X_n$ be independent, and assume that each X_i has the normal distribution with mean μ and variance σ^2. Consider the problem of finding a most powerful unbiased test for

(3.42)
Hypothesis: $\mu \le 0$, $\sigma^2 \in]0, \infty[$

Alternative: $\mu > 0$, $\sigma^2 \in]0, \infty[$.

The power function for any test $\phi(\mathbf{x})$ is given by

$$\mathbf{P}_\phi(\mu, \sigma^2) = \int_{R^n} \phi(\mathbf{x})(2\pi\sigma^2)^{-n/2} \exp\left[-\frac{1}{2\sigma^2} \sum_i^n (x_i - \mu)^2\right] \prod_1^n dx_i.$$

Since the integrand is a continuous function of (μ, σ^2) and since in any neighborhood of a value of (μ, σ^2) it is bounded by an integrable function,

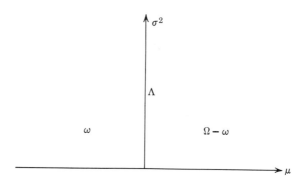

Figure 11. The parameter space Ω in Example 3.6.

it follows that the power is a continuous function of (μ, σ^2). The common boundary for ω and $\Omega - \omega$ is given by $\Lambda = \{(\mu, \sigma^2)|\mu = 0,$ $\sigma^2 \in]0, \infty[\}$. By the argument above we look for a most powerful similar test of

$$\Lambda : \quad \mu = 0, \quad \sigma^2 \in]0, \infty[,$$
$$\text{Alt:} \quad \mu > 0, \quad \sigma^2 \in]0, \infty[.$$

But by Example 3.5 the most powerful similar test is the ordinary t test.

We now check to see if the ordinary t test is unbiased. Suppose that t_α has been chosen so that

$$\Pr_{0\sigma}\left\{\frac{n^{1/2}\bar{X}}{s_X} > t_\alpha\right\} = \alpha$$

when $\mu = 0$. Consider a value of $\mu > 0$; then

$$E_{\mu\sigma}\{\phi(\mathbf{X})\} = \Pr_{\mu\sigma}\left\{\frac{n^{1/2}\bar{X}}{s_X} > t_\alpha\right\}$$
$$= \Pr_{\mu\sigma}\{n^{1/2}\bar{X} > t_\alpha s_X\}$$
$$\geq \Pr_{\mu\sigma}\{n^{1/2}\bar{X} - n^{1/2}\mu > t_\alpha s_X\}$$
$$= \Pr_{\mu\sigma}\left\{\frac{n^{1/2}(\bar{X} - \mu)}{s_X} > t_\alpha\right\}$$
$$= \alpha.$$

Similarly, if $\mu < 0$, we obtain

$$E_{\mu\sigma}\{\phi(\mathbf{X})\} \leq \alpha.$$

These two results establish that $\phi(\mathbf{x})$ is unbiased of size α, and hence is the most powerful unbiased test for the original problem (3.42).

3.7. Invariant Tests.   In this section a third restriction on the class of tests is considered—the restriction to invariant tests.   The general ideas of the invariance method were introduced in Section 2.3, and we only briefly outline them here.

For many problems there are transformations that can be applied to the outcome and that produce a transformed problem statistically the same as the original problem.   The invariance restriction is then to consider only those decision or test functions that have the same values for the transformed outcomes as for the corresponding original outcomes; such tests are called invariant tests.   It is certainly a reasonable restriction.   For, if the problem is not altered by the transformations, then why should the result of applying a test function be altered?

Let the class of probability measures be $\{P_\theta | \theta \in \Omega\}$ over the space $\mathscr{X}(\mathscr{A})$.   Then a class $\mathscr{G}$ of measurable transformations sx from $\mathscr{X}$ into $\mathscr{X}$ is called *invariant* for the probability structure if it satisfies

(1) $\mathscr{G}$ *is a group.*

(2)   *The class of measures* $\{P_\theta | \theta \in \Omega\}$ *is closed under* $\mathscr{G}$; *that is, if X has the measure* $P_\theta(\theta \in \Omega)$, *then* sX *for* $s \in \mathscr{G}$ *has the probability measure* $P_{\bar{s}\theta}$ *where* $\bar{s}\theta \in \Omega$.

The class $\mathscr{G}$ of transformation $\bar{s}$ on Ω forms a group homomorphic to $\mathscr{G}$ (Problems 18 and 19).

Consider now the hypothesis testing problem;

(3.43)   Hypothesis: $\theta \in \omega$,
           Alternative: $\theta \in \Omega - \omega$.

If the transformations in $\mathscr{G}$ do not alter this hypothesis testing problem, then the measures of the hypothesis must remain measures of the hypothesis, and the measures of the alternative must remain measures of the alternative.   We summarize this in

(3)   If $\theta \in \omega$, then $\bar{s}\theta \in \omega$; if $\theta \in \Omega - \omega$, then $\bar{s}\theta \in \Omega - \omega$.

The invariance principle for hypothesis testing is to confine attention to the invariant test functions:

$\phi(x)$ *is an invariant test function re* $\mathscr{G}$ *if*

$$\phi(sx) = \phi(x)$$

for all $s \in \mathscr{G}$ *and* $x \in \mathscr{X}$.

In some problems a weaker form of invariance is useful:

$\phi(x)$ *is almost invariant for* $\mathscr{G}$ *if, for each* $s \in \mathscr{G}$,

$$\phi(sx) = \phi(x)$$

for almost all $\{P_\theta\}x$.

In order to apply the invariance method we need some way of describing the invariant test function. This can be done quite simply by the use of a maximal invariant function. For any statistic $\phi(x)$ there is a corresponding partition of $\mathscr{X}$; this was described at the end of Section 1 in Chapter 1. If the statistic is invariant, we call the partition invariant. An invariant partition has, of course, the property that x and sx are always in the same set of the partition. If one partition of $\mathscr{X}$ is formed by the sets $\{A\}$ and another partition is formed by the sets $\{B\}$, then the totality of sets $A \cap B$ also forms a partition of $\mathscr{X}$, the *intersection partition*. Similarly, any class of partitions will produce an intersection partition. However, if the original partitions were induced by statistics, that is, measurable functions, the question naturally arises of the measurability of a function inducing the intersection partition. But we can always make it measurable by appropriately defining the σ-algebra on the range of values of the function. We take the natural σ-algebra as given by formula (2.2) in Chapter 1. It follows very easily that, if the original partitions were invariant, then the intersection partition is also invariant (see Problem 34). *The maximal invariant partition is the intersection partition of all invariant partitions.* From its definition the maximal invariant partition is the finest invariant partition in the sense that no set of the partition can have a proper subset belonging to an invariant partition. Sometimes it is convenient to think of a maximal invariant function, say $m(x)$. This is any function whose partition is the maximal invariant partition. The values of the function $m(x)$ are unimportant except that $m(x) = m(x')$ if x and x' are in the same set of the maximal invariant and $m(x) \neq m(x')$ if x and x' are in different sets. As mentioned above we make $m(x)$ measurable by choosing the natural σ-algebra on the space of values of $m(x)$.

Another definition of the maximal invariant partition is also of interest. With any point $x \in \mathscr{X}$ we associate a set containing it defined by

$$T_x = \{x' \,|\, x' = sx\};$$

that is, all points obtained from x by transformations in $\mathscr{G}$. If we took any point $x^* = s^*x$ in T_x and considered T_{x^*}, we would have

$$\begin{aligned} T_{x^*} &= \{x' \,|\, x' = sx^*\} \\ &= \{x' \,|\, x' = ss^*x\} \\ &= T_x. \end{aligned}$$

Thus the sets T_x form a partition of $\mathscr{X}$. The sets T_x are obviously closed under the transformations s, and certainly no proper subset of any T_x would be closed. Therefore this is the maximal invariant partition.

THEOREM 3.7. Any invariant statistic $\phi(x)$ can be expressed as a measurable function of the maximal invariant function $m(x)$.

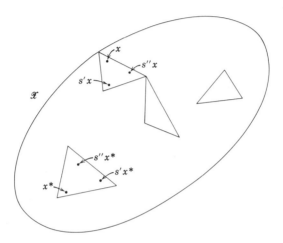

Figure 12. Typical sets of an invariant partition.

Proof. A function $\phi(x)$ can be written in terms of another function $m(x)$ if, whenever for a set of values of x $m(x)$ is constant, then so also is $\phi(x)$. This is easily seen because $\phi(x)$ then has a unique value for all x giving rise to a value for $m(x)$. In terms of partitions this is equivalent to the $m(x)$ partition being a subpartition of the $\phi(x)$ partition. But the maximal invariant partition is a subpartition of any invariant partition; therefore we can write $\phi(x) = f(m(x))$.

To complete the proof we need only show that $f(m)$ is a measurable function. Let B be any measurable set in the range of ϕ or equivalently of f. We want to prove that $f^{-1}(B)$ is a measurable set. But the measurable sets M in the range of m are those for which $m^{-1}(M) \in \mathscr{A}$. Therefore we want to prove that $m^{-1}f^{-1}(B)$ is measurable; that is, $\in \mathscr{A}$. But $m^{-1}f^{-1}(B) = (fm)^{-1}B = \phi^{-1}(B)$. Since ϕ is measurable, $\phi^{-1}(B) \in \mathscr{A}$; that is, $m^{-1}f^{-1}(B) \in \mathscr{A}$. This completes the proof.

By our Theorem 3.7 any invariant function is equivalent to a function of the maximal invariant function. Thus, in a hypothesis testing problem, if we wish to restrict our attention to invariant test functions, we equivalently examine the test functions based on the maximal invariant. We have, then, the following invariance method for treating a hypothesis testing problem. Find a group $\mathscr{G}$ of transformations which is invariant for the problem; for this group find a maximal invariant function; calculate the induced measures for the maximal invariant function, and consider the hypothesis testing problem for these; then look for a best test for this related problem. The resulting test expressed in terms of the original outcome by means of the maximal invariant will be the best invariant test.

For the transformations $\bar{\mathscr{G}}$ on Ω, we can define a maximal invariant partition. Let $\bar{m}(\theta)$ stand for the corresponding maximal invariant function. It would be natural to suspect that, for the reduced problem in terms of $m(x)$, the probability measures can be expressed in terms of the maximal invariant $\bar{m}(\theta)$ as the parameter. For this we have the theorem:

THEOREM 3.8. If $\phi(x)$ is invariant re $\mathscr{G}$, then the probability measure for $\phi(X)$ is constant over each set of the maximal invariant ($\mathscr{G}$) partition of Ω; that is, the distributions for ϕ depend on θ through $\bar{m}(\theta)$.

Proof. We wish to show that

$$\Pr_{\theta}\{\phi(X) \in B\} = \Pr_{\theta'}\{\phi(X) \in B\}$$

for all $B \in \mathscr{B}$ whenever θ and θ' belong to the same set of the maximal invariant partition on Ω; that is, whenever $\theta' = \bar{s}\theta$. We have

$$\begin{aligned}
\Pr_{\theta'}\{\phi(X) \in B\} &= \Pr_{\bar{s}\theta}\{\phi(X) \in B\} \\
&= \Pr_{\theta}\{\phi(sX) \in B\} \\
&= \Pr_{\theta}\{\phi(X) \in B\},
\end{aligned}$$

where the last step follows from the invariance property of $\phi(x)$; viz., $\phi(sx) = \phi(x)$ for all s.

EXAMPLE 3.7. Let $X_1, \cdots, X_n$ be independent, and assume that each X_i has the normal distribution with mean μ and variance σ^2. Consider the hypothesis testing problem

(3.44)
$$\begin{aligned}
&\text{Hypothesis:} \quad \mu \leq 0, \quad \sigma^2 \in \,]0, \infty[\\
&\text{Alternative:} \quad \mu > 0, \quad \sigma^2 \in \,]0, \infty[.
\end{aligned}$$

By Theorem 3.2 we can restrict attention to tests based on the sufficient statistic $(u, v^2) = (\bar{x}, \Sigma(x_i - \bar{x})^2)$.

Consider the class of tranformation $\mathscr{G}*$,

$$\mathscr{G} = \{x_i' = cx_i \,(i = 1, \cdots, n) \,\big|\, c \in \,]0, \infty[\}.$$

These transformations obviously form a group. Because each transformation is just a change of scale about the origin, a normal distribution remains a normal distribution and the new mean is $c\mu$, and the new variance is $c^2\sigma^2$. Therefore the class of induced transformations on Ω is

$$\bar{\mathscr{G}} = \{\mu' = c\mu,\ \sigma'^2 = c^2\sigma^2 \,\big|\, c \in \,]0,\,\infty[\}.$$

Now, since the hypothesis and alternative are transformed by elements of $\mathscr{G}$ into themselves, respectively, the class $\mathscr{G}$ is an invariant class of transformations for the problem.

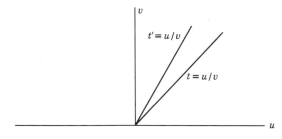

Figure 13. The partition for $t = u/v$.

The induced class of transformations on the sufficient statistic is

$$(3.45)\qquad \mathscr{G}^* = \{u' = cu,\ v'^2 = c^2v^2 \,\big|\, c \in \,]0,\,\infty[\}.$$

We now show that $t = u/v$ is a maximal invariant function. In Fig. 13, two typical sets t, t' of the partition for $t = u/v$ are exhibited. This partition is invariant. For the transformed value of t, $t' = cu/cv$, is equal to the untransformed value $t = u/v$ for all transformations and all points (u, v). To show that the partition is the maximal invariant partition, we show that there is no subpartition that is invariant. Consider a set of the partition, say the one indexed by t'. Obviously any point in that set can be transformed into any other by a suitable value of c; hence the set has no proper subset left unchanged by the elements of $\mathscr{G}^*$. Thus the partition does not have an invariant subpartition and hence is maximal invariant.

To state the problem in terms of the maximal invariant t, we need to derive the induced probability distribution of t. For this, it is more convenient to use the equivalent statistic $t^* = n^{1/2}t$. Now, since

$$(3.46)\qquad t^* = \frac{n^{1/2}u}{v} = \frac{n^{1/2}u/\sigma}{v/\sigma},$$

we can represent the induced distribution of t^* by

$$T^* = \frac{Z}{\chi},$$

where the distribution of Z is normal with mean $n^{1/2}\mu/\sigma$ and variance 1,

and the distribution of χ^2 is the χ^2-distribution with $n - 1$ degrees of freedom. If we write $n^{1/2}\mu/\sigma = \delta$, then the joint probability density function for Z and χ can be written

$$(2\pi)^{-1/2} \exp\left[-\frac{1}{2}(z - \delta)^2\right]\left[2^{(n-1)/2}\, \Gamma\left(\frac{(n-1)}{2}\right)\right]^{-1} \chi^{n-3} \exp\left(-\frac{\chi^2}{2}\right) 2\chi.$$

By expanding the exponential, we obtain

$$(2\pi)^{-1/2} \exp\left(-\frac{\delta^2}{2}\right) \sum_{r=0}^{\infty} \frac{(z\delta)^r}{r!} \exp\left(-\frac{z^2}{2}\right) \times$$

$$\left[2^{(n-1)/2}\, \Gamma\left(\frac{n-1}{2}\right)\right]^{-1} \chi^{n-3} \exp\left(-\frac{\chi^2}{2}\right) 2\chi.$$

The transformation ($t^* = z/\chi,\ \chi = \chi$) has the Jacobian χ^{-1}; therefore the density function for ($t^*,\ \chi$) is

$$(2\pi)^{-1} \exp\left(-\frac{\delta^2}{2}\right) \sum_{r=0}^{\infty} \frac{(\chi t^*)^r \delta^r}{r!} \exp\left[-\frac{(\chi t^*)^2}{2}\right] \times$$

$$\left[2^{(n-1)/2}\, \Gamma\left(\frac{n-1}{2}\right)\right]^{-1} \chi^{n-3} \exp\left(-\frac{\chi^2}{2}\right) 2\chi^2.$$

Now, integrating with respect to χ to obtain the marginal probability density for t^*, we have

$$\frac{2}{(2\pi)^{1/2} 2^{(n-1)/2} \Gamma\left(\dfrac{n-1}{2}\right)} \exp\left(-\frac{\delta^2}{2}\right) \sum_{r=0}^{\infty} \frac{(t^*\delta)^r}{r!} \times$$

$$\int_0^\infty \chi^r \exp\left[-\frac{(\chi t^*)^2}{2}\right] \chi^{n-1} \exp\left(-\frac{\chi^2}{2}\right) d\chi$$

$$= \left[\pi^{1/2} 2^{(n-2)/2}\, \Gamma\left(\frac{n-1}{2}\right)\right]^{-1} \exp\left(-\frac{\delta^2}{2}\right) \sum_{r=0}^{\infty} \frac{(t^*\delta)^r}{t!} f_r(t^*),$$

where

$$f_r(t^*) = \int_0^\infty \chi^{n+r-1} \exp\left[-\frac{1}{2}\chi^2(1 + t^{*2})\right] d\chi$$

$$= \int_0^\infty (\chi^2)^{(n+r-2)/2} \exp\left[-\frac{1}{2}\chi^2(1 + t^{*2})\right] d\frac{\chi^2}{2}$$

$$= 2^{(n+r-2)/2}(1 + t^{*2})^{-(n+r)/2} \int_0^\infty w^{(n+r-2)/2}\, e^{-w}\, dw$$

$$= 2^{(n+r-2)/2}(1 + t^{*2})^{-(n+r)/2}\, \Gamma\left(\frac{n+r}{2}\right).$$

Therefore the induced probability density function for t^* is

$$(3.47) \quad \pi^{-1/2} \exp\left(-\frac{\delta^2}{2}\right) \sum_{r=0}^{\infty} 2^{r/2} \frac{\delta^r}{r!} \frac{\Gamma\left(\dfrac{n+r}{2}\right)}{\Gamma\left(\dfrac{n-1}{2}\right)} \frac{(t^*)^r}{(1+t^{*2})^{(n+r)/2}},$$

and, if $\delta = 0$, is

$$(3.48) \quad \pi^{-1/2} \frac{\Gamma\left(\dfrac{n}{2}\right)}{\Gamma\left(\dfrac{n-1}{2}\right)} \frac{1}{(1+t^{*2})^{n/2}}.$$

This last expression is the density function for $(n-1)^{-1/2}$ times a random variable with the Student distribution.

The distribution of t^* depends only on δ and n. n has a given value for this problem while δ is a parameter which indexes the different distributions of t^*. In agreement with Theorem 3.8 we find that the parameter δ is constant over each set of the maximal invariant partition; in fact $\delta = n^{1/2}\mu/\sigma$, and μ/σ is obviously a maximal invariant function.

The problem for the induced distributions of t^* is

$$(3.49) \qquad \begin{array}{ll} \text{Hypothesis:} & \delta \leq 0, \\ \text{Alternative:} & \delta > 0. \end{array}$$

We consider first a simple alternative $\delta = \delta_1$. At least favorable distribution for the parameter of the hypothesis would seemingly be to apply all probability to the single value $\delta = 0$. We apply the fundamental lemma to the simplified problem,

$$(3.50) \qquad \begin{array}{ll} \text{Hypothesis:} & \delta = 0, \\ \text{Alternative:} & \delta = \delta_1, \end{array}$$

and obtain, as the most powerful test function,

$$\phi(t^*) = 1 \quad \text{if} \quad \frac{\pi^{-1/2} \exp\left(-\dfrac{\delta^2}{2}\right) \sum\limits_{r=0}^{\infty} 2^{r/2} \dfrac{\delta^r}{r!} \dfrac{\Gamma\left(\dfrac{n+r}{2}\right)}{\Gamma\left(\dfrac{n-1}{2}\right)} \dfrac{(t^*)^r}{(1+t^{*2})^{(n+r)/2}}}{\pi^{-1/2} \dfrac{\Gamma\left(\dfrac{n}{2}\right)}{\Gamma\left(\dfrac{n-1}{2}\right)} \dfrac{1}{(1+t^{*2})^{n/2}}} > c$$

$$= 0$$

$$\text{if} \quad \Sigma\, 2^{r/2} \frac{\delta^r}{r!} \Gamma\left(\frac{n+r}{2}\right) \frac{(t^*)^r}{(1+t^{*2})^{r/2}} \quad \begin{array}{l} < c, \\ > c \\ < c. \end{array}$$

We shall show that the function in the last line is a monotone-increasing function of t^*, but first we complete the derivation of the most powerful test for our problem.

$$\phi(t^*) = 1 \quad \text{if} \quad t^* > c$$
$$= 0 \quad\quad\quad < c.$$

Using the probability distribution ($\delta = 0$) which is very simply related to the Student distribution, we find that $c = (n-1)^{-1/2}t_\alpha$ where t_α is exceeded with probability α according to the Student distribution with $n-1$ degrees of freedom. Therefore

$$\phi(t^*) = 1 \quad \text{if} \quad t^* > (n-1)^{-1/2}t_\alpha$$
$$= 0 \quad\quad\quad < (n-1)^{-1/2}t_\alpha.$$

To show that our choice of λ distribution was least favorable, we must prove that $\phi(t^*)$ is of correct size for the composite hypothesis in (3.49).

$$E_\delta\{\phi(T^*)\} = \Pr_\delta\{T^* > (n-1)^{-1/2}t_\alpha\}$$
$$= \Pr_\delta\left\{\frac{Z}{\chi} > (n-1)^{-1/2}t_\alpha\right\}$$
$$= \Pr_\delta\{Z - \delta > (n-1)^{-1/2}t_\alpha\chi - \delta\},$$

where $Z - \delta$ has the normal distribution with mean 0 and variance 1 and χ is independent of Z. Then for $\delta \leq 0$ we have

$$E_\delta\{\phi(T^*)\} \leq \Pr_\delta\{Z - \delta > (n-1)^{-1/2}t_\alpha\chi\}$$
$$= \Pr_0\{Z > (n-1)^{-1/2}t_\alpha\chi\}$$
$$= \alpha,$$

with the last step obtained directly from the definition for t_α. Thus the test $\phi(t^*)$ is a size-α test for the hypothesis $H : \delta \leq 0$. Also, the test does not depend on δ_1. It is therefore a uniformly most powerful test for the problem expressed in terms of t^*. From the theory at the beginning of this section, it is then the most powerful invariant test for the original problem (3.44). It is to be noted that the test is the same as the ordinary t test:

$$\phi(t^*) = 1 \quad \text{if} \quad t^* > (n-1)^{-1/2}t_\alpha$$
$$= 0 \quad\quad\quad\quad < (n-1)^{-1/2}t_\alpha,$$
$$\text{if} \quad \frac{n^{1/2}u}{v} > (n-1)^{-1/2}t_\alpha$$
$$< (n-1)^{-1/2}t_\alpha,$$
$$\text{if} \quad \frac{n^{1/2}\bar{x}}{[\Sigma(x_i - \bar{x})^2]^{1/2}} > (n-1)^{-1/2}t_\alpha$$
$$< (n-1)^{-1/2}t_\alpha,$$
$$\text{if} \quad \frac{n^{1/2}\bar{x}}{s_x} > t_\alpha$$
$$< t_\alpha,$$

where s_x^2 is the sample variance, $(n-1)^{-1}\Sigma(x_i - \bar{x})^2$.

We now show that, for $\delta > 0$,

$$\sum_{r=0}^{\infty} 2^{r/2} \frac{\delta^r}{r!} \Gamma\left(\frac{n+r}{2}\right) \frac{t^r}{(1+t^2)^{r/2}}$$

is a monotone-increasing function of t. Since $t/(1 + t^2)^{1/2}$ is monotone-increasing and since $2^{1/2}$ can be combined with the arbitrary positive δ, it suffices to show that

$$\sum_{r=0}^{\infty} \frac{\Gamma\left(\frac{n+r}{2}\right)}{r!} \delta^r t^r$$

or that

$$h_n(t) = \sum_{r=0}^{\infty} \Gamma\left(\frac{n+r}{2}\right) \frac{t^r}{r!}$$

is monotone-increasing. Since $h_n(t)$ is, except for positive constants, the ratio of two nonzero probability density functions, it must be positive everywhere. Also it is easily seen that

$$\frac{d}{dt} h_n(t) = h_{n+1}(t).$$

The function $h_n(t)$ has a positive derivative. Hence it must be a monotone-increasing function.

3.8. Stringency. For a number of problems we looked for test functions having maximum power for each parameter value of the alternatives. When such test functions did not exist we restricted our attention to those satisfying some reasonable property such as unbiasedness, similarity, or invariance and then again looked for tests having maximum power for each parameter value of the alternative. However, some of the simplest problems do not have such tests. We need, therefore, for choosing a test, some criterion which provides a compromise to maximizing the power uniformly over the alternative. We now formulate such a criterion—stringency.

First we define a function called the envelope power which exhibits the maximum power attainable for each parameter value of the alternative. *The envelope power function for tests of size α is*

$$\beta_\alpha(\theta) = \sup_{\phi} \mathbf{P}_\phi(\theta),$$

where the supremum is taken over the test functions $\phi(x)$ of size α:

$$E_\theta\{\phi(X)\} \leq \alpha$$

for all $\theta \in \omega$.

A reasonable thing to examine for any test function is the amount by which its power falls short of the maximum possible at each parameter value of the alternative:

$$\beta_\alpha(\theta) - \mathbf{P}_\phi(\theta).$$

Earlier in this section our attempts have been to effectively minimize this expression for each θ in the alternative. Here we take $\beta_\alpha(\theta) - \mathbf{P}_\phi(\theta)$

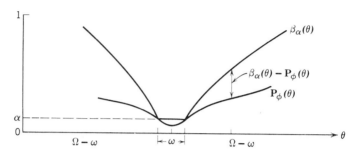

Figure 14. The envelope power $\beta_\alpha(\theta)$.

as a measure of the "shortcoming" of the test ϕ for the alternative θ; then

$$\sup_{\theta \in \Omega - \omega} (\beta_\alpha(\theta) - \mathbf{P}_\phi(\theta))$$

is the most extreme shortcoming of the test under the alternative. We use

$$\sup_{\theta \in \Omega - \omega} [\beta_\alpha(\theta) - \mathbf{P}_\phi(\theta)]$$

to compare different tests; a test that minimizes this is called a *most stringent test*.

A test function $\phi(x)$ is a most stringent size α test if it is of size α and if

$$\sup_{\theta \in \Omega - \omega} [\beta_\alpha(\theta) - \mathbf{P}_\phi(\theta)] \leq \sup_{\theta \in \Omega - \omega} [\beta_\alpha(\theta) - \mathbf{P}_{\phi*}(\theta)]$$

for any other size α test, $\phi*(x)$.

▶ One possible procedure for obtaining most stringent tests is given in the following theorem.

THEOREM 3.9. (HUNT AND STEIN). If $\Omega - \omega$ is partitioned into disjoint subsets Ω_δ such that the envelope power $\beta(\theta)$ is constant on each Ω_δ and if $\phi_\delta(x)$, the test that maximizes $\inf_{\theta \in \Omega_\delta} \mathbf{P}_\phi(\theta)$, is independent of δ ($\phi_\delta(x) = \phi(x)$), then ϕ is most stringent.

Proof. Since $\beta(\theta)$ is constant over Ω_δ, maximizing $\inf\limits_{\theta\in\Omega_\delta} \mathbf{P}_\phi(\theta)$ is clearly equivalent to minimizing $\sup\limits_{\theta\in\Omega_\delta} -\mathbf{P}_\phi(\theta)$ or $\sup\limits_{\theta\in\Omega_\delta} (\beta(\theta) - \mathbf{P}_\phi(\theta))$. Therefore the test function $\phi(x)$ minimizes $\sup\limits_{\theta\in\Omega_\delta} (\beta(\theta) - \mathbf{P}_\phi(\theta)$ for each δ. But the minimizing of $\sup\limits_{\theta\in\Omega_\delta} (\beta(\theta) - \mathbf{P}_\phi(\theta))$ for each δ implies that $\sup\limits_{\delta} \sup\limits_{\theta\in\Omega_\delta} (\beta(\theta) - \mathbf{P}_\phi(\theta))$ is minimized. The theorem follows by noting that the operation $\sup\limits_{\delta} \sup\limits_{\theta\in\Omega_\delta}$ is equivalent to $\sup\limits_{\theta\in\Omega-\omega}$.

To apply this theorem, however, we need a method for obtaining tests which satisfy a size condition

$$E_\theta\{\phi(X)\} \le \alpha$$

and which maximize the minimum power

$$\inf\limits_{\theta\in\Omega_\delta} \mathbf{P}_\phi(\theta)$$

over a composite alternative Ω_δ. This can sometimes be accomplished by the method of least favorable distributions introduced in Section 3.3. We try to find a P_ϕ (θ in Ω_δ) or a weighted average of P_ϕ's (θ in Ω_δ) which most resembles the measures of the hypothesis. If we find the test that maximizes the power for this representative alternative and if the power elsewhere in the alternative Ω_δ is at least as large, then the test maximizes the minimum power over Ω_δ. For, if $\phi(x)$ is the size α test that maximizes the power for the alternative

$$\int_{\Omega_\delta} P_\theta(A)\,d\eta(\theta),$$

then, using the assumption that the power is at least as large for the other θ's in the alternative, we have

$$
\begin{aligned}
\inf\limits_{\phi\in\Omega_\delta} \mathbf{P}_\phi(\theta) &= \int_{\Omega_\delta} \mathbf{P}_\phi(\theta)\,d\eta(\theta) \\
&\ge \int_{\Omega_\delta} \mathbf{P}_{\phi*}(\theta)\,d\eta(\theta) \\
&\ge \inf\limits_{\Omega_\delta} \mathbf{P}_{\phi*}(\theta)
\end{aligned}
$$

This proves the following theorem.

THEOREM 3.10. If $\phi(x)$ is the size-α test that maximizes the power for the simple alternative $\int_{\Omega_\delta} P_\phi(A)\,d\eta(\theta)$ and if this maximized power is less than or equal the test's power at each θ in Ω_δ, then $\phi(x)$ maximizes the minimum power over Ω_δ.

This theorem assumes that the measurability conditions are satisfied which allow the interchange of order of integration with respect to x and θ. As examples of the application of this theorem see Problems 39, 40.

Another possible procedure for obtaining most stringent tests is provided by the method of invariance. For this we need to define four types of transformation groups.

(i) $\{sx = x + c \,|\, c \in \,]-\infty, +\infty[\,\}$, x a real variable.
(ii) $\{sx = ax \,|\, a \in \,]0, \infty[\,\}$, x a real variable.
(iii) The group of orthogonal transformations on a Euclidean space.
(iv) Any finite group.

We give without proof the following lemma of Hunt and Stein.

THEOREM 3.11. (HUNT AND STEIN). If $\mathscr{G}$ can be factored by normal subgroups such that the normal subgroup at each stage and the final factor group are of types (i), $\cdots$, (iv) then, for any function $\phi(x)$ over $\mathscr{X}$ $(0 \leq \phi(x) \leq 1)$, there exists a function $\psi(x)$ invariant under $\mathscr{G}$ $(0 \leq \psi(x) \leq 1)$ such that

$$\inf_{s \in \mathscr{G}} \int_{\mathscr{X}} \phi(sx)\, p(x)\, d\mu(x) \leq \int_{\mathscr{X}} \psi(x)\, p(x)\, d\mu(x) \leq \sup_{s \in \mathscr{G}} \int_{\mathscr{X}} \phi(sx)\, p(x)\, d\mu(x).$$

for all integrable functions $p(x)$.

Let $\mathscr{G}$ be a group of transformations which leaves invariant the hypothesis testing problem

$$\text{Hypothesis:} \quad \theta \in \omega,$$

$$\text{Alternative:} \quad \theta \in \Omega - \omega;$$

and let $m(x)$ and $\bar{m}(\theta)$ be the maximal invariant functions over $\mathscr{X}$ and Ω. Then we have the following theorem of Hunt and Stein.

THEOREM 3.12. (HUNT AND STEIN). If $\mathscr{G}$ satisfies the conditions in Theorem 3.11, if the measures $\{P_\theta \,|\, \theta \in \Omega\}$ are dominated by a measure $\mu(x)$, and if there is a most powerful invariant size-α test for the alternative $\bar{m}(\theta) = \bar{m}$, then this test, among size-α tests, maximizes the minimum power over those θ's having $\bar{m}(\theta) = \bar{m}$.

Proof. First we note by Theorem 3.8 that $\bar{m}(\theta) = \bar{m}$ gives a simple alternative for the problem of finding invariant tests. For the invariant partition of Ω induced by $\bar{m}(\theta)$, let $\Omega_{\bar{m}}$ be the set for which $\bar{m}(\theta) = \bar{m}$. Also let θ, θ' be typical elements of $\Omega_{\bar{m}}$. Since $\mathscr{G}$ is a group, there is a transformation in $\bar{\mathscr{G}}$ such that $\theta' = s\theta$. Therefore we have

$$\inf_{s \in \mathscr{G}} \int_{\mathscr{X}} \phi(sx P_\theta(x)\, d\mu(x) = \inf_{s \in \mathscr{G}} E_\theta\{\phi(sX)\}$$

$$= \inf_{s \in \mathscr{G}} E_{s\theta}\{\phi(X)\}$$

$$= \inf_{\theta' \in \Omega_{\bar{m}}} E_{\theta'}\{\phi(X)\}.$$

Now applying Theorem 3.11, we have the existence of an invariant test function $\psi(x)$ such that

$$\inf_{\theta' \in \Omega_{\bar{m}}} E_{\theta'}\{\phi(X)\} \leq \int_{\mathcal{X}} \psi(x)\, p_\theta(x)\, d\mu(x)$$

$$\leq E_\theta\{\psi(X)\}.$$

for $\theta \in \Omega_{\bar{m}}$. Of course $E_{\bar{m}}\{\psi(X)\}$ is constant over $\Omega_{\bar{m}}$, as is easily seen by applying Theorem 3.8 to the invariant function $\psi(x)$.

Now by the result in the theorem above, we may restrict our attention to invariant test functions if our only concern is to maximize $\inf\limits_{\theta \in \Omega_{\bar{m}}} \mathbf{P}_\phi(\theta)$. Hence, if there is a uniformly most powerful invariant function, it maximizes the minimum power over each set of the partition induced by $\bar{m}(\theta)$.

THEOREM 3.13. If $\mathscr{G}$ satisfies the condition in Theorem 3.11 and if the measures $\{P_\theta \,|\, \theta \in \Omega\}$ are dominated by a measure $\mu(x)$, then a uniformly most powerful invariant test is most stringent.

Proof. Follows directly from Theorems 3.9 and 3.12.

If we introduce a loss function, then the next theorem used with either Theorem 3.10 or Theorem 3.12 provides a possible procedure for obtaining minimax test functions.

THEOREM 3.14. (LEHMANN). If a test function maximizes the minimum power over each set of a partition Ω_δ, then it has minimax risk with respect to any loss function which is constant on each set Ω_δ.

Note. Because of the size restriction on the tests under consideration, we ignore that part of the loss function concerned with an incorrect decision under the hypothesis; in effect, we let $W_2(\theta) = 0$.

Proof. Let $W_1(\theta)$ be the loss function for an incorrect decision under the alternative, and by assumption it is constant-valued over each set Ω_δ. Then, if $\phi(x)$ maximizes for each δ

$$\inf_{\theta \in \Omega_\delta} \mathbf{P}_{\phi*}(\theta),$$

it minimizes

$$\sup_{\theta \in \Omega_\delta} (1 - \mathbf{P}_{\phi*}(\theta))$$

or equivalently minimizes

$$\sup_{\theta \in \Omega_\delta} W_1(\theta)(1 - \mathbf{P}_{\phi*}(\theta))$$

$$= \sup_{\theta \in \Omega_\delta} \mathbf{R}_{\phi*}(\theta).$$

But, since $\sup\limits_{\delta} \sup\limits_{\theta \in \Omega_\delta}$ is an equivalent operation to $\sup\limits_{\theta \in \Omega - \omega}$, we have that $\phi(x)$ minimizes the maximum risk—is minimax.

Problem 36 is to use these theorems to show that the ordinary F test of the general linear hypothesis is most stringent, and minimax with respect to any invariant loss function. ◀

3.9. Consistency and Efficiency. In many statistical problems the outcome **x** is a point in a product space $\mathscr{X} = \mathscr{X}_1 \times \cdots \times \mathscr{X}_n$, where the $\mathscr{X}_i$ are identical spaces, say $\mathscr{X}$. Also, each probability measure is the power product of a measure on $\mathscr{X}$. It is then of interest to inquire whether a test defined for each "sample size" n has good properties when n is large. One such property is that of consistency.

Let P_θ^X be a probability measure over $\mathscr{X}$, and let $P_\theta^{\mathbf{X}}$ be the power-product measure over $\mathscr{X} = \mathscr{X}_1 \times \cdots \times \mathscr{X}_n$; then

A sequence of size α test functions $\{\phi_n(\mathbf{x})\}$ for the hypothesis: $\theta \in \omega$ is consistent for the alternative $\theta \in \Omega - \omega$ if

$$\lim_{n \to \infty} \mathbf{P}_{\phi_n}(\theta) = 1$$

for each $\theta \in \Omega - \omega$.

This means that, for any $\theta \in \Omega - \omega$, the power of ϕ_n can be made arbitrarily close to 1 by taking n sufficiently large.

Often it is desirable to compare sequences of test functions for certain values of the parameter in the alternative. Since most test sequences under consideration for any problem will be consistent over most of the alternative, it is usually necessary to take values of θ that change with the sample size and become "close" to the hypothesis as the sample size becomes large. Let $\{\phi_n\}$, $\{\phi_n^*\}$ be two sequences of size-α tests. Also let $\{n_i\}$, $\{n_i^*\}$ be two increasing sequences of positive integers such that

$$\lim_{i \to \infty} \mathbf{P}_{\phi_{n_i}}(\theta_i) = \lim_{i \to \infty} \mathbf{P}_{\phi_{n_i^*}^*}(\theta_i)$$

with the two limits existing not equal 0 or 1. Then

The relative efficiency of $\{\phi_n\}$ re $\{\phi_n^*\}$ is

$$e(\{\phi_n\}; \{\phi_n^*\}) = \lim_{i \to \infty} \frac{n_i^*}{n_i}$$

if the limit exists the same for all sequences $\{n_i\}$, $\{n_i^*\}$.

Thus efficiency is the limiting ratio of sample sizes such that the tests have the same limiting power for the sequence $\{\theta_i\}$ in the alternative.

4. CONFIDENCE REGIONS

In Section 2 we consider the estimation of real parameters. The purpose there was to find a procedure for calculating from the outcome an estimate which on the average would be close to the parameter value. Here, our purpose is quite similar. We want to find an interval or region which on the average will tend to contain the correct parameter value and not contain other values of it. Surprisingly though, the technique and analysis for this fit closely the work of the preceding section on hypothesis testing. In this section we shall define confidence regions and establish the analogy with hypothesis testing. An example to illustrate the connection with the material in Section 3 and a series of problems in Section 6 will complete the general discussion.

We first illustrate the idea of confidence regions by means of an example. Let $X_1, \cdots, X_n$ be independent and each be normally distributed with mean μ and variance 1. $(\mu \in]-\infty, +\infty[)$. Suppose we are interested in the parameter μ, but, instead of wanting an estimate $d(x_1, \cdots, x_n)$ which comes close to μ, we want to calculate a set on the real line which we hope will contain the value of the parameter μ. Consider the interval $[\bar{x} - 1.96n^{-1/2}, \bar{x} + 1.96n^{-1/2}]$. It is calculated from the outcome $(x_1, \cdots, x_n)$, and, as we shall see later, it tends to do better than other sets as far as containing the actual value of μ, and not containing other values of μ.

With a confidence interval we associate a *confidence level*, a number β (often 0.90, 0.95, or 0.99). This is the probability with which the confidence region contains the actual value of the parameter. For our example the confidence level is 0.95; that is, with probability 0.95 the interval $[\bar{X} \pm 1.95n^{-1/2}]$ will contain the actual value of μ. We check this probability statement:

$$\Pr_{\mu}\{\mu \in [\bar{X} \pm 1.96n^{-1/2}]\}$$

$$= \Pr_{\mu}\{\bar{X} - 1.96n^{-1/2} \leq \mu \leq \bar{X} + 1.96n^{-1/2}\}$$

$$= \Pr_{\mu}\{\bar{X} - \mu - 1.96n^{-1/2} \leq 0 \leq \bar{X} - \mu + 1.96n^{-1/2}\}$$

$$= \Pr_{\mu}\{\mu + 1.96n^{-1/2} \geq \bar{X} \geq \mu - 1.96n^{-1/2}\}$$

$$= \Pr_{\mu}\{-1.96 \leq \frac{\bar{X} - \mu}{n^{-1/2}} \leq +1.96\}$$

$$= \Pr\{-1.96 \leq Z \leq +1.96\}$$

$$= 0.95,$$

where Z designates a random variable with the normal distribution having mean 0 and variance 1. At the end of this section we shall prove that in a certain sense this interval is the best confidence region with confidence level 0.95.

We first give a general definition of confidence regions, and then we shall consider some optimum properties to look for. Let $\{P_{\theta} | \theta \in \Omega\}$ be a class of probability measures over $\mathscr{X}(\mathscr{A})$, and let $\eta(\theta)$ be a parameter taking its values in a parameter space H. $\eta(\theta)$ need not be real or vector-valued as we required in the theory of estimation. *The function $S(x)$ from*

$\mathscr{X}$ *into the space of subsets of H is a* β *confidence region for* $\eta(\theta)$ *if*

$$\mathrm{Pr}_\theta\{\eta(\theta) \in S(X)\} \geq \beta,$$

or equivalently if

$$P_\theta(\{x \mid \eta(\theta) \in S(x)\}) \geq \beta.$$

It is to be noted that the probability statement concerns a condition on the random variable X. This definition describes a function $S(x)$, which chooses a set of possible values for the parameter $\eta(\theta)$ such that the

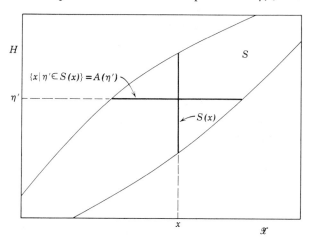

Figure 15. The structure of a confidence region $S(x)$.

probability is at least β that these values will contain the actual value of the parameter in the experiment.

In line with the use of randomized decision functions we now define a randomized confidence region.

The function $S(x, r)$ *from* $\mathscr{X} \times [0, 1]$ *into the space of subsets of H is a* β *confidence region for* $\eta(\theta)$ *if*

$$\mathrm{Pr}_\theta\{\eta(\theta) \in S(X, R)\} \geq \beta$$

where R has the uniform distribution [0, 1].

There is nothing essential in the use of a uniform distribution or in the use of a real-valued random variable R. It is just a convenient method of introducing randomness and·with the availability of random digits is easy to apply.

In Fig. 15 we exhibit the form of a confidence region $S(x)$ in relation to the sample space $\mathscr{X}$ and the parameter space H. For a given x, $S(x)$ is a subset of H. However, for the construction of a confidence region we are interested in the section of the combined confidence regions corresponding to a given value of the parameter, say η'. The resulting set $A(\eta') = \{x \mid \eta' \in S(x)\}$ is a subset of $\mathscr{X}$, and we assume it measurable for each η'. The probability statement says that for each P_θ having $\eta(\theta) = \eta'$ the probability measure of $A(\eta')$ must be β or more. Hence, confidence regions can always be constructed in the following manner. For each η' a subset $A(\eta')$ of $\mathscr{X}$ is determined such that

$$P_\theta(A(\eta')) \geq \beta$$

for each θ having $\eta(\theta) = \eta'$. A β confidence region is the x intersection of these sets arrayed as in Fig. 15:

$$S(x) = \{\eta \mid x \in A(\eta)\}.$$

Obviously $S(x)$ satisfies the requirements in the definition.

For a confidence region it is convenient to define a characteristic function $\phi_\eta(x)$. In the nonrandomized case

$$\phi_\eta(x) = 1 \quad \text{if} \quad \eta \in S(x)$$
$$= 0 \quad\quad\quad \notin S(x),$$

and for the randomized case

$$\phi_\eta(x) = \Pr_R \{\eta \in S(x, R)\},$$

where the probability is taken with respect to the random variable R. In the nonrandomized case, if we think of $\phi_\eta(x)$ as a function of two variables, then it is the characteristic function for the combined confidence regions S as exhibited in Fig. 15, and, if we think of it as a function of x for a given η, it is the characteristic function for the horizontal section $A(\eta)$, which of course must have probability at least β for the corresponding θ's. For a given x in the randomized case, $\phi_\eta(x)$ gives a "probability evaluation" of the different η's in the parameter space H.

In terms of the characteristic function we can restate our definition of a confidence region.

The function $S(x)$ from $\mathscr{X}$ into the space of subsets of H is a β confidence region for η if the corresponding characteristic function satisfies

$$E_\theta\{\phi_{\eta(\theta)}(X)\} \geq \beta.$$

for all $\theta \in \Omega$.

THEOREM 4.1. For any function $\phi_\eta(x)$ with values in $[0, 1]$ and satisfying

$$E_\theta\{\phi_{\eta(\theta)}(X)\} \geq \beta,$$

there corresponds at least one β confidence region.

Proof. We define a function $S(x, r)$ by the equation,

$$S(x, r) = \{\eta \mid \phi_\eta(x) \geq r\}.$$

This is a β confidence region since

$$\Pr_\theta\{\eta(\theta) \in S(X, R)\}$$
$$= E_\theta\{\Pr_R [\eta(\theta) \in S(X, R)]\}$$
$$= E_\theta\{\Pr_R [\phi_\eta(X) \geq R]\}$$
$$= E_\theta\{\phi_\eta(X)\}$$
$$\geq \beta.$$

The theorem and the definition preceding it show that, for any construction or theory of confidence regions, we can equivalently work with characteristic functions. It will be by means of characteristic functions that we establish the connection with hypothesis testing. However, to do this it is convenient to introduce a function very simply related to the characteristic function; we call it the auxiliary function $\psi_\eta(x)$:

$$\psi_\eta(x) = 1 - \phi_\eta(x).$$

It is the characteristic function for the complement of the confidence region in the nonrandomized case. In terms of $\psi_\eta(x)$ the condition for a β confidence region becomes

$$E_\theta\{\psi_{\eta(\theta)}(X)\} \leq 1 - \beta.$$

It is this condition that we associate with the size in hypothesis testing. When β is one of the usual values 0.90, 0.95, 0.99, then $1 - \beta$ is one of the values 0.10, 0.05, 0.01 which are frequently used for the size in hypothesis testing.

For a clear picture of the relationship between a confidence region and the corresponding hypothesis testing problems, it is helpful to give a verbal description. Suppose $\psi_\eta(x)$ is a size $1 - \beta$ test for the problem

$$\text{Hypothesis:} \quad \eta(\theta) = \eta,$$

$$\text{Alternative:} \quad \eta(\theta) \neq \eta.$$

Then for a given outcome we "test" each η and decide whether to reject it or accept it. The η's we reject become points outside the confidence region; those we accept become points inside the confidence region. This constructs a confidence region for that x, and by the theory above it will have confidence level β.

We define the power of a confidence region:

The power of the confidence region $S(x, r)$ at the parameter value η is

$$\mathbf{P}(\theta; \eta) = E_\theta\{\psi_\eta(X)\}.$$

The power $\mathbf{P}(\theta; \eta)$ of a confidence region is the probability that it does not cover η when the probability measure is given by θ. Of course, when $\eta = \eta(\theta)$, we want this probability to be less than $1 - \beta$ in order to satisfy the size condition. However, when $\eta \neq \eta(\theta)$ the power is the probability of not covering a value η which is not the value of the parameter $\eta(\theta)$ in the experiment. This probability we want to be large.

In terms of the auxiliary function we have *the condition for a confidence region*:

$$\mathbf{P}(\theta; \eta) = E_\theta\{\psi_\eta(X)\} \leq 1 - \beta$$

for all θ, η having $\eta = \eta(\theta)$; and, in order to obtain a good confidence region, we want to *maximize*

$$\mathbf{P}(\theta; \eta) = E_\theta\{\psi_\eta(X)\}$$

for all θ, η having $\eta \neq \eta(\theta)$.

To establish the connection with hypothesis testing we partition the space Ω by the function $\eta(\theta)$ and obtain sets Ω_η:

$$\Omega_\eta = \{\theta \,|\, \eta(\theta) = \eta\}.$$

Now by examining the conditions above it is seen that to obtain the auxiliary function of a good β confidence region is to obtain a good test function $\psi_\eta(x)$ of size $1 - \beta$ for the hypothesis testing problem,

$$\text{Hypothesis:} \quad \theta \in \Omega_\eta,$$

$$\text{Alternative:} \quad \theta \notin \Omega_\eta.$$

Then by applying the straightforward connection with hypothesis testing we can have most powerful confidence regions, most powerful similar, unbiased or invariant confidence regions, or most stringent confidence regions.

EXAMPLE 4.1. Let $X_1, \cdots, X_n$ be independent and each be normally distributed with mean μ and variance σ^2, where $\mu \in R^1$ and $\sigma^2 \in {]0, \infty[}$. Consider the problem of finding a β confidence region for the parameter μ.

According to the theory above we partition Ω into sets

$$\Omega_{\mu'} = \{(\mu', \sigma^2) | \sigma^2 \in {]0, \infty[}\},$$

and look for a good test function of size $1 - \beta$ for the problem:

$$\text{Hypothesis:} \quad \mu = \mu', \quad \sigma^2 \in {]0, \infty[},$$

$$\text{Alternative:} \quad \mu \neq \mu', \quad \sigma^2 \in {]0, \infty[}.$$

By Problem 35 the ordinary t test is most stringent; it is

$$\psi_\mu(x) = 1 \quad \text{if} \quad \frac{n^{1/2}|\bar{x} - \mu'|}{s_x} > t_{(1-\beta)/2}$$

$$= 0 \qquad\qquad\qquad < t_{(1-\beta)/2}$$

where t_α is the point exceeded with probability α according to Student's distribution with $n - 1$ degrees of freedom. Now, transferring to the characteristic function for the confidence region, we obtain

$$\phi_\mu(x) = 1 \quad \text{if} \quad \frac{n^{1/2}|\bar{x} - \mu|}{s_x} < t_{(1-\beta)/2}$$

$$= 0 \qquad\qquad\qquad > t_{(1-\beta)/2}.$$

The confidence region $S(x)$ is then given by

$$S(x) = \{\mu \,|\, \phi_\mu(x) = 1\}$$

$$= \{\mu \,|\, \bar{x} - \mu| < n^{-1/2}s_x t_{(1-\beta)/2}\}$$

$$= [\bar{x} \pm n^{-1/2}s_x t_{(1-\beta)/2}]$$

This is a most stringent β confidence region.

5. TOLERANCE LIMITS

When an article is mass-produced, a certain amount of variability is inevitable, but, if an individual item from production deviates excessively from the desired form, it may be unacceptable for the use to which the articles are being put. The limits that divide an acceptable article from a defective article are called *tolerance limits*—limits that define the tolerable variability. In many applications, production is considered satisfactory if 95% (or 99%) of the articles fall within the tolerance limits.

Statistical tolerance limits are somewhat different. After production has commenced, a sample from production may be used to calculate limits which the statistician feels reasonably sure contain a fraction, say 95%, of the articles being produced. Such limits are called statistical tolerance limits, or merely tolerance limits when there is no chance of confusion. In effect, the statistician on the basis of a sample is trying to find a region in the range of the article's variability, containing 95% of production, a *statistical tolerance region*. A statistical tolerance region may be calculated for various reasons: to find out what sort of an article is being produced, to compare with the tolerance limits to see if most of the articles being produced are acceptable, or to keep a check on the production equipment to see that it produces the acceptable type of article. We shall consider only the statistical tolerance regions.

As an example consider $X = (X_1, \cdots, X_4)$ where the X_i are independently distributed and each has the same probability measure on the real line. Let $F_\theta(x)$ be the distribution function for an X_i, and assume that it is a continuous function.   If we take the smallest, $x_{(1)}$, and the largest, $x_{(4)}$, of the measurements in the outcome $(x_1, \cdots x_4)$ and form the interval $[x_{(1)}, x_{(4)}]$, then we have a region in the space of the probability measure being sampled, and this region is a function of the outcome $(x_1, \cdots, x_4)$.

We are interested in the proportion of future sampled articles in this region; that is, in the probability in this region:

$$P_\theta([x_{(1)}, x_{(4)}]) = F_\theta(x_{(4)}) - F_\theta(x_{(1)}).$$

This probability is a function of the outcome $(x_1, \cdots, x_4)$ and hence has an induced probability distribution corresponding to the distribution $F_\theta(x)$ for each x_i.   We now calculate the probability that the interval $[X_{(1)}, X_{(4)}]$ contains 95% of the probability for the distribution $F_\theta(x)$.

$$\Pr_\theta \{P_\theta([X_{(1)}, X_{(4)}]) \geq 0.95\} = \Pr_\theta \{F_\theta(X_{(4)}) - F_\theta(X_{(1)}) \geq 0.95\}.$$

This probability is simple to evaluate because $F_\theta(X_{(4)}) - F_\theta(X_{(1)})$ has a very simple probability distribution when the same value of θ gives the distribution for the X_i.   As we shall see in Chapter 4, this is a β distribution with parameters 3, 2.

$$\Pr_\theta \{P_\theta([X_{(1)}, X_{(4)}]) \geq 0.95\}$$

$$= \frac{\Gamma(5)}{\Gamma(3)\Gamma(2)} \int_{0.95}^1 x^2(1 - x)\, dx$$

$$= 12 \int_0^{0.05} x^1(1 - x)^2\, dx$$

$$= 12 \int_0^{0.05} (x - 2x^2 + x^3)\, dx$$

$$= 12 \left[\frac{x^2}{2} - 2\frac{x^3}{3} + \frac{x^4}{4}\right]_0^{0.05}$$

$$= 12 \left[\frac{0.0025}{2} - \tfrac{2}{3}(0.000125) + \tfrac{1}{4}(0.00000625)\right]$$

$$\doteq 0.015.$$

Thus there is only 0·015 probability that the interval $[X_{(1)}, X_{(4)}]$ will contain 95% of the probability of the distribution.   Certainly we need more than a sample of four to pin down 95% of the probability.

We now generalize these ideas on tolerance regions and consider a number of different definitions.   Let $\{P_\theta | \theta \in \Omega\}$ be a class of probability measures over the measurable space $\mathcal{X}(\mathcal{A})$. We shall consider tolerance regions based on a sample of say n from one of these probability measures. Therefore, the sample space for the problem will be $\mathcal{X}^n$, and each measure in the class for $\mathcal{X}^n$ will be the power product of a measure in $\{P_\theta \,|\, \theta \in \Omega\}$. Now by the above example we see that, for each value of the outcome $(x_1, \cdots, x_n)$, we wish to associate a subset of the space $\mathcal{X}$. Accordingly, our first requirement is that *a tolerance region* $S(x_1, \cdots, x_n)$ *be a mapping from* $\mathcal{X}^n$ *into* $\mathcal{A}$. The thing of interest about the region $S(x_1, \cdots, x_n)$ for a given outcome is the probability in the region as determined by the probability measure P_θ which gave rise to that outcome. The probability measure of S using P_θ is

$$P_\theta(S(x_1, \cdots, x_n));$$

it is a real number between 0 and 1. This function of the outcome has an induced probability distribution corresponding to the product measure of P_θ over $\mathcal{X}^n$. It is this distribution that tells us how the probability content of $S(x_1, \cdots, x_n)$ varies in repeated sampling from a given probability measure. If we are interested in how often the region $S(x_1, \cdots, x_n)$ contains at least a proportion p of the probability, then we calculate

$$\mathrm{Pr}_\theta\{P_\theta(S(X_1, \cdots, X_n)) \geq p\}.$$

DEFINITION 5.1. $S(x_1, \cdots, x_n)$ is a β tolerance region for a proportion p if

$$\inf_{\theta \in \Omega} \ \mathrm{Pr}_\theta\{P_\theta(S(X_1, \cdots, X_n)) \geq p\} = \beta.$$

The probability of containing a proportion p of the probability may change with θ. The lower bound of this probability is the *confidence level* with which we are able to assert that $S(x_1, \cdots, x_n)$ contains at least a proportion p of the probability. Using the frequency interpretation of probability, we can rephrase the definition as follows: $S(x_1, \cdots, x_n)$ is a β tolerance region for a proportion p if at least β of the time in repeated sampling the region $S(X_1, \cdots, X_n)$ contains at least p of the probability as determined by the measure producing the sample elements x_i.

Another definition which has much stronger requirements is sometimes used in the hope of obtaining tolerance regions with more regular behavior.

DEFINITION 5.2. $S(x_1, \cdots, x_n)$ is a distribution-free tolerance region for $\{P_\theta \,|\, \theta \in \Omega\}$ over $\mathcal{X}(\mathcal{A})$ if the induced probability distribution of

$$P_\theta(S(x_1, \cdots, x_n)),$$

corresponding to P_θ for each x_i, is independent of $\theta \in \Omega$.

The induced distribution function, say $G_\theta(p)$ for $P_\theta(S(X_1, \cdots, X_n))$, is given by

$$G_\theta(p) = \mathrm{Pr}_\theta\{P_\theta(S(X_1, \cdots, X_n)) \leq p\}.$$

The definition then states that $G_\theta(p) = G(p)$. The example of a tolerance region at the beginning of this section was distribution-free. In fact, the distribution of the probability content of the region was a fixed β distribution. We shall see in Chapter 4 that there is a large class of tolerance regions for which the β distribution is the induced distribution of the probability content of the region.

It is possible to give analytic conditions under which a tolerance region satisfies Definition 5.2. For this we need to define the characteristic function of a tolerance region, $\phi_y(x_1, \cdots, x_n)$.

$$\phi_y(x_1, \cdots, x_n) = 1 \qquad \text{if} \quad y \in S(x_1, \cdots, x_n)$$
$$= 0 \qquad\qquad \notin S(x_1, \cdots, x_n).$$

Then it is easily seen that $P_\theta(S(x_1, \cdots, x_n)) = E_\theta^Y\{\phi_Y(x_1, \cdots, x_n)\}$, where the expectation applies to the random variable Y with probability measure P_θ.

THEOREM 5.1. A necessary and sufficient condition that $S(x_1, \cdots, x_n)$ be a distribution-free tolerance region is that there exist a sequence $\alpha_1, \alpha_2, \cdots$ such that

$$\phi_{y_1}(x_1, \cdots, x_n) - \alpha_1, \cdots, \prod_{j=1}^r \phi_{y_j}(x_1, \cdots, x_n) - \alpha_r, \cdots$$

are, respectively, unbiased estimators of zero over $\mathscr{X}^{n+1}, \cdots, \mathscr{X}^{n+r}, \cdots$ for the power-product measures of $\{P_\theta | \theta \in \Omega\}$. The sequence $\alpha_1, \alpha_2, \cdots$ is the moment sequence for the distribution of $P_\theta(S(X_1, \cdots, X_n))$.

Proof. A distribution-free tolerance region has the distribution function $G_\theta(p)$ independent of θ. Now, since a distribution function on a bounded interval is uniquely determined by the corresponding moment sequence (see [4]), it is equivalent to state that the moment sequence for $G_\theta(p)$ should be independent of θ. The rth moment for $G_\theta(p)$ is given by α_r.

$$\alpha_r = \int_0^1 p^r \, dG_\theta(p)$$
$$= \int_{\mathscr{X}^n} [P_\theta(S(x_1, \cdots, x_n))]^r \prod_{i=1}^n dP_\theta(x_i)$$
$$= \int_{\mathscr{X}^n} [E_\theta^Y(\phi_Y(x_1, \cdots, x_n))]^r \prod_{i=1}^n dP_\theta(x_i)$$
$$= \int_{\mathscr{X}^n} \left[\int_{\mathscr{X}} \phi_y(x_1, \cdots, x_n) \, dP_\theta(y) \right]^r \prod_{i=1}^n dP_\theta(x_i)$$
$$= \int_{\mathscr{X}^{n+r}} \prod_{j=1}^r \phi_{y_j}(x_1, \cdots, x_n) \prod_{j=1}^r dP_\theta(y_j) \prod_{i=1}^n dP_\theta(x_i).$$

Therefore $\prod_{j=1}^r \phi_{y_j}(x_1, \cdots, x_n) - \alpha_r$ is an unbiased estimate of zero over

$\mathscr{X}^{n+r}$. Thus the statement that $F_\theta(p)$ is independent of θ is equivalent to the above expression being an unbiased estimate of zero for all r.

Another definition for tolerance regions is concerned with the average or expected probability in a tolerance region. For it, we can set up a correspondence with hypothesis testing which will permit us to find tolerance regions with optimum properties.

DEFINITION 5.3. $S(x_1, \cdots, x_n)$ is a β-expectation tolerance region if

$$E_\theta\{P_\theta(S(X_1, \cdots, X_n))\} = \beta$$

for all $\theta \in \Omega$.

In terms of the characteristic function the above condition becomes

$$\int_{\mathscr{X}^{n+1}} \phi_y(x_1, \cdots, x_n) \prod_{i=1}^{n} dP_\theta(x_i) \, dP_\theta(y) = \beta.$$

In order to introduce the notion of a good tolerance region we need a function that will tell us the relative merits of sets S in $\mathscr{A}$ when the probability measure is P_θ. Let the "desirability" of a set S when the probability measure is θ be given by a probability measure $Q_\theta(S)$ defined for all $S \in \mathscr{A}$. We assume that

$$Q_\theta(S) = \int_S f_\theta(y) \, dP_\theta(y).$$

Then the measure of merit or *power* of a tolerance region will be given by

$$E_\theta\{Q_\theta(S(X_1, \cdots, X_n))\},$$

or in terms of the characteristic function by

$$\int_{\mathscr{X}^{n+1}} \phi_y(x_1, \cdots, x_n) \prod_{i=1}^{n} dP_\theta(x_i) f_\theta(y) \, dP_\theta(y).$$

Thus to find the characteristic function of a good tolerance region is to find a good similar test function $\phi_y(x_1, \cdots, x_n)$ for the hypothesis testing problem

Hypothesis: $Y, X_1, \cdots, X_n$ independent, each with measure P_θ $(\theta \in \Omega)$,

Alternative: $X_1, \cdots, X_n$ independent, each with measure P_θ Y independent of the X_i and with measure Q_θ $(\theta \in \Omega)$.

If the test function should turn out to be randomized, then we need a definition of a randomized tolerance region; this can be given in the same way that a randomized confidence region was introduced in the last section. For further reading on the construction of best β-expectation tolerance regions, see Fraser and Guttman [13].

6. PROBLEMS FOR SOLUTION

1. A complete class of decision functions is called *minimal* if it does not contain a proper subset which is complete. Show that, if a minimal complete class exists, it is identical to the class of admissible decision functions.

2. For Example 1.1 consider the class $\mathscr{D}_f^*$ of decision functions of the form

$$d(x) = d_1 \quad \text{if} \quad \frac{\Sigma x_i}{n} \leq b$$

$$= d_2 \quad\quad\quad > b,$$

where b takes any real value. Sketch the power function for a typical b; also sketch the risk function, using the given loss function with $a = 1$. Find a minimax decision procedure.

3. Let X have the probability measure $P_p(1) = p$, $P_p(0) = q = 1 - p$ (binomial distribution with $n = 1$), and consider the estimation of $p \in [0, 1]$ when the loss function is

$$W(d, p) = 1 \quad \text{if} \quad |d - p| \geq \tfrac{1}{4}$$

$$= 0 \quad \text{if} \quad |d - p| < \tfrac{1}{4}.$$

Plot the risk function for the decision function $d_1(x)$ which estimates $p = \tfrac{1}{4}, \tfrac{3}{4}$ when $x = 0, 1$, respectively:

$$d_1(0) = \tfrac{1}{4}$$

$$d_1(1) = \tfrac{3}{4}.$$

Show that $\sup_p R_{d_1}(p) = 1$. Consider a randomized estimator defined symbolically by $d_2(x) = Y$ where Y is a random variable with the uniform distribution $[0, 1]$. This estimator ignores the outcome and estimates by means of a number uniformly chosen from $[0, 1]$. Plot the risk function for $d_2(x)$. Show that $\sup_p R_{d_2}(p) = \tfrac{3}{4}$. Which would you prefer on a minimax basis?

4. If $W(y)$ is a convex function defined over R^1 (or any open interval) show that $W(y)$ is continuous. *Hint*: consider the derivatives to the left and right.

5. Prove the last statement in Theorem 2.2.

6. Prove Theorem 2.3.

7. Prove that the first two loss functions in formula (2.5) are strictly convex.

8. Prove that the first loss function in formula (2.7) is strictly convex.

9. Prove that any sum of convex functions is convex; that any finite sum of strictly convex functions is strictly convex.

10. Let $X_1, \cdots, X_n$ be independent, and let each have the normal distribution with mean μ and variance σ^2.

(a) If $\mu \in R^1$ and $\sigma^2 = 1$, what is the complete sufficient statistic?

(b) If $\mu = 0$ and $\sigma^2 \in \,]0, \infty[$, what is the complete sufficient statistic?

(c) If $(\mu, \sigma^2) \in R \times \,]0, \infty[$, what is the complete sufficient statistic? (See problems in Chapter 1.)

For each of the above cases find minimum-risk (convex-loss) unbiased estimators for the parameters: μ, σ^2, σ, (μ, σ^2), $E(X^2)$, $E^2(X)$, $E(X^3)$, $E^3(X)$, $E(X - \mu)^3$.

11. Let $X_1, \cdots, X_n$ be independent, and let each have the binomial distribution $\Pr(X = 1) = p$, $\Pr(X = 0) = q = 1 - p$. Show that Σx_i is a complete sufficient statistic. Find minimum variance unbiased estimates of p, $p(1 - p)$.

12. Let $Y_1, \cdots, Y_n$ be independent, and let each have the Poisson distribution with mean m. What is the complete sufficient statistic? Find minimum-risk (convex-loss) unbiased estimates of m, m^2.

13. The hypergeometric distribution is defined by

$$\Pr(Y = y) = \frac{\dbinom{D}{y}\dbinom{N - D}{n - y}}{\dbinom{N}{n}} \qquad (0 \leq y \leq \min D, n).$$

What s the complete sufficient statistic for the class corresponding to $D = 0, 1, \cdots, n$? Find a minimum variance unbiased estimate of D, D^2.

14. Let $X_1, \cdots, X_n$ be independent, and let each have the same absolutely continuous distribution on R^1. For the class of all such distributions, what is the complete sufficient statistic? Find minimum-variance, minimum-risk (convex-loss) unbiased estimates of $\mu = E(X)$, $\sigma^2 = E(X - \mu)^2$, (μ, σ^2), $E(X^2)$, $E^2(X)$, $E(X^3)$, $E^3(X)$, $E(X - \mu)^3$.

15. Let $X_1, \cdots, X_r$ be independent, and let each have the binomial distribution with parameter (n, p). What is a complete sufficient statistic? These values $x_1, \cdots, x_r$ could correspond to the numbers of defectives in r successive lots from a production line. A parameter of interest might be the probability P that an individual lot passes a quality inspection. If the inspection plan is to accept or reject a lot according as $x \leq 2$ or $x > 2$, an unbiased estimate of P is $1/r$ (number of lots accepted). Find a minimum-variance unbiased estimate.

16. For the measures of Problem 12, find a minimum-variance unbiased estimate of e^{-m}, $e^{-m}(1 + m)$.

17. Complete the proof of Theorem 2.7 by inserting the details necessary in the last paragraph.

18. For the invariance theory in Section 2.3, show that each $\bar{s}$ maps Ω onto Ω; .e., is a one-to-one mapping.

19. For the invariance theory in Section 2.3, show that $\bar{\mathscr{G}}$ is a group homomorphic to $\mathscr{G}$.

20. For the regression example at the end of Section 2.3, show that the suggested estimator has minimum risk among invariant estimators (loss function being a weighting of the squared errors).

21. Prove that, if for tests in $\mathscr{D}_t$ there does not exist one having maximum power for the parameter value $\theta(\theta \in \Omega - \omega)$, there does exist a sequence of tests for which the power approaches the supremum.

22. If for a hypothesis testing problem there does not exist a minimax test, show that at least there exists a sequence of tests having the minimax property in the limit.

23. Show that for any two measures $P(A)$, $P'(A)$ over $\mathscr{X}$ ($\mathscr{A}$) there exists a dominating measure $\mu(x)$: $P << \mu$, $P' << \mu$.

24. If $P(A) = \displaystyle\int_A f(x)\, d\mu(x)$, then prove that $\Pr\{f(X) = 0\} = 0$. If X has the measure $P(A)$, prove that

$$\Pr\left\{\frac{g(X)}{f(X)} = +\infty \text{ or is undefined}\right\} = 0,$$

where $g(x) \geq 0$. What are the implications for Theorem 3.1?

25. Let $X_1, \cdots, X_n$ be independent, and let each have the normal distribution with means 0 and variance σ^2. Find a most powerful size α test for

$$\text{Hypothesis:} \quad \sigma = \sigma_0,$$
$$\text{Alternative:} \quad \sigma > \sigma_0,$$

and hence for

$$\text{Hypothesis:} \quad \sigma \leq \sigma_0,$$
$$\text{Alternative:} \quad \sigma > \sigma_0.$$

Find a most powerful size-α test for

$$\text{Hypothesis:} \quad \sigma \geq \sigma_0,$$
$$\text{Alternative:} \quad \sigma < \sigma_0.$$

26. For the binomial distributions with parameters n, p, find a most powerful size-α test for

$$\text{Hypothesis:} \quad p = p_0,$$
$$\text{Alternative:} \quad p > p_0,$$

and for

$$\text{Hypothesis:} \quad p = p_0,$$
$$\text{Alternative:} \quad p < p_0.$$

27. Let $X_1, \cdots, X_n$ be independent, and let each have the normal distribution with mean μ and variance σ^2. Find a most powerful size-α test for

$$\text{Hypothesis:} \quad \sigma = \sigma_0, \quad \mu \in R^1,$$
$$\text{Alternative:} \quad \sigma = \sigma_1(<\sigma_0), \quad \mu = \mu_1.$$

For what larger alternative is the test most powerful? Is it most powerful against the

$$\text{Alternative:} \quad \sigma < \sigma_0, \quad \mu \in R^1?$$

28. Let $X_1, \cdots, X_m, Y_2, \cdots, Y_n$ be independent, and let each X_i be normally distributed with mean μ and variance σ^2 and each Y_i be normally distributed with mean ν and variance τ^2. If $\sigma = \tau = 1$, find a most powerful size-α test for

$$\text{Hypothesis:} \quad \mu = \nu, \quad \mu \in R^1,$$
$$\text{Alternative:} \quad \mu = \mu_1, \quad \nu = \nu_1 \quad (\mu_1 < \nu_1).$$

For what extended alternative is the test uniformly most powerful?

29 (Continuation). If $\mu = \nu = 0$, find a most powerful size test for

$$\text{Hypothesis:} \quad \sigma = \tau \in \,]0, \infty[,$$
$$\text{Alternative:} \quad \sigma = \sigma_1, \quad \tau = \tau_1.$$

For what extended alternative is the test uniformly most powerful?

30 (Continuation). Find a most powerful size-α test for

$$\text{Hypothesis:} \quad \mu, \nu \in R_1, \quad \sigma = \tau \in \,]0, \infty[,$$
$$\text{Alternative:} \quad \mu = \mu_1, \quad \nu = \nu_1, \quad \sigma = \sigma_1, \quad \tau = \tau_1.$$

For what extended alternative is the test uniformly most powerful?

31. Let $X_1, \cdots, X_n$ be independent, and let each be normally distributed with mean μ and variance σ^2. Find a most powerful similar test of size α for

Hypothesis: $\sigma = \sigma_0$, $\mu \in R^1$,

Alternative: $\sigma < \sigma_0$, $\mu \in R^1$.

32. For the measures of Problem 31 find a most powerful unbiased test for

Hypothesis: $\sigma \geq \sigma_0$, $\mu \in R^1$,

Alternative: $\sigma < \sigma_0$, $\mu \in R^1$.

33. Let X have the binomial distribution with parameters n, p, and let Y have the binomial distribution with parameter m, p^*. Find a most powerful similar size-α test for

Hypothesis: $p = p^*$,

Alternative: $p < p^*$.

34. If $P_\alpha = \{A_\alpha\}$ is an invariant partition of $\mathscr{X}$ with respect to the group $\mathscr{G}$ for each α belonging to an index set I, show that $\{\bigcap_{\alpha \in I} A_\alpha \,|\, A_\alpha \in P_\alpha\}$ is a partition and is invariant.

35. Let $X_1, \cdots, X_n$ be independent and each be normally distributed with mean μ and variance σ^2. For the problem

Hypothesis: $\mu = 0$, $\sigma \in \,]0, \infty[$,

Alternative: $\mu \neq 0$, $\sigma \in \,]0, \infty[$,

show that $|\bar{x}| [\Sigma(x_i - \bar{x})^2]^{-1/2}$ or $\bar{x}^2/\Sigma(x_i - \bar{x})^2$ is a maximal invariant function for the problem in terms of the sufficient statistic. What is the maximal invariant parameter? Find a most powerful invariant test. Show that the test is most stringent and minimax re any invariant loss function.

36. The general linear hypothesis problem can be described as follows: $X_1, \cdots, X_n$ are independently distributed, and each X_i is normally distributed with mean μ_i and variance σ^2. $\mu_i = \sum_{j=1}^{s} a_{ij}\theta_j \ (s \leq n)$ and $\|a_{ij}\|$ has rank s. $\Omega = \{(\sigma^2, \theta_1, \cdots, \theta_s) \,|\, \sigma^2 \in \,]0, \infty[, \theta_i \in R^1\}$. The problem is

Hypothesis: $b_{11}\theta_1 + \cdots + b_{1s}\theta_s = c_1$,

$b_{r1}\theta_1 + \cdots + b_{rs}\theta_s = c_r$,

Alternative: At least one inequality in the relations of the hypothesis.

There are $s + 1$ parameters, $\sigma^2, \theta_1, \cdots, \theta_s$, and the hypothesis imposes r restrictions on the s θ's. Many of the standard problems of regression theory and the analysis of variance are of this type.

(a) Define the orthogonal transformations and changes of origin that put this problem into the canonical form: $Y_1, \cdots, Y_n$ are independently distributed; $Y_1, \cdots, Y_s$ are normally distributed with means $\eta_1, \cdots, \eta_s$ and variance σ^2; and $Y_{s+1}, \cdots, Y_n$ are normally distributed with means 0 and variance σ^2; the problem is

Hypothesis: $\eta_1 = \cdots = \eta_r = 0$,

Alternative: At least one inequality in the hypothesis.

(b) Define the group of transformations which leave the general linear hypothesis problem invariant. Show that a maximal invariant (in terms of the Y's) is

$$F = \frac{\sum\limits_{1}^{r} Y_i^2}{\sum\limits_{s+1}^{n} Y_i^2},$$

or the corresponding F ratio (i.e., with the division by the degrees of freedom).

(c) Show that the maximal invariant under the induced group on the parameter space is

$$\psi^2 = \frac{1}{\sigma^2} \sum_{i=1}^{r} \eta_i^2,$$

in terms of the parameters of the problem in canonical form.

(d) The distribution of the noncentral F (again ignoring the division by the degrees of freedom) has the p.d.f.

$$f_{\eta_1 \cdots \eta_r \sigma^2}(F) = \exp\left(\frac{-\psi^2}{2}\right) \sum_{h=0}^{\infty} \frac{(\psi^2/2)^h}{h!} \frac{\Gamma\left(\dfrac{n_1 + n_2}{2} + h\right)}{\Gamma\left(\dfrac{n_1}{2} + h\right) \Gamma\left(\dfrac{n_2}{2}\right)} \frac{F^{n_1/2}}{(1 + F)^{\frac{n_1 + n_2}{2} + h}}$$

It is interesting to note that this is a weighted average of a series of F densities, starting with the central F and increasing the numerator degrees of freedom successively by 2, (again omitting the divisions by degrees of freedom). The weights are the Poisson probabilities with mean $\psi^2/2$. Show that the most powerful invariant test is the ordinary F test. Show that the F test is minimax re any invariant loss function.

37. Show that the two-sided t test (Problem 35) is most stringent. Show that the F test (Problem 36) is most stringent.

38. For the Problem 32 with the

$$\text{Hypothesis: } \sigma \geq \sigma_0, \quad \mu \in R^1,$$

$$\text{Alternative: } \sigma < \sigma_0, \quad \mu \in R^1,$$

find a most powerful invariant size-α test. Is it most stringent? Is it minimax with respect to any invariant loss function?

39. Use Theorem 3.10 to find a most stringent test for Problem 38.

40. Let $X_1, \cdots, X_n$ be independent and each be normally distributed with mean μ and variance σ^2. Apply Theorem 3.10 to find a size-α test which maximizes the minimum power over the alternative of the problem,

$$\text{Hypothesis: } \mu = 0,$$

$$\text{Alternative: } \mu = \pm\mu_1.$$

What is a most stringent size-α test for

$$\text{Hypothesis: } \mu = 0,$$

$$\text{Alternative: } \mu \neq 0.$$

41. Let $X_1, \cdots, X_n$ be independent and each be normally distributed with mean μ and variance σ^2.

(a) If $\Omega = \{(\mu, \sigma^2) \mid \mu \in R^1, \sigma^2 = 1\}$ find a most stringent confidence region for μ.

(b) If $\Omega = \{(\mu, \sigma^2) \mid \mu \in R^1, \sigma^2 \in]0, \infty[\}$, find a most stringent confidence region for μ.

42. For the general linear hypothesis Problem 36, find a most stringent confidence region for a parameter, say η_i (in canonical form); for a θ_i.

43. Let $X_1, \cdots, X_n$ be independent and each be normally distributed with mean μ and variance σ^2.

(a) If $\sigma^2 = 1$ and *power* is obtained from the normal density with the same mean but with $\sigma^2 = \epsilon \, (<1)$, find a most stringent β-expectation tolerance region (the center of the distribution is being weighted).

(b) If $\mu \in R^1$, $\sigma \in]0, \infty[$ and power is obtained from the normal density with the same mean but with variance decreased by a proportion ϵ, find a most stringent β-expectation tolerance region.

REFERENCES AND BIBLIOGRAPHY

1. A. Wald, *Statistical Decision Functions*, John Wiley & Sons, 1950.

2. J. von Neumann and O. Morgenstern, *Theory of Games and Economic Behaviour*, Princeton University Press, 1944.

3. J. L. Hodges Jr. and E. L. Lehmann, "Some application of the Cramér-Rao Inequality," *Proc. 2d Berkeley Symposium*, University of California Press, Berkeley, 1951.

4. H. Cramér, *Mathematical Methods of Statistics*, Princeton University Press, 1946.

5. G. Hardy, J. Littlewood, and G. Polya, *Inequalities*, Cambridge University Press, 1934.

6. D. Blackwell, "Conditional expectation and unbiased sequential estimation," *Ann. Math. Stat.*, Vol. 18 (1947), pp. 105–110.

7. E. L. Lehmann, "Theory of Estimation," mimeographed notes, University of California, 1950.

8. E. L. Lehmann and H. Scheffé, "Completeness, similar regions and unbiased estimation," *Sankhyā*, Vol. 10 (1950), pp. 305–340.

9. D. A. S. Fraser, "A regression problem and the invariance method," unpublished.

10. E. Lehmann, "Theory of hypothesis testing," mimeographed notes, University of California 1949.

11. E. L. Lehmann, "Some principles of the theory of testing hypothesis," *Ann. Math. Stat.*, Vol. 21 (1950), pp. 1–26.

12. D. A. S. Fraser, "Nonparametric theory. Scale and location parameters," *Can. J. Math.*, Vol. 6 (1953), pp. 46–48.

13. D. A. S. Fraser and I. Guttman, "Tolerance regions," *Ann. Math. Stat.*, Vol. 27 (1956), pp. 16–32.

14. H. Robbins, "Mixture of distributions," *Ann. Math. Stat.*, Vol. 19 (1948), p. 360.

CHAPTER 3

Nonparametric Problems

1. INTRODUCTION

Much of the statistical theory developed in the past has been concerned with *parametric problems*. In these, the probability distribution has some simple functional form such as that of the normal distribution and is completely specified by one, two, or at most a countable number of real parameters. The essential feature is the finite or countable number of *parameters*, parameters in the traditional sense of real-valued parameters. There are some good reasons for this concentration on parametric problems. For many applications the normal, or some of the distributions derived therefrom, do resemble the theoretical distributions as indicated by repeated sampling. Second, and this is mainly a justification for the theoretician, it was for the normal distribution that much of the mathematical analysis was singularly tractable, and direct attempts to extend the analysis to other distribution forms led to great increases in complexity.

More recently, much effort has been expended in trying to increase the field of application of statistics. This has taken place in two directions. The standard statistical procedures derived under the assumption of normal distributions have been examined under various modifications of the assumptions—usually that the functional form of the distribution has been altered in some simple manner. These investigations have been primarily concerned with the effect on the size of tests. We shall not be considering this approach, although we obtain, incidentally, some answers to the problems arising in this direction. The second approach has been to restate the standard problems in quite general terms and then look for adequate statistical procedures. In this case the class of probability distributions considered is quite large—so large, in fact, that it can no longer be indexed by a finite number of real parameters. This field of investigation has been given the title *nonparametric* statistics; that is, statistics without parameters in the traditional sense of the term parameter.

125

We propose the following as a rough description of nonparametric theory: *that portion of statistical inference for which the parameter space cannot be simply represented as a subset of a real space of a finite number of dimensions.* Unfortunately, this would include a simple sequential problem involving normal distributions and a countable number of means. Such a problem properly belongs to the parametric theory concerning normal distributions. On the other hand, a problem involving a sample from a continuous distribution function has a parameter space representable as a countable number of real coordinates (the values of the distribution function at the rationals). Such a problem we wish to call nonparametric. So without a clear-cut definition of nonparametric theory we emphasize that its purpose is the statistical treatment of the standard problems under quite general assumptions.

In the remaining section we sketch a few nonparametric formulations for standard problems. For a first reading this may well be omitted since the problems are introduced one by one in the later chapters. They are collected here to amplify the discussion above and for comparison of one problem with another.

2. SINGLE SAMPLE PROBLEMS

▶ The basic assumption in a single sample problem is that a set of real- (or vector-) valued random variables forms a sample from a distribution over R^1 (or over R^k). The problem is to test some hypothesis concerning this distribution, to estimate or form a confidence interval for some real-valued parameter, or to construct a tolerance region. For later reference we classify some of the more usual assumptions:

ASSUMPTION 2. $X_1, \cdots, X_n$ are independent, each has the same distribution and either

(a) X_i has the distribution P_θ over R^1; $\{P_\theta | \theta \in \Omega\}$ is the class of absolutely continuous distributions over R^1 and is equivalently given by the class $\{f_\theta(x) | \theta \in \Omega\}$ of density functions re Lebesgue measure over R^1, or

(b) $\mathbf{X}_i = (X_{i1}, \cdots, X_{ik})$, has a distribution P_θ over R^k; $\{P_\theta | \theta \in \Omega\}$ is the class of all discrete distributions over R^k (each has probability on at most a countable number of points), or

(c) $\mathbf{X}_i = (X_{i1}, \cdots, X_{ik})$ has a distribution P_θ over R^k; $\{P_\theta | \theta \in \Omega\}$ is the class of absolutely continuous distributions over R^k and is equivalently given by the class $\{f_\theta(\mathbf{x}) | \theta \in \Omega\}$ of density functions re Lebesgue measure over R^k.

Some hypothesis testing problems that come under these assumptions are outlined in the following subsections.

2.1. The Problem of Fit. Historically, this is perhaps the first problem with a nonparametric formulation. Karl Pearson as early as 1900 proposed the problem and offered the now classical χ^2 test of fit.

The problem of fit is to test whether a sample is from some particular distribution against the alternative that it is from some other distribution in the class $\{P_\theta \mid \theta \in \Omega\}$; this is expressed by

(2.1)
$$\text{Hypothesis:} \quad \theta = \theta_0,$$
$$\text{Alternative:} \quad \theta \in \Omega - \theta_0.$$

For application, however, the statistician might be more interested in testing whether a sample is from a distribution close to a particular distribution or from a quite different distribution. We can make this precise by introducing the notion of distance between two probability distributions. Let $F_\theta(x)$, $F_{\theta'}(x)$ be two distribution functions over the real line. Then we could define a "distance" between them as

$$d_1(F_\theta, F_{\theta'}) = \sup_x \left| F_{\theta'}(x) - F_\theta(x) \right|$$

or

$$d_2(F_\theta, F_{\theta'}) = \int_R (F_{\theta'}(x) - F_\theta(x))^2 \, dF_\theta(x).$$

The first definition satisfies the usual axioms for a measure of distance; namely

(1)
$$d_1(F_\theta, F_{\theta'}) = d_1(F_{\theta'}, F_\theta),$$

(2)
$$d_1(F_\theta, F_\theta) = 0,$$

(3)
$$d_1(F_\theta, F_{\theta'}) + d_1(F_{\theta'}, F_{\theta''}) \geq d_1(F_\theta, F_{\theta''}).$$

The second definition produces a directed distance which in general fails axiom (1). However, for our purposes it is satisfactory. We can modify these definitions by introducing a positive weight function $W(u)$ to depend on the value of $F_\theta(x)$:

$$d_3(F_\theta, F_{\theta'}) = \sup_x \left| F_{\theta'}(x) - F_\theta(x) \right| W(F_\theta(x))$$

$$d_4(F_\theta, F_{\theta'}) = \int_R [F_{\theta'}(x) - F_\theta(x)]^2 W(F_\theta(x)) \, dF_\theta(x).$$

Both these definitions in general produce directed distances.

Using one of these definitions to measure the distance of a distribution from F_{θ_0},

$$d(F_\theta) = d_i(F_{\theta_0}, F_\theta),$$

we can describe the modified hypothesis testing problem by

(2.2)
$$\text{Hypothesis:} \quad \theta \in \{\theta \mid d(F_\theta) \leq \delta\},$$
$$\text{Alternative:} \quad \theta \in \{\theta \mid d(F_\theta) > \delta\},$$

or more compactly by

(2.3)
$$\text{Hypothesis:} \quad d(F_\theta) \leq \delta,$$
$$\text{Alternative:} \quad d(F_\theta) > \delta.$$

2.2. The Problem of Location.   This problem is concerned with the location of a probability distribution.   To describe the problem we need the concept of a location parameter—a real number which is calculated from a distribution and which measures where the distribution is 'located'.   In as general a class of distribution as given by Assumption 2a, the median is usually used.   However, if the location of one or other end of the distribution was of prime importance, some other percentile could be used.   In [2] the problem of defining a location parameter for a general class of distributions is considered, and, under a mild restriction on the transformation properties of the parameter, it is shown that the location parameter must be a percentile.   We designate the pth percentile of a distribution F by $\xi_p(F)$, and we have, under Assumption 2a, the defining equation $F(\xi_p) = p$.   A more general definition is given by (2.4) in Chapter 2.

One form of the location parameter problem is to test the hypothesis that the location parameter has a specified value ξ_0 against the alternative that it has a larger value:

(2.4)
$$\text{Hypothesis:} \quad \xi_p(F_\theta) = \xi_0, \quad \theta \in \Omega,$$
$$\text{Alternative:} \quad \xi_p(F_\theta) > \xi_0, \quad \theta \in \Omega.$$

Sometimes a more general hypothesis is wanted—that the location parameter takes a value less than or equal to the specified value ξ_0:

(2.5)
$$\text{Hypothesis:} \quad \xi_p(F_\theta) \leq \xi_0, \quad \theta \in \Omega,$$
$$\text{Alternative:} \quad \xi_p(F_\theta) > \xi_0, \quad \theta \in \Omega.$$

Such location problems are called one-sided because the alternative values of the location parameter are all larger than ξ_0 (or for the analogous problem are smaller).   The two-sided location parameter problem is given by

(2.6)
$$\text{Hypothesis:} \quad \xi_p(F_\theta) = \xi_0, \quad \theta \in \Omega,$$
$$\text{Alternative:} \quad \xi_p(F_\theta) \neq \xi_0, \quad \theta \in \Omega.$$

With the median as the location parameter there is another form of the problem which has had frequent consideration in the literature.   It differs from those above in that there is an over-all assumption that the distributions are symmetric about the median.   The probability measure P_θ with median $\xi_{0.5}$ is said to be symmetric if

$$P_\theta\{]\xi_{0.5} - x, \xi_{0.5}]\} = P_\theta\{[\xi_{0.5}, \xi_{0.5} + x[\}$$

for all positive x.   In terms of the distribution function F_θ the condition is

$$F_\theta(\xi_{0.5} - x) = 1 - F_\theta(\xi_{0.5} + x - 0)$$

for all positive x.   Then a modified form of the one-sided location problem is

(2.7)
$$\text{Hypothesis:} \quad \xi_{0.5}(F_\theta) = \xi_0, \quad F_\theta \text{ symmetric}, \quad \theta \in \Omega,$$
$$\text{Alternative:} \quad \xi_{0.5}(F_\theta) > \xi_0, \quad F_\theta \text{ symmetric}, \quad \theta \in \Omega,$$

and of the two-sided problem is

(2.8)
$$\text{Hypothesis:} \quad \xi_{0.5}(F_\theta) = \xi_0, \quad F_\theta \text{ symmetric}, \quad \theta \in \Omega,$$
$$\text{Alternative:} \quad \xi_{0.5}(F_\theta) \neq \xi_0, \quad F_\theta \text{ symmetric}, \quad \theta \in \Omega.$$

2.3. Location and Symmetry. This problem differs from the last above in that the alternative is increased to include all distributions for which either the symmetry is lost, or the location parameter is different from the hypothesis value, or both. In short, the problem is to test whether the distribution is symmetric about a specified value.

(2.9)
$$\text{Hypothesis:} \quad \xi_{0.5}(F_\theta), = \xi_0, \quad F_\theta \text{ symmetric}, \quad \theta \in \Omega$$

$$\text{Alternative:} \quad \xi_{0.5}(F_\theta) \neq \xi_0 \quad \text{or} \quad F_\theta \text{ not symmetric}, \quad \theta \in \Omega.$$

2.4. Independence. The problem of independence is to test whether a vector-valued random variable has independent components. If the components are not independent, then there is a probability connection or association between them. It is for this reason that a test for the problem of independence is sometimes called a test for association. We describe the simplest form of the problem—to test whether two real random variables are independent. Let $F_\theta(x^{(1)}, x^{(2)})$ be a bivariate distribution function, and let $F_\theta'(x^{(1)})$ and $F_\theta''(x^{(2)})$ be the corresponding marginal distribution functions; then the problem is

(2.10)
$$\text{Hypothesis:} \quad F_\theta(x^{(1)}, x^{(2)}) = F_\theta'(x^{(1)})F_\theta''(x^{(2)})$$

$$\text{for all } x^{(1)}, x^{(2)}; \quad \theta \in \Omega,$$

$$\text{Alternative:} \quad F_\theta(x^{(1)}, x^{(2)}) \neq F_\theta'(x^{(1)})F_\theta''(x^{(2)})$$

$$\text{for some } x^{(1)}, x^{(2)}; \quad \theta \in \Omega.$$

3. RANDOMNESS PROBLEMS

In the single-sample problems considered above the over-all assumption was that a set of n random variables forms a sample from some probability distribution. In randomness problems this assumption becomes the hypothesis and is tested against alternatives for which the n random variables are from different distributions or have a degreee of dependence. We give first some general assumptions.

ASSUMPTION 3. $X_1, \cdots, X_n$ are independent, and either
(a) X_i has the distribution P_{θ_i} over R^1; $\{P_\theta | \theta \in \Omega\}$ is the class of absolutely continuous distributions over R^1 and is equivalently given by the class $\{f_\theta(x) | \theta \in \Omega\}$ of densities re Lebesgue measure; $(\theta_1, \cdots, \theta_n) \in \Omega^n$, or
(b) $X_i = (X_{i1}, \cdots, X_{ik})$ has the distribution P_{θ_i} over R^k; $\{P_\theta | \theta \in \Omega\}$ is the class of absolutely continuous distributions over R^k and is equivalently given by the class $\{f_\theta(\mathbf{x}) | \theta \in \Omega\}$ of density functions; $(\theta_1, \cdots, \theta_n) \in \Omega^n$.

3.1. The Two-Sample Problem. In the two-sample problem there are two sets of random variables, each being a sample from a probability distribution. The problem is to test whether the distributions are the same; that is, whether the two samples can be regarded as a single sample. Let the first $n_1 X_i$'s correspond to one sample and the remaining $n_2 X_i$'s correspond to the second sample; then $n = n_1 + n_2$.

(3.1)

Hypothesis: X_i has measure P_θ $(i = 1, \cdots, n);$ $\theta \in \Omega,$

Alternative: X_i has measure P_{θ_1} $(i = 1, \cdots, n_1);$ $\theta_1 \in \Omega,$

X_{n_1+j} has measure P_{θ_2} $(j = 1, \cdots, n_2);$ $\theta_2 \in \Omega.$

$\theta_1 \neq \theta_2.$

Sometimes a more restricted alternative is considered in which the distribution for one sample has the same form as for the second sample but is shifted in location. For example, if $k = 1$, we might have the two distribution functions under the alternative connected by $F_1(x) = F_2(x + d)$ for all $x(d \neq 0)$.

3.2. c-Sample Problem. This is an extension of the previous problem to a consideration of c samples. Assuming $n = n_1 + \cdots + n_c$, we have

(3.2)

Hypothesis: X_i has measure P_θ $(i = 1, \cdots, n);$ $\theta \in \Omega,$

Alternative: X_i has measure P_{θ_1} $(i = 1, \cdots, n_1);$ $\theta_1 \in \Omega,$

X_{n_1+j} has measure P_{θ_2} $(j = 1, \cdots, n_2);$ $\theta_2 \in \Omega,$

$\cdot \quad \cdot \quad \cdot$

$\theta_1, \theta_2, \cdots, \theta_c$ not all equal.

A number of more restricted alternatives have been considered. In these the distributions for the different samples are usually assumed to be the same except for a shift of location; these are called slippage alternatives.

3.3. The Regression Alternative. This alternative to randomness is a linear regression model in which the 'errors' are independent and identically distributed according to a distribution in the Ω defined at the beginning of this section. More precisely, we assume that the random variables X_i can be described by

$$X_i = \xi c_i + Y_i,$$

where $c_1, \cdots, c_n$ are given numbers for the experiment, and $Y_1, \cdots, Y_n$ are independent, and each has the same distribution in the class Ω given in Assumption 3a. ξ is called the regression coefficient, the c_i are values of the independent variable, and the Y_i are the errors about regression. If we let $\bar{c} = n^{-1} \Sigma c_i$, then we can write

$$X_i = \xi(c_i - \bar{c}) + (Y_i + \xi\bar{c})$$

$$= \xi(c_i - \bar{c}) + Y_i',$$

and once again the Y_i' are independent, and each has the same distribution in Ω. Thus, without loss of generality for our purposes here, we assume $\Sigma c_i = 0$.

The randomness problem with one-sided regression alternative is given by

(3.3)
$$\text{Hypothesis:} \quad \xi = 0, \quad \theta \in \Omega,$$
$$\text{Alternative:} \quad \xi > 0, \quad \theta \in \Omega,$$

and the two-sided problem by

(3.4)
$$\text{Hypothesis:} \quad \xi = 0, \quad \theta \in \Omega,$$
$$\text{Alternative:} \quad \xi \neq 0, \quad \theta \in \Omega.$$

3.4. Two-Sample Scale Problem. This problem for normal distributions is to test whether two distributions have the same variances. However, for the general class of distributions given by Assumption 3a the variance seems entirely unsuited to measuring the scale or spread of a distribution, particularly so because it takes the value $+ \infty$ for some quite simple distributions. There are reasonable nonparametric scale parameters such as the difference between two specified percentiles (see [2]), but the formulations we propose below do not need the definition of a scale parameter.

Let $X_1, \cdots, X_{n_1}$ be independent and each have the same distribution function $F_\theta(x)$, $\theta \in \Omega$; also let $X_{n_1+1}, \cdots, X_{n_1+n_2}$ be independent and each have the same distribution function $F_\eta(x)$, $\eta \in \Omega$. Then we have

(3.5)
$$\text{Hypothesis:} \quad F_\theta(x) = F_\eta(x + c) \quad \text{for all } x; \quad \theta, \eta \in \Omega,$$
$$\text{Alternative:} \quad \xi_{p_2}(F_\theta) - \xi_{p_1}(F_\theta) < \xi_{p_2}(F_\theta) - \xi_{p_1}(F_\eta)$$
$$\text{for all } p_2 > p_1; \quad \theta, \eta \in \Omega.$$

A formulation with a more general alternative is given by

(3.6)
$$\text{Hypothesis:} \quad F_\theta(x) = F_\eta(x + c) \quad \text{for all } x; \quad \theta, \eta \in \Omega,$$
$$\text{Alternative:} \quad \Pr\{|Y_1 - Y_1'| < |Y_2 - Y_2'|\} > \tfrac{1}{2}$$

where Y_1, Y_1' designate random variables with distribution F_θ; Y_2, Y_2' designate random variables with distribution F_η; $\theta, \eta \in \Omega$.

In each case the alternatives are one-sided with the second distribution more "spread out" than the first distribution.

4. RANDOMIZED BLOCKS AND MORE GENERAL DESIGNS

For the more general experimental designs there are many ways in which the assumptions can be made nonparametric. If the assumptions are too liberal, it can happen that a parameter to be estimated or about which a hypothesis is to be tested may be lost within the freedom of the probability distribution—be *nonidentifiable.* This is one of the difficulties encountered with the general linear hypothesis. However, for the randomized block problem we pose several formulations of which two, as we shall see later, have solutions with quite satisfactory properties.

4.1. Randomized Blocks. The randomized-block design corresponds to the classical agricultural experiment in which a number of treatments, say c, are applied randomly to c 'plots' in a 'block' of land, and then this is repeated a number of times to make a total of, say, b blocks. The first nonparametric formulation that comes to mind is to keep all the usual assumptions but the one concerning the distribution of the 'error' and add the general assumption that errors have some absolutely continuous distribution. Precisely, let X_{ij} designate the random variable for the ith block and the jth treatment, and assume that

$$X_{ij} = \alpha + \rho_i + \gamma_j + Y_{ij},$$

where the Y_{ij} are independent, and each has the same absolutely continuous distribution over R^1 with distribution function $F_\theta(x)$, $\theta \in \Omega$. Also, we assume without loss of generality that $\Sigma \gamma_i = \Sigma \rho_j = 0$.

(4.1)
Hypothesis: $\gamma_1 = \cdots = \gamma_c = 0$; $\alpha, \rho_1, \cdots, \rho_b \in R^1$; $\theta \in \Omega$,

Alternative: Not all $\gamma_j = 0$; $\alpha, \rho_1, \cdots, \rho_b \in R^1$; $\theta \in \Omega$.

We can generalize this model by allowing the errors to have different distributions from block to block but the same within any block. Let the Y_{ij} be independent and each Y_{ij} have an absolutely continuous distribution over R^1 with distribution function $F_{\theta_i}(x)$, $\theta_i \in \Omega$.

(4.2)
Hypothesis: $\gamma_1, \cdots, \gamma_c = 0$; $\alpha, \rho_1, \cdots, \rho_b \in R^1$; $\theta_1, \cdots, \theta_b \in \Omega$,

Alternative: Not all $\gamma_j = 0$; $\alpha, \rho_1, \cdots, \rho_b \in R^1$; $\theta_1, \cdots, \theta_b \in \Omega$.

In some applications it is not unreasonable to expect the errors within a block to be dependent. Let $(X_{11}, \cdots, X_{1c}), \cdots, (X_{b1}, \cdots, X_{bc})$ be independent, and let $(X_{i1}, \cdots, X_{ic})$ have an absolutely continuous distribution over R^c with density function $f_{\theta_i}(x_{i1}, \cdots, x_{ic})$, $\theta_i \in \Omega$. If we assume that each block has the same distribution, then one possible formulation is

(4.3)
Hypothesis: $f_\theta(x_{i1}, \cdots, x_{ic})$ symmetric in $x_{i1}, \cdots, x_{ic}$;
$\theta \in \Omega$,

Alternative: $f_\theta(x_{i1}, \cdots, x_{ic})$ not symmetric for all
$(x_{i1}, \cdots, x_{ic})$; $\theta \in \Omega$.

Since it is assumed that the treatments are randomly assigned within a block, then equivalence of treatments implies that in each block the distribution is symmetric with respect to the treatments; hence the hypothesis above. The alternative above is simply that the treatments are not equivalent. A more restricted alternative might be of more interest in many applications.

If we no longer assume the distributions identical from block to block, then the following formulation might be appropriate.

(4.4)
Hypothesis: $f_{\theta_i}(x_{i1}, \cdots, x_{ic})$ symmetric; $\theta_1, \cdots, \theta_b \in \Omega$,

Alternative: $f_{\theta_i}(x_{i1}, \cdots, x_{ic})$ not symmetric for all

$(x_{i1}, \cdots, x_{ic})$; $\theta_1, \cdots, \theta_b \in \Omega$.

This alternative is quite general. Once again a more restricted alternative may be preferred for some problems.

A third type of formulation might be appropriate if we were little concerned about small differences between treatments but wished to test whether in some general sense they had an equivalent effect. Let $(X_{i1}, \cdots, X_{ic}), \cdots, (X_{b1}, \cdots, X_{bc})$ be independent and each $(X_{i1}, \cdots, X_{ic})$ have a continuous distribution over R^c with distribution function $F_\theta(x_1, \cdots, x_c)$, $\theta \in \Omega$ (Ω here indexes all the continuous distributions over R^c). Then, if $(Y_1, \cdots, Y_c)$ designates a random variable with distribution function $F_\theta(y_1, \cdots, y_c)$, we have

(4.5)
Hypothesis: $\Pr_\theta\{Y_{j_1} < \cdots < Y_{j_c}\} = (c!)^{-1}$; $\theta \in \Omega$,

Alternative: Not all $\Pr_\theta\{Y_{j_1} < \cdots < Y_{j_c}\} = (c!)^{-1}$; $\theta \in \Omega$.

$(j_1, \cdots, j_c)$ represents a typical permutation of $(1, \cdots, c)$.

4.2. The General Linear Hypothesis. The general linear hypothesis problem is to test whether a number of regression coefficients are equal to zero. Let $(X_1, \cdots, X_n)$ be a random variable with structure

$$X_i = \sum_{j=1}^{c} \xi_j a_{ij} + \sum_{k=1}^{r} \eta_k b_{ik} + Y_i,$$

where the a's and b's are treated as a known set of constants in any application. The ξ's and η's are called regression coefficients, and the Y_i's are called error terms.

For the first formulation we assume that $Y_1, \cdots, Y_n$ are independent and that each has the same absolutely continuous distribution over R^1 with distribution function $F_\theta(x)$. Let $\theta, \in \Omega$, index those absolutely continuous distribution functions having $F_\theta(0) = \frac{1}{2}$; that is, having median equal to zero.

(4.6)
Hypothesis: $\xi_1 = \cdots = \xi_c = 0$; $\eta_1, \cdots, \eta_r \in R^1$; $\theta \in \Omega$,

Alternative: Not all $\xi_j = 0$; $\eta_1, \cdots, \eta_r \in R^1$; $\theta \in \Omega$.

The second formulation admits a degree of dependence among the errors. Let $(Y_1, \cdots, Y_n)$ have an absolutely continuous distribution over R^n with probability density function $f_\theta(y_1, \cdots, y_n)$. Also let $\theta, \in \Omega$, index those density functions $f_\theta(y_1, \cdots, y_n)$ which are spherically symmetric about $(0, \cdots, 0)$; that is, for which f_θ can be written

$$f_\theta(y_1, \cdots, y_n) = g_\theta(y_1^2 + \cdots + y_n^2)$$

(4.7)
Hypothesis: $\xi_1 = \cdots = \xi_c = 0$; $\eta_1, \cdots, \eta_r \in R^1$; $\theta \in \Omega$,

Alternative: Not all $\xi_j = 0$; $\eta_1, \cdots, \eta_r \in R^1$; $\theta \in \Omega$.

5. PROBLEMS FOR SOLUTION

1. Show that $d_1(F, F')$ defined in Section 2.1 satisfies the axioms for a distance function.

2. Which axioms do d_2, d_3, d_4 satisfy?

3. The two-sample problem is a particular case of the regression alternative in Section 3.3. Define the c_i which give the two-sample problem.

4. The randomized-block problem is a particular case of the general linear hypothesis problem. Define the constants a_{ij}, b_{ik} which produce the randomized-block problems. ◀

REFERENCES AND BIBLIOGRAPHY

1. K. Pearson, "On the criterion that a given system of deviations from the probable in the case of a correlated system is such that it can be reasonably supposed to have arisen from random samplings," *Phil. Mag.*, Series 5, Vol. 50 (1900), p. 157.

2. D. A. S. Fraser, "Nonparametric theory. Scale and location parameters," *Can. J. Math.*, Vol. 6 (1955), p. 46.

CHAPTER 4

The Estimation of Real Parameters
and Tolerance Regions

1. INTRODUCTION

In parametric problems the model for an experiment often forms a unit
by itself, there being no subspace with a distribution from which the
over-all random variable forms a sample. In such cases, however, the
simple structure involving only a finite number of parameters usually
permits sufficient control that parameters can be estimated and tests made
without repetitions of the experiment. When the assumptions are
weakened to make a problem nonparametric, there is a much greater need
for repetitions so that the over-all random variable forms a sample from
a distribution over a component space. Of course, there is need too for
theory to cover the more complex problems, but little has been developed
for this purpose. The estimation and tolerance region theory developed
in this chapter will assume that the over-all random variable is a sample
from a distribution over a component space.

2. THE ESTIMATION OF REAL PARAMETERS

Let $\mathscr{X}$ be a space with a class of probability measures $\{P_\theta \mid \theta \in \Omega\}$.
For a sample of n from a distribution in this class, we have the sample
space $\mathscr{X} = \mathscr{X}_1 \times \cdots \times \mathscr{X}_n$ where each $\mathscr{X}_i$ is identical to $\mathscr{X}$. Also, we
have the class $\{P_\theta^{\mathbf{X}} \mid \theta \in \Omega\}$ where each measure $P_\theta^{\mathbf{X}}$ is the product measure
of P_θ over each component space. In the examples at the end of this
section, $\mathscr{X}$ will be the real line or a Euclidean space R^k of k dimensions and
the class of distributions will comprise the absolutely continuous or the
discrete distributions, or subclasses of these. (See Assumptions 2 in
Chapter 3.)

Of the different properties on which our choice of estimator can be based, unbiasedness is most easily applied in nonparametric theory. The classical estimator of the median of a distribution on the real line is the sample median. And it is possible to show that there does not exist an unbiased estimator for the median of an arbitrary continuous distribution on the real line. Nevertheless we restrict ourselves to estimation based on unbiasedness and in passing indicate the need for a general theory of median estimation.

A real-valued parameter $g(\theta)$ is called *estimable* if it has an unbiased estimator; that is, *if there exists a statistic $f(x_1, \cdots, x_n)$ such that*

$$(2.1) \qquad E_\theta\{f(X_1, \cdots, X_n)\} = \int_{\mathscr{X}^n} f(x_1, \cdots, x_n) \prod_{i=1}^n dP_\theta(x_i)$$

$$= g(\theta)$$

for all $\theta \in \Omega$. An estimable parameter is sometimes called a *regular parameter*.

Similarly, a vector-valued parameter $\mathbf{g}(\theta) = (g_1(\theta), \cdots, g_p(\theta))$ is called estimable if there exists a vector-valued statistic $\mathbf{f}(x_1, \cdots, x_n) = (f_1(x_1, \cdots, x_n), \cdots, f_p(x_1, \cdots, x_n))$ such that

$$(2.2) \qquad E_\theta\{\mathbf{f}(X_1, \cdots, X_n)\} = \left(\int_{\mathscr{X}^n} f_1(x_1, \cdots, x_n) \prod_{i=1}^n dP_\theta(x_i), \cdots \right)$$

$$= \mathbf{g}(\theta)$$

The degree m of an estimable parameter is defined to be *the smallest sample size for which the parameter has an unbiased estimator*; it is the minimum value of n for which there is an equation (2.1) or (2.2).

Any unbiased estimator of a parameter based on the minimum sample size m is called a *kernel*. It is easily seen that there is always a *symmetric kernel*. For, if $f(x_1, \cdots, x_m)$ is a kernel, then there is a symmetric statistic $f_s(x_1, \cdots, x_m)$ defined by

$$f_s(x_1, \cdots, x_m) = \frac{1}{m!} \sum_P f(x_{i_1}, \cdots, x_{i_m}),$$

where the summation is over all permutations $(i_1, \cdots, i_m)$ of $(1, \cdots, m)$. This statistic is an average of $m!$ forms, each of which is an unbiased estimator of the parameter. From the properties of expectation it follows that the symmetric function $f_s(x_1, \cdots, x_m)$ is an unbiased estimator and hence is a kernel of the parameter.

It is interesting to note some properties of estimable parameters. If $g_1(\theta)$, $g_2(\theta)$ are estimable parameters of degrees m_1, m_2, then the sum $g_1(\theta) + g_2(\theta)$ and the product $g_1(\theta) g_2(\theta)$ are also estimable parameters and have degrees, respectively, less than or equal to $m = \max(m_1, m_2)$ and $m_1 + m_2$. For, if $f_i(x_1, \cdots, x_{m_i})$ is a kernel of $g_i(\theta)$, then

$$\int_{\mathscr{X}^m} [f_1(x_1, \cdots, x_m) + f_2(x_1, \cdots, x_{m_2})] \prod_{i=1}^{m} dP_\theta(x_i)$$

$$= g_1(\theta) + g_2(\theta)$$

and

$$\int_{\mathscr{X}^{m_1+m_2}} f_1(x_1, \cdots, x_{m_1}) f_2(x_{m_1+1}, \cdots, x_{m_1+m_2}) \prod_{i=1}^{m_1+m_2} dP_\theta(x_i)$$

$$= g_1(\theta) g_2(\theta).$$

Thus we have unbiased estimators of degrees $m = \max(m_1 m_2)$ and $m_1 + m_2$, respectively. As a more general result, it follows that any polynomial in estimable parameters is also an estimable parameter. If the parameters are vectors, then we interpret addition and multiplication to be the addition and multiplication of corresponding coordinates.

Corresponding to any estimator $f(x_1, \cdots, x_m)$ of an estimable parameter $g(\theta)$, we define a U statistic for a sample of n $(n > m)$:

(2.3) $$U(x_1, \cdots, x_n) = \frac{1}{\binom{n}{m}} \sum_C f_s(x_{i_1}, \cdots, x_{i_m}),$$

where the summation C is over all $\binom{n}{m}$ combinations $(i_1, \cdots, i_m)$ of m integers chosen from $(1, \cdots, n)$, and f_s is the symmetrized statistic corresponding to $f(x_1, \cdots, x_m)$. Of course, we could also write

$$U(x_1, \cdots, x_n) = \frac{(n-m)!}{n!} \sum_P f(x_{i_1}, \cdots x_{i_m}),$$

where the summation is over all permutation P of m integers $(i_1, \cdots, i_m)$ chosen from $1, \cdots, n$. From this last expression it is seen that $U(x_1, \cdots, x_n)$ is the symmetrized form of $f(x_1, \cdots, x_m)$ considered as a function of $(x_1, \cdots, x_n)$. Now, since

$$E_\theta\{f(X_1, \cdots, X_m)\} = g(\theta),$$

we obtain easily that

$$E_\theta\{U(X_1, \cdots, X_n)\} = g(\theta),$$

and therefore that the U statistic is an unbiased estimator of $g(\theta)$.

EXAMPLE 2.1. Let $\mathscr{X}$ be the real line and $\{P_\theta | \theta \in \Omega\}$ be the class of absolutely continuous distributions. Now consider the three real-valued parameters μ_X, σ_X^2, μ_X^2 (μ_X, σ_X^2 stand for the mean and variance of the random variable X).

μ_X is obviously an *estimable* parameter because it can be written

$$\mu_X = E_\theta\{X\}.$$

It can be estimated on the basis of a sample of one; hence it is of *degree* 1. The corresponding U statistic for a sample of n is $n^{-1}\Sigma x_i$.

μ_X^2 is a simple polynomial in μ_x and hence is estimable. We have

$$\mu_X^2 = [E_\theta\{X\}]^2$$
$$= E_\theta\{X_1 X_2\};$$

therefore μ_X^2 is of degree less than or equal to 2. A simple example can be constructed to show that the degree is not 1 and hence is 2. (See Problem 2.) It is easily seen that the corresponding U statistic for a sample of n is

$$\frac{1}{n(n-1)} \sum_{i \neq j} x_i x_j.$$

σ_X^2 can also be written as a polynomial in parameters which are obviously estimable:

(2.4) $$\sigma_X^2 = E_\theta\{[X - \mu_X]^2\}$$
$$= E_\theta\{X^2\} - [E_\theta\{X\}]^2.$$

Of the two parameters in terms of which σ_X^2 has been expressed, the first is obviously of degree 1 and the second was stated above to be of degree 2. For a sample of 2, $x_1^2 - x_1 x_2$ is an unbiased estimate of σ_X^2:

$$E_\theta(X_1^2) - E_\theta(X_2 X_2) = \sigma_X^2.$$

There cannot be an estimate from a sample of one since by rearrangement and noting the breakdown (2.4) we could obtain an estimate of $[E_\theta(X)]^2$ based on a sample of one, and this is contradictory to the degree of $[E_\theta(X)]^2$ being 2. Hence σ_X^2 is a regular parameter of degree 2, and $x_1^2 - x_1 x_2$ is a kernel. The corresponding *symmetric kernel* is

$$\frac{x_1^2 - x_1 x_2 + x_2^2 - x_1 x_2}{2}$$

$$= \frac{(x_1 - x_2)^2}{2}.$$

For a sample of n the corresponding U statistic is

$$U(x_1, \cdots, x_n) = \frac{2}{n(n-1)} \sum_{i<j} \frac{(x_i - x_j)^2}{2}$$

$$= \frac{1}{n(n-1)} \left\{ (n-1) \Sigma x_i^2 - 2 \sum_{i<j} x_i x_j \right\}$$

$$= \frac{1}{n} \Sigma x_i^2 - \frac{1}{n(n-1)} [(\Sigma x_i)^2 - \Sigma x_i^2]$$

$$= \frac{1}{n-1} \Sigma x_i^2 - \frac{1}{n(n-1)} (\Sigma x_i)^2$$

$$= \frac{1}{n-1} [\Sigma x_i^2 - n\bar{x}^2]$$

$$= s_x^2,$$

where $\bar{x} = n^{-1} \Sigma x_i$ and s_x^2 is the sample variance.

The moments μ_r of the distribution P_θ are all estimable since

$$\mu_r = E_\theta \{ X^r \}$$

From this equation it is seen that the moments are estimable of degree 1 and that x^r is a kernel for μ_r. For a sample of n the U statistic corresponding to x^r is

$$\frac{1}{n} \Sigma x_i^r,$$

the sample rth moment.

The central moments μ_r' for P_θ are defined by

$$\mu_r' = E_\theta \{ (X - \mu_1)^r \}$$

$$= E_\theta \{ (X - E_\theta(X))^r \}.$$

By expanding the rth power and taking the expectation it is seen that μ_r' is a polynomial in the moments $\mu_1, \cdots, \mu_r$. Hence it is estimable.

From the polynomial relationship of the cumulants of P_θ to the moments, it is easily obtained that they too are estimable parameters.

For the remaining results in this section we need a particular statistic defined over $\mathscr{X}^n$ and called the *order statistic*. In Section 7 of Chapter 1 order statistic was defined for the case $\mathscr{X} = R^1$; we give the general definition now. As was mentioned in Chapter 1, statistics are used to condense the outcome of an experiment. For instance, if $(x_1, \cdots, x_n)$ is the outcome of an experiment, one condensation of the information in $(x_1, \cdots, x_n)$ is to record the different values $x_1, \cdots, x_n$ but neglect to record the order in which these values occurred in the outcome. This can be described mathematically by means of the statistic $t(x_1, \cdots, x_n)$ called the *order statistic* and defined by

$$(2.5) \qquad t(x_1, \cdots, x_n) = \{x_1, \cdots, x_n\}$$

where the braces stand for the *set* consisting of the n points $x_1, \cdots, x_n$. This statistic loses the information about the order of the x's in the outcome $(x_1, \cdots, x_n)$ because it records only the set of x's and knowing a set does not carry any knowledge about ordering within the set.

This definition of order statistic is equivalent to that introduced in Section 7 of Chapter 1. There the order statistic for $(x_1, \cdots, x_n)$ with real-valued x_i was defined to be $(x_{(1)}, \cdots x_{(n)})$, where $x_{(1)}, \cdots, x_{(n)}$ are the number $x_1, \cdots, x_n$ arranged in order of magnitude, so that $x_{(1)} \leq x_{(2)} \cdots \leq x_{(n)}$. Clearly the two definitions produce statistics which extract the same amount of information from the outcome $(x_1, \cdots, x_n)$.

We now describe a simple property of the order statistic $t(x_1, \cdots, x_n)$. Let $f(x_1, \cdots, x_n)$ be an arbitrary statistic over $\mathscr{X}^n$. Then, if $f(x_1, \cdots, x_n)$ *is a symmetric function, it can be written as a function of the order statistic*

$$f(x_1, \cdots, x_n) = h(t(x_1, \cdots, x_n)),$$

and conversely, if $f(x_1, \cdots, x_n)$ can be written as a function of the order statistic, it is a symmetric function. The proof in both directions follows easily by noting that each of the two conditions is equivalent to stating that $f(x_1, \cdots, x_n)$ is constant-valued over the $n!$ points $(x_{i_1}, \cdots, x_{i_n})$ corresponding to the $n!$ permutations $(i_1, \cdots, i_n)$ of $(1, \cdots, n)$.

Now, returning to the probability structure descriptive of a sample of n from a distribution in $\{P_\theta \mid \theta \in \Omega\}$, we shall prove that the order statistic $t(\mathbf{x})$ is a sufficient statistic. For this it is convenient to think of the statistic as a partition of the sample space $\mathscr{X}^n$. We let $t'(x_1, \cdots, x_n)$ designate the set of the partition containing the outcome $(x_1, \cdots, x_n)$. The set $t'(x_1, \cdots, x_n)$ then consists of the point $(x_1, \cdots, x_n)$ and all points $(x_{i_1}, \cdots, x_{i_n})$ obtained by permuting the coordinates $x_1, \cdots, x_n$; $t'(\mathbf{x})$ contains $n!$ points (or fewer if some of the coordinates are equal).

Let P_θ be one of the measures over $\mathscr{X}^n$. We look for a convenient way of describing the induced distribution of the statistic $t'(x_1, \cdots, x_n)$. A set of values attained by $t'(x_1, \cdots, x_n)$ can be exhibited as a set in $\mathscr{X}^n$, the union of the sets $t'(x_1, \cdots, x_n)$. It will, of course, be a set that is symmetric with respect to the n coordinates. The induced probability measure of a set of values of $t'(x_1, \cdots, x_n)$ is the $P_\theta^{\mathbf{X}}$ measure of this symmetric set in

$\mathscr{X}^n$. Hence, the induced measure is given directly in terms of the measure over $\mathscr{X}^n$, and integration with respect to it can be done over $\mathscr{X}^n$.

Let $A \subset \mathscr{X}^n$ and $P(A \mid \{x_1, \cdots, x_n\})$ stand for the conditional probability of falling in the set A, given the order statistic $\{x_1, \cdots, x_n\}$. We shall show that

(2.6)
$$P(A \mid \{x_1, \cdots, x_n\}) = \frac{i(A, \{x_1, \cdots, x_n\})}{n!}$$

is a determination of the conditional probability; $i(A, \{x_1, \cdots, x_n\})$ is defined to be the number of the $n!$ permutations $(x_{i_1}, \cdots, x_{i_n})$ that fall in A. Let B be a symmetric set in $\mathscr{X}^n$ standing for a set of values of the statistic $t'(x_1, \cdots, x_n)$. Examining the definition of conditional probability in Section 4 of Chapter 1, we need only show that the following equation holds for all B:

(2.7)
$$P_\theta^{\mathbf{X}}(A \cap B) = \int_B \frac{i(A, \{x_1, \cdots, x_n\})}{n!} \prod_{i=1}^n dP_\theta(x_i).$$

The left-hand side of this equation can be written

$$\int_B \phi_A(x_1, \cdots, x_n) \prod_{i=1}^n dP_\theta(x_i)$$

where $\phi_A(x_1, \cdots, x_n)$ is the characteristic function of the set A and is defined by

$$\phi_A(x_1, \cdots, x_n) = 1 \qquad \text{if} \quad (x_1, \cdots, x_n) \in A$$
$$= 0 \qquad\qquad\qquad \notin A.$$

Since the probability measure over $\mathscr{X}^n$ is symmetric in the coordinates and so also is the set B, we have that the left-hand side is equal to

$$\int_B \phi_A(x_{i_1}, \cdots, x_{i_n}) \prod_{i=1}^n dP_\theta(x_i),$$

where $(i_1, \cdots, i_n)$ is any permutation of $(1, \cdots, n)$. Therefore, we can write the left-hand side as the average of the $n!$ equal expressions obtained by taking the $n!$ permutations of $(1, \cdots, n)$:

$$\int_B \frac{\sum_P \phi_A(x_{i_1}, \cdots, x_{i_n})}{n!} \prod_{i=1}^n dP_\theta(x_i).$$

It is easy to see that $\sum_P \phi_A(x_{i_1}, \cdots, x_{i_n})$ is just the number of permutations of $(x_1, \cdots, x_n)$ that fall in A; that is, is equal to $i(A, \{x_1, \cdots, x_n\})$. This establishes the equality (2.7) above.

Examining the expression for the conditional probability $P(A | \{x_1, \cdots, x_n\})$, we see that it does not depend on θ. Therefore, $t'(\mathbf{x}) = \{x_1, \cdots, x_n\}$ is a sufficient statistic for the class of measures $\{P_\theta^{\mathbf{X}} | \theta \in \Omega\}$ over $\mathscr{X} = \prod_{i=1}^{n} \mathscr{X}_i$ defined at the beginning of this section.

We now have a theorem which in part shows the importance of U statistics in nonparametric estimation.

THEOREM 2.1. If $f(x_1, \cdots, x_n)$ is an unbiased estimator over $\mathscr{X}^n$ of the parameter $g(\theta)$ re the measures $\{P_\theta^{\mathbf{X}} | \theta \in \Omega\}$ (the power-product measures of a sample of n), then the corresponding U statistic is also an unbiased estimator of $g(\theta)$ and $\sigma_U^2(\theta) \leq \sigma_f^2(\theta)$ with equality only if $f(x_1, \cdots, x_n)$ is equal the U statistic almost everywhere $P_\theta^{\mathbf{X}}$; and, using a strictly convex loss function $\mathbf{R}_U(\theta) \leq \mathbf{R}_f(\theta)$, with equality only if $f(x_1, \cdots, x_n)$ is equal the U statistic almost everywhere $P_\theta^{\mathbf{X}}$.

Note. If the variance or risk of f is $+\infty$, the variance or risk of the U statistic may also be unbounded without the equality almost everywhere of f and U.

Proof. The proof follows easily from the Rao–Blackwell Theorem 2.6 in Chapter 2. We have proved that the order statistic $t(x_1, \cdots, x_n)$ is a sufficient statistic for our class of measures. To be able to use the Rao–Blackwell theorem and complete the proof, we need only show that the U statistic is the conditional expectation of $f(x_1, \cdots, x_n)$, given the order statistic $\{x_1, \cdots, x_n\}$. Almost everywhere $P_\theta^{\mathbf{X}}$ we have

$$E\{f(X_1, \cdots, X_n) | \{x_1, \cdots, x_n\}\}$$

$$= \frac{1}{n!} \sum_{P} f(x_{i_1}, \cdots, x_{i_n})$$

$$= U(x_1, \cdots, x_n),$$

where $U(x_1, \cdots, x_n)$ is the U statistic corresponding to $f(x_1, \cdots, x_n)$.

The next theorem adds importance to the U statistic by showing that under suitable conditions the U statistic for an estimable parameter is essentially unique.

THEOREM 2.2. If the order statistics $t(\mathbf{x}) = \{x_1, \cdots, x_n\}$ is complete re the class $P_\theta^{\mathbf{X}}$ over $\mathscr{X}^n$ (a sample of n from $\{P_\theta | \theta \in \Omega\}$), then the U statistic corresponding to any estimable parameter is essentially unique, and it has uniformly minimum variance and risk (convex loss) among the unbiased estimators of the parameter. For vector estimation minimum variance is replaced by minimum concentration ellipsoid.

Note. Theorems 7.1, 7.2, 7.3 give sufficient conditions on $\{P_\theta | \theta \in \Omega\}$ for the order statistic to be complete.

Note. We can permit an estimable parameter $g(\theta)$ to take the values $+\infty$, $-\infty$ and even not exist, provided that for a statistic unbiased for $g(\theta)$ the integral

$$g(\theta) = \int_{\mathscr{X}^n} f(x_1, \cdots, x_n) \prod_{i=1}^{n} dP_\theta(x_i),$$

respectively, converges to $+\infty$, converges to $-\infty$, and diverges. In such a case, we add the requirement that $t(x_1, \cdots, x_n)$ *be complete* with respect to the subclass of distributions corresponding to $\Omega_0 = \{\theta | g(\theta) \in R^1\}$; Ω_0 *consists of those θ for which $g(\theta)$ is finite.*

Proof. We proved above that the order statistic $t(x_1, \cdots, x_n)$ was a sufficient statistic. The theorem then follows immediately from the Lehmann–Scheffé Theorem 2.8 in Chapter 2.

In Chapter 6 we shall prove a theorem concerning the distribution of a U statistic as the sample size n approaches infinity. If $f(x_1, \cdots, x_m)$ is a statistic unbiased for the parameter $g(\theta)$ and $U_n(x_1, \cdots, x_n)$ is the corresponding U statistic for a sample of n, then this theorem says that, as $n \to \infty$, the distribution of $n^{1/2}(U_n - g(\theta))$ approaches the normal distribution having mean zero and finite variance, provided only that the second moment of $f(X_1, \cdots, X_m)$ exists. As a consequence of this theorem we have

THEOREM 2.3. If $f(x_1, \cdots, x_m)$ is an unbiased estimate of $g(\theta)$ and if $E_\theta\{f^2(X_1, \cdots, X_m)\}$ exists, then the corresponding U statistic for a sample of n is a consistent estimate of $g(\theta)$ as $n \to \infty$.

Proof. By the theorem mentioned above, $n^{1/2}(U_n - g(\theta))$ has a limiting normal distribution with mean zero and finite variance. We have

$$\mathrm{Pr}_\theta \{g(\theta) - \varepsilon \le U_n \le g(\theta) + \varepsilon\}$$

$$= \mathrm{Pr}_\theta \{-n^{1/2}\varepsilon \le n^{1/2}(U_n - g(\theta)) \le +n^{1/2}\varepsilon\},$$

and, since $n^{1/2}\varepsilon \to \infty$ as $n \to \infty$, this last probability expression approaches the value 1. Thus, as $n \to \infty$, the probability that U_n is in any small neighborhood of $g(\theta)$ approaches 1, and we say that U_n approaches $g(\theta)$ in probability and write p-lim $U_n = g(\theta)$.
$$\underset{n \to \infty}{}$$

EXAMPLE 2.2. We consider further the parameters introduced in Example 2.1. There the sample space was R^n, and the class of probability distributions were those of a sample of n from an absolutely continuous distribution on R^1.   Theorem 7.1 in Chapter 1 proved the order statistic complete corresponding to the uniform distributions over intervals on R^1. Using Theorem 6.2 in Chapter 1, we obtain the completeness for the larger class of absolutely continuous distributions.   The conditions for our Theorem 2.2 are fulfilled.

The parameters we considered in Example 2.1 do not exist over the whole parameter space.   However, they do exist for each of the uniform distributions over intervals.   Hence, the additional requirement in our first note after the theorem is fulfilled.

For the parameter $E_\theta(X)$, it follows that the U statistic $n^{-1}\Sigma x_i$ is the unique U statistic which is an unbiased estimator of $E_\theta(X)$.   It has minimum variance and risk (convex loss) among the unbiased estimators of $E_\theta(X)$.

For the parameter $[E_\theta(X)]^2$ we obtained a kernel $x_1 x_2$ for a sample of 2. The corresponding U statistic is

$$\frac{\sum\limits_{i \neq j=1}^{n} x_i x_j}{n(n-1)}$$

By our theorem it is the only unbiased estimator that is symmetric in the x's, and it has minimum variance among the unbiased estimators.

For the parameter σ_x^2 we obtained the symmetric kernel $\frac{1}{2}(x_1 - x_2)^2$. The corresponding U statistic is

$$\frac{1}{n-1} \Sigma(x_i - \bar{x})^2.$$

By the theorem it is the only unbiased estimator that is symmetric in the x's, and it has minimum variance among the unbiased estimators of σ_x^2.

For the unbiased estimation of the cumulants R. A. Fisher proposed the k statistics.   They are unbiased estimators, and, because they are symmetric, they are functions of the order statistic.   From Theorem 2.2 it follows that they are the minimum-variance and risk (convex-loss) estimators of the cumulants.

As a measure of the concentration or of the spread of a distribution, the parameter Δ_θ has been used:

$$\Delta_\theta = E_\theta\{|X_1 - X_2|\}$$
$$= \int\int |x_1 - x_2| \, dF_\theta(x_1) \, dF_\theta(x_2),$$

where F_θ is the distribution function for the parameter value θ.   Obviously the parameter is estimable and has a kernel $|x_1 - x_2|$. The corresponding U statistic is

$$d = \frac{1}{n(n-1)} \sum_{\alpha \neq \beta} |x_\alpha - x_\beta|$$

and is called Gini's mean difference [13]. It has minimum variance among unbiased estimators of Δ_θ.

The probability measure of a set is also an estimable parameter; consider $P_\theta(A)$, where A is a set on the real line. Let $\phi_A(x)$ be the characteristic function for A:

$$\phi_A(x) = 1 \qquad \text{if} \quad x \in A$$
$$= 0 \qquad \notin A.$$

Then

$$E_\theta\{\phi_A(X)\} = P_\theta(A),$$

and the parameter is estimable of degree 1. The minimum-variance unbiased estimator for a sample of n is m/n, where m is the number of x's in the set A.

EXAMPLE 2.3. For a sample of n from an arbitrary discrete distribution on the real line, we have from Theorem 7.3 in Chapter 1 that the order statistic is complete. We can then apply our Theorem 2.2, and all the results in the example above apply also to the discrete distributions on the real line.

EXAMPLE 2.4. Let $\mathbf{X} = (X_1, \cdots, X_{n_1})$, where the X_i are independent and each has the same distribution P_θ, where $\{P_\theta | \theta \in \Omega\}$ are the absolutely continuous distributions on R^1. Similarly, let $\mathbf{Y} = (Y_1, \cdots, Y_{n_2})$, where the Y_i are independent and each has the same distribution P_η, where $\{P_\eta | \eta \in \Omega\}$ are the absolutely continuous distributions. We consider the combined experiment with random variable $(\mathbf{X}, \mathbf{Y})$ and $(\theta, \eta) \in \Omega^2$.

For the X's we know that $t_1(x) = \{x_1, \cdots, x_{n_1}\}$ is a sufficient and complete statistic. Similarly $t_2(y_1, \cdots, y_{n_2}) = \{y_1, \cdots, y_{n_2}\}$ is a complete sufficient statistic for the Y's. By Theorem 5.3 in Chapter 1 the combined statistic $(\{x_1, \cdots, x_{n_1}\}, \{y_1, \cdots, y_{n_2}\})$ is sufficient for the combined experiment. Theorem 6.3 in Chapter 1 is not easily applied to show the combined statistic complete. However, Theorem 7.1 of Chapter 1 can be extended in a straightforward manner and gives this result.

Then directly from the Lehmann–Scheffé Theorem 2.8 in Chapter 2 it follows that, for any estimable parameter, there is essentially only one unbiased estimate based on $(\{x_1, \cdots, x_{n_1}\}, \{y_1, \cdots, y_{n_2}\})$. It is interesting to note that a function of this statistic is symmetric in the x's and symmetric in the y's, and conversely.

Consider the estimation of $E(XY)$. Obviously, an unbiased estimator is x_1y_1. By averaging we make x_1y_1 symmetric in x's and obtain

$$\frac{\sum\limits_{1}^{n} x_i}{n_1}\, y_1;$$

similarly, making it symmetric in the y's, we obtain

$$\frac{\sum\limits_{1}^{n_1} x_i \sum\limits_{1}^{n_2} y_j}{n_1 n_2}.$$

This is the only unbiased estimator symmetric in the x's and in the y's, and it has minimum variance.

By a similar argument we can show that the minimum variance unbiased estimator of σ_{X+Y}^2 is

$$\frac{\sum\limits_{1}^{n_1} (x_i - \bar{x})^2}{n_1 - 1} + \frac{\sum\limits_{1}^{n_2} (y_i - \bar{y})^2}{n_2 - 1}.$$

EXAMPLE 2.5.   Let $(X_1, Y_1), \cdots, (X_n, Y_n)$ be independent and each (X_i, Y_i) have the same distribution P_θ over R^2, where $\{P_\theta \,|\, \theta \in \Omega\}$ is the class of absolutely continuous distributions. The order statistic is $\{(x_1, y_1), \cdots, (x_n, y_n)\}$ and is of course a sufficient statistic. Any function of the order statistic is a symmetric function of the n entries $(x_1, y_1), \cdots,$ (x_n, y_n). By Theorem 7.3 in Chapter 1, it is complete.

For the estimation of the parameter $E(XY)$ we have an unbiased estimate x_1y_1. The corresponding U statistic is

$$\frac{\sum\limits_{i=1}^{n} x_i y_i}{n},$$

and it is essentially unique and has minimum variance and risk (convex loss).

For the estimation of σ_{X+Y}^2 we have by Example 2.2 the unbiased estimator

$$\tfrac{1}{2}[x_1 + y_1 - (x_2 + y_2)]^2.$$

The corresponding U statistic is

$$\frac{1}{n-1} \sum_1^n (x_i + y_i - \overline{x+y})^2$$

where $\overline{x+y} = n^{-1}\Sigma(x_i + y_i)$, and it has minimum variance among unbiased estimators.

3. TOLERANCE REGIONS

Again let the sample space be $\mathscr{X} = \mathscr{X}_1 \times \cdots \times \mathscr{X}_n$, and let the class of probability measures $\{P_\theta^{\mathbf{X}} \mid \theta \in \Omega\}$ correspond to a sample of n from a measure in $\{P_\theta \mid \theta \in \Omega\}$ over the component space $\mathscr{X} = \mathscr{X}_i$. In Section 5 of Chapter 2 we introduced the concept of a statistical tolerance region and gave several definitions. Each of these definitions has applications, but the one of particular importance is Definition 5.2 for a distribution-free tolerance region. Such a region has regularity properties which make it particularly attractive in nonparametric theory. Also distribution-free tolerance regions give quite general examples of the other types of region. For convenience we repeat the definition:

$S(x_1, \cdots, x_n)$ is a distribution-free tolerance region for $\{P_\theta \mid \theta \in \Omega\}$ over $\mathscr{X}(\mathscr{A})$ if $S(x_1, \cdots, x_n)$ takes values in $\mathscr{A}$ and if the induced distribution of the function

$$P_\theta(S(x_1, \cdots, x_n))$$

corresponding to the measure $P_\theta^{\mathbf{X}}$ over $\mathscr{X}^n$ is independent of the parameter $\theta \in \Omega$.

Later in this section we shall have a theorem which gives a method for constructing distribution-free tolerance regions, but first we develop some necessary distribution theory.

Let $f(x)$ be a real-valued statistic defined over the component space $\mathscr{X}$. For an outcome $\mathbf{x} = (x_1, \cdots, x_n)$ from $\mathscr{X}$ we can calculate the value of the statistic for each coordinate and obtain n real numbers: $f(x_1), \cdots, f(x_n)$. The first theorem is concerned with the rth largest of these n numbers, and we need a symbol to designate it. Let $\max_{i=1}^{n}(r) \, t_i$ designate the rth largest of the n real numbers $t_1, \cdots, t_n$. The theorem is concerned with the conditional distribution over $\mathscr{X}$, given the real-valued statistic $\max(r) \, f(x_i)$; that is, loosely, the conditional distribution of a sample given the value for the rth largest $f(x_i)$ from the sample.

THEOREM 3.1.   If the distribution of the real statistic $f(x)$ induced from P_θ over $\mathscr{X}$ is continuous, then, for a sample of n, $\mathbf{X} = (X_1, \cdots, X_n)$, from P_θ, the conditional distribution, given $\max\limits_{i=1}^{n}(r) \, f(x_i) = t$ is that of a sample of $r - 1$ from P_θ restricted to $\{x \,|\, f(x) > t\}$, an independent sample of $n - r$ from P_θ restricted to $\{x \,|\, f(x) < t\}$ and an independent sample of one from $P_\theta(\,|\, f(X) = t)$.

Note.   For an extension of this theorem to cover the case where the induced distribution of $f(x)$ is discontinuous see [12].

Proof.   When the n x's in the outcome are ordered by the real statistic $f(x)$, there are $n!$ possible orderings.   Each of these orderings has the same conditional probability $1/n!$, given the order statistic $t(x_1, \cdots, x_n) = \{x_1, \cdots, x_n\}$.   This obtains immediately from formula (2.6) in the previous section.   The statement of the theorem omits to mention this "equal likely" conditional distribution, given the order statistic, and just gives the distribution of the $r - 1$ x's having $f(x) > t$, the $n - r$ x's having $f(x) < t$, and one x having $f(x) = t$.   Actually, there are $n!/(r - 1)! \, (n - r)!$ such arrangements of the original outcome into this partition, and each has the same probability.

We have assumed that the induced distribution of the statistic $f(x)$ is continuous.   Hence, for a sample of n from P_θ over $\mathscr{X}$, the probability is zero that any of the values $f(x_1), \cdots, f(x_n)$ are equal.   We therefore omit from further consideration the outcomes $(x_1, \cdots, x_n)$ for which any of $f(x_1), \cdots, f(x_n)$ are equal.

From the symmetry of the probability measure over $\mathscr{X} = \mathscr{X}^n$, each of the $n!/(r - 1)! \, 1! \, (n - r)!$ cases with $r - 1$, 1, $n - r$ x's having $f(x)$, respectively, $>, =, < t$ will have the same probability distribution.   We therefore consider one of these, say the one for which $f(x_1), \cdots, f(x_{r-1}) > t$, $f(x_r) = t$, and $f(x_{r+1}), \cdots, f(x_n) < t$.   To find the conditional distribution, given this condition, we need three simple properties of conditional probabilities.   First, if a condition has positive probability of being fulfilled, then the conditional measure is the given measure normalized to the region for which the condition is fulfilled, [see first definition of conditional probability (4.6) in Chapter 1]; for example, if $P_X(A)$ is the measure over $\mathscr{X}$, then by this measure normalized for the condition $\{x \,|\, f(x) > t\}$ we mean

$$(3.1) \qquad P_X\{A \,|\, f(x) > t\} = \frac{P_X[A \cap \{x \,|\, f(x) > t\}]}{P_X[\{x \,|\, f(x) > t\}]}$$

Second, a conditional probability measure can be obtained in steps.   For, if $P_X(A \,|\, C_1 C_2)$ is the conditional measure from $P_X(A)$, given conditions

C_1 and C_2, it is equal $P_{X|C_1}(A|C_2)$, the conditional measure from $P_X(A|C_1)$, given condition C_2. This holds for both definitions of conditional probability, provided the conditional probability is a measure (see Problem 7). Third, if Y and Z are independent random variables and the conditional measure of Y is wanted, given a condition on Z, it is just the given unconditioned measure for Y. This is immediately obtained from the fact that the measure over $\mathscr{Y} \times \mathscr{Z}$ is a product measure.

We now apply the three properties to finding our conditional probability. We first impose the single condition $f(x_r) = t$ on the product measure over $\mathscr{X} = \mathscr{X}^n$. The conditional measure is that of a sample of $n - 1$ from P_θ over $\mathscr{X}$, giving the coordinates other than x_r and an independent sample of one from $P_\theta(A|f(x) = t)$ for the coordinate x_r. We now impose the additional conditions $f(x_1), \cdots, f(x_{r-1}) > t$ and $f(x_{r+1}), \cdots, f(x_n) < t$. The resultant conditional measure is that of a sample of $r - 1$ from P_θ restricted to $\{x|f(x) > t\}$, giving the first $r - 1$ coordinates, an independent sample of one from $P_\theta(A|f(x) = t)$, and an independent sample of $n - r$ from $P_\theta(A)$ restricted to $\{x|f(x) < t\}$. This proves the theorem.

We now consider some probability distributions derived from sampling from the uniform distribution on the interval $[0, 1]$. Let U designate a real random variable with the uniform distribution on $[0, 1]$. It will have the density function $f(u)$ defined by

$$
\begin{aligned}
f(u) &= 1 && \text{if} \quad u \in \,]0, 1[\\
&= 0 && \notin \,]0, 1[.
\end{aligned}
$$

(3.2)

For a sample of n we have the random variable $(U_1, \cdots, U_n)$, where the U's are independent and each has the above distribution. $(U_1, \cdots, U_n)$ has the uniform distribution over $[0, 1]^n$.

The n-dimensional cube $]0, 1[^n$ can be partitioned into $n!$ regions, a typical one being $\{(u_1, \cdots, u_n)|0 < u_{i_1} < \cdots < u_{i_n} < 1\}$, and a region in which at least two of the coordinates $u_1, \cdots, u_n$ are equal. This last set has Lebesgue measure zero and hence probability zero. Letting $u_{(1)}, \cdots, u_{(n)}$ designate the smallest, $\cdots$, the largest of the numbers $u_1, \cdots, u_n$ and using these as coordinates in each of the $n!$ regions, we find the $n!$ regions to be the same; viz., $\{(u_{(1)}, \cdots, u_{(n)})|0 < u_{(1)} < \cdots < u_{(n)} < 1\}$. Also the density function has the same value over each. It follows then that the induced distribution of $(U_{(1)}, \cdots, U_{(n)})$ has density function $h(u_1, \cdots, u_n)$ given by

$$
\begin{aligned}
h(u_1, \cdots, u_n) &= n! && \text{if} \quad 0 < u_1 < \cdots < u_n < 1, \\
&= 0 && \text{otherwise;}
\end{aligned}
$$

(3.3)

it is the uniform distribution over the region given by $0 < u_1 < \cdots < u_n < 1$.

We define new variables $c_1, \cdots, c_{n+1}$ by the equations

$$c_1 = u_{(1)}$$
$$c_2 = u_{(2)} - u_{(1)}$$
$$\cdot \quad \cdot \quad \cdot \quad \cdot$$
$$\cdot \quad \cdot \quad \cdot \quad \cdot$$
$$c_n = u_{(n)} - u_{(n-1)}$$
$$c_{n+1} = 1 - u_{(n)}.$$

These are the successive differences between the values $0, u_{(1)}, \cdots, u_{(n)}, 1$, and they obviously satisfy the relation $\sum_1^{n+1} c_i = 1$. The c's are sometimes called *coverages*; for example, the value of $c_i = u_{(i)} - u_{(i-1)}$ is just the probability measure (or *coverage*) of the interval $[u_{(i-1)}, u_{(i)}]$ as given by the uniform distribution.

We now find the induced distribution of $(c_1, \cdots, c_{n+1})$. If we choose any n of the c's and consider the transformation from the $u_{(i)}$'s, the Jacobian will have absolute value one. For consider the first n c's; we have the Jacobian

$$\frac{\partial(c_1, \cdots, c_n)}{\partial(u_{(1)}, \cdots, u_{(n)})} = \begin{vmatrix} 1 & -1 & 0 & \cdot & \cdot & \cdot & \cdot \\ 0 & 1 & -1 & \cdot & \cdot & \cdot & \cdot \\ 0 & 0 & 1 & \cdot & \cdot & \cdot & \cdot \\ \cdot & \cdot & \cdot & \cdot & \cdot & \cdot & \cdot \\ \cdot & \cdot & \cdot & \cdot & 1 & -1 & 0 \\ \cdot & \cdot & \cdot & \cdot & 0 & 1 & -1 \\ \cdot & \cdot & \cdot & \cdot & 0 & 0 & 1 \end{vmatrix}$$

$$= 1,$$

and similarly for any other n c's. Thus, the distribution of $(u_{(1)}, \cdots, u_{(n)})$ as given by

$$P(A) = \int_A n! \, du_{(1)}, \cdots, du_{(n)}$$

with $A \subset \{(u_1, \cdots, u_n) | 0 < u_1 \cdots < u_n < 1\}$ yields for $c_1, \cdots, c_n$ the induced distribution

(3.4) $$P'(B) = \int_B n! \, dc_1, \cdots, dc_n,$$

where $B \subset \{(c_1, \cdots, c_n) | 0 < c_i < 1, \Sigma c_i < 1\}$. This distribution of the c's is uniform and has complete symmetry with respect to the n c's involved. The same is true for any other set of n c's. It follows then that the distribution of the $n + 1$ c's is uniform over the region

$$\{(c_1, \cdots, c_{n+1}) | 0 < c_i, \sum_1^{n+1} c_i = 1\}.$$

We now consider the induced distribution of the sum of r c's. Let such a sum be designated by C_r. Because of the symmetry of the distribution of the c's, the distribution of C_r is the same as the distribution of the sum of the first r c's, $\sum_1^r c_i$, and from the definition of the c's we have

$$C_r = \sum_1^r c_i = u_{(r)}.$$

The distribution function of $u_{(r)}$ is given by

$$(3.5) \qquad \Pr\{U_{(r)} \le y\} = n! \int_{u_{(r)} \le y} du_{(1)} \cdots du_{(n)}$$

$$= n! \int_0^{u_2} du_1 \cdots \int_0^{u_r} du_{r-1} \int_{u_{n-1}}^1 du_n \cdots \int_{u_r}^1 du_{r+1} \int_0^y du_r$$

$$= n! \int_0^y \frac{u_r^{r-1}}{(r-1)!} \frac{(1 - u_r)^{n-r}}{(n-r)!} du_r$$

$$= \frac{\Gamma(n+1)}{\Gamma(r)\Gamma(n-r+1)} \int_0^y u^{r-1}(1-u)^{n-r} du.$$

Thus C_r has the β distribution with parameters $p = r$ and $q = n - r + 1$; the β distribution function is

$$I_y(p, q) = \frac{\Gamma(p+q)}{\Gamma(p)\Gamma(q)} \int_0^y u^{p-1}(1-u)^{q-1} du,$$

the so-called incomplete β function. The expected value of C_r is easily obtained from the distribution function (3.5). However, it is obtained immediately from the symmetry of the distribution for $c_1, \cdots, c_{n+1}$. We have

$$1 = E\{1\}$$

$$= E\left\{\sum_1^{n+1} c_i\right\}$$

$$= \sum_1^{n+1} E(C_i)$$

$$= (n+1)E(C_1),$$

from which we obtain $E(c_i) = (n + 1)^{-1}$; therefore

$$E(C_r) = r \cdot E(c_i)$$

(3.6)
$$= \frac{r}{n + 1}.$$

We consider one more probability distribution. Let X be a real-valued random variable with a continuous distribution function $F(x)$. We prove that the induced distribution of $F(X)$ is the uniform distribution on the interval $[0, 1]$.

For any x define $x-$ and $x+$ by

$$x- = \inf_{F(x') = F(x)} x'$$

$$x+ = \sup_{F(x') = F(x)} x';$$

they are respectively the inf and sup of the x' having $F(x') = F(x)$. Because of the continuity of the function $F(x)$, $F(x-) = F(x) = F(x+)$. From the definition of $x-$, $x+$, we have the set-inclusion relations

$$\{x' | x' \leq x-\} \subset \{x' | F(x') \leq F(x)\} \subset \{x' | x' \leq x+\}.$$

Consequently we have

$$\Pr\{X \leq x-\} \leq \Pr\{F(X) \leq F(x)\} \leq \Pr\{X \leq x+\}.$$

Since the outside expressions are each equal to $F(x)$, then

$$\Pr\{F(X) \leq F(x)\} = F(x);$$

but, since $F(x)$ takes all values on $]0, 1[$, we have

(3.7) $$\Pr\{F(X) \leq y\} = y$$

for $y \in]0, 1[$. Thus $F(X)$ has the uniform distribution on $[0, 1]$.

We now define a construction procedure whereby, corresponding to n points $x_1, \cdots, x_n$ in $\mathscr{X}$, the region $\mathscr{X}$ is partitioned into $n + 1$ disjoint subsets (numbered from 1 to $n + 1$) and referred to as *blocks*, and a further n disjoint subsets referred to as *cuts*. The theorem at the end of this section will prove that a distribution-free tolerance region can be formed by taking any r of the numbered blocks.

The construction procedure is given by two sequences of functions $[\phi_1(x), \cdots, \phi_n(x)]$ and $[p_1, \cdots, p_n]$. $\phi_j(x) = \phi_j(x; r_1, \cdots, r_{j-1})$ is a real-valued measurable function of x which may depend on $j - 1$ real variables $r_1, \cdots, r_{j-1}$. When the function ϕ_j is used, the real values $r_1, \cdots, r_{j-1}$ are values, respectively, of the function $\phi_1, \cdots, \phi_{j-1}$. $p_j = p_j(r_1, \cdots, r_{j-1})$ is an integer in $1, \cdots, n$, and which integer it is may depend on $j - 1$ real variables $r_1, \cdots, r_{j-1}$, which once again will be values attained, respectively, by the functions $\phi_1, \cdots, \phi_{j-1}$. Further, for a given sequence of numbers $r_1, \cdots, r_{n-1}$, the set of integers $(p_1, \cdots, p_n)$ is a permutation of the set $(1, \cdots, n)$; thus there can be no two integers the same in the sequence.

For the construction procedure it is convenient to think of the outcome $(x_1, \cdots, x_n)$ as n points $x_1, \cdots, x_n$ in the space $\mathcal{X}$. Now, corresponding to $\{\phi_j(x)\}$ and $\{p_j\}$ and n points $x_1, \cdots, x_n$ in $\mathcal{X}$, we construct $n+1$ disjoint blocks by making n cuts or divisions of $\mathcal{X}$. The first is made by using the function $\phi_1(x)$ and the integer p_1. The n values $\phi_1(x_1), \cdots, \phi_1(x_n)$ are examined and the p_1 largest value chosen, $\max_{i=1}^{n}(p_1)\ \phi_0(x_i)$. $\mathcal{X}$ is then divided into two regions,

$$S_{1\cdots p_1} = \left\{x \,\middle|\, \phi_1(x) > \max_{i=1}^{n}(p_1)\ \phi_1(x_i)\right\}$$

and

$$S_{p_1+1\cdots n+1} = \left\{x \,\middle|\, \phi_1(x) < \max_{i=1}^{n}(p_1)\ \phi_1(x_i)\right\}$$

by means of the cut

$$T_{p_1} = \left\{x \,\middle|\, \phi_1(x) = \max_{i=1}^{n}(p_1)\ \phi_1(x_i)\right\}.$$

There will, of course, be at least one x_i having $\phi(x_i) = \max(p_1)\ \phi(x_i)$, and, when we apply our construction procedure, there will with probability one be only one such x_i. We therefore assume that there is exactly one x_i in T_{p_1}. It follows then that there are exactly $p_1 - 1$ x_i's in $S_{1\cdots p_1}$ and exactly $n - p_1$ in $S_{p_1+1\cdots n+1}$.

The second cut is made by using the function $\phi_2(x)$ and the integer p_2. These, however, depend on r_1, which stands for the value of the function $\phi_1(x)$ at the cut $T_{p_1} : r_1 = \max(p_1)\ \phi_1(x_i)$. Hence

$$\phi_2(x) = \phi_2(x;\ \max_{i=1}^{n}(p_1)\ \phi_1(x_i)),$$

$$p_2 = p_2(\max_{i=1}^{n}(p_1)\ \phi_1(x_i)).$$

If p_2 is one of the integers $1, \cdots, p_1 - 1$, then we divide the region $S_{1\cdots p_1}$ into $S_{1\cdots p_2}$ and $S_{p_2+1\cdots p_1}$ and the cut T_{p_2}. This is done by calculating the p_2 largest value of $\phi_2(x_i)$ for x_i in $S_{1\cdots p_1}$ and dividing $S_{1\cdots p_1}$ into

$$S_{1\cdots p_2} = S_{1\cdots p_1} \cap \{x \,|\, \phi_2(x) > \max_{x_i \in S_{1\cdots p_1}}(p_2)\ \phi_2(x_i)\}$$

and

$$S_{p_2+1\cdots p_1} = S_{1\cdots p_1} \cap \{x \,|\, \phi_2(x) < \max_{x_i \in S_{1\cdots p_1}}(p_2)\ \phi_2(x_i)\}$$

by means of the cut

$$T_{p_2} = S_{1 \cdots p_1} \cap \{x \mid \phi_2(x) = \max_{x_i \in S_{1 \cdots p_1}} (p_2) \; \phi_2(x_i)\}.$$

If p_2 is one of the integers $p_1 + 1, \cdots, n$, then we divide the region $S_{p_1+1 \cdots n+1}$ into $S_{p_1+1 \cdots p_2}$ and $S_{p_2+1 \cdots n+1}$ and the cut T_{p_2}. This is done by calculating the $p_2 - p_1$ largest† $\phi_2(x_i)$ for x_i in $S_{p_1+1 \cdots n+1}$ and dividing $S_{p_1+1 \cdots n+1}$ into

$$S_{p_1+1 \cdots p_2} = S_{p_1+1 \cdots n+1} \cap \{x \mid \phi_2(x) > \max_{x_i \in S_{p_1+1 \cdots n+1}} (p_2 - p_1) \; \phi_2(x_i)\}$$

and

$$S_{p_2+1 \cdots n+1} = S_{p_1+1 \cdots n+1} \cap \{x \mid \phi_2(x) < \max_{x_i \in S_{p_1+1 \cdots n+1}} (p_2 - p_1) \; \phi_2(x_i)\}$$

by means of the cut

$$T_{p_2} = S_{p_1+1 \cdots n+1} \cap \{x \mid \phi_2(x) = \max_{x_i \in S_{p_1+1 \cdots n+1}} (p_2 - p_1) \; \phi_2(x_i)\}.$$

This procedure is continued. For the jth stage $\phi_j(x)$ and p_j are used with $r_1, \cdots, r_{j-1}$ replaced by the values of $\phi_1, \cdots, \phi_{j-1}$ at their respective cuts. The set divided is the one having p_j in its index set, and the x_i in that set are ordered by $\phi_j(x)$ and the $p_j - p_{j_0}$ largest value chosen to represent the cut. p_{j_0} stands for the largest of the $p_1, \cdots, p_{j-1}$ which are less than p_j; it is one less than the smallest index in the set being divided. The set is then divided into a set having $\phi_j(x)$ values greater than the value representing the cut, a set having $\phi_j(x)$ values less than the value representing the cut, and the cut T_{p_j}.

By this procedure we obtain finally $n + 1$ regions $S_1, \cdots, S_{n+1}$ and n cuts $T_1, \cdots, T_n$. Then, provided the conditions of the theorem are fulfilled, we can choose any r of these $n + 1$ regions to form a tolerance region, and its coverage will have the simple distribution of $U_{(r)}$, the rth order statistic in a sample of n from the uniform distribution $[0, 1]$. An example illustrating this procedure is given after the theorem.

THEOREM 3.2. If $\phi_1(x), \cdots, \phi_n(x)$ each have a continuous induced distribution corresponding to the measure P over $\mathscr{X}$, then the coverages $P(S_1), \cdots, P(S_{n+1})$ of the $n + 1$ regions $S_1, \cdots, S_{n+1}$ defined by the procedure above in terms of a sample $X_1, \cdots, X_n$ from P have the uniform distribution of coverages (3.4) for a sample from the uniform distribution $[0, 1]$. Any r of the regions will have a coverage with the β distribution having parameters $p = r, q = n - r + 1$.

---

† If we treat the $p_1 x_i$'s in $T_{1 \cdots p_1}$ as being "largest" and then order the x_i's in $T_{p_1+1 \cdots n}$ by means of the function $\phi_2(x_i)$, then the p_2 "largest" x_i is used to form the cut.

The requirement of continuity of the induced distribution of the ϕ's may be modified to hold almost everywhere (P) with respect to the auxiliary arguments of the ϕ functions.

Proof. The proof is done stepwise, corresponding to the stages in the constructional procedure, and a correspondence is set up with the simple case of sampling from the uniform distribution. For this latter case the distributions were obtained earlier in this section, and they are as given in the statement of the theorem.

Consider the distribution of $\phi_1(X)$ corresponding to P over $\mathscr{X}$. It has a continuous distribution function, say $F(y)$. To simplify the proof we assume that $F(y)$ is a strictly increasing function; it is a matter of detail to remove this restriction. By the last probability result at the beginning of this section, we know that $F(\phi_1(X))$ has as induced distribution the uniform distribution $[0, 1]$. Then, for a sample of n from P, we have that $F(\phi_1(X_1)), \cdots, F(\phi_1(X_n))$ are independent, each with the uniform distribution $[0, 1]$. Therefore $\max(p_1) \{F(\phi_1(X_1)), \cdots, F(\phi_1(X_n))\}$ has the distribution of the p_1th largest order statistic $U_{(n-p_1+1)}$ from the uniform distribution. But, because of the strict monotonicity of $F(y)$, we have

$$\max(p_1) \ F(\phi_1(x_i)) = F(\max(p_1) \ \phi_1(x_i)).$$

Then, from the definition of $F(y)$, we obtain

$$P(S_{1 \cdots p_1}) = 1 - F(\max(p_1) \ \phi_1(x_i)),$$
$$P(S_{p_1+1 \cdots n+1}) = F(\max(p_1) \ \phi_1(x_i)).$$

Because of these relations, the distribution of the coverages of $S_{1 \cdots p_1}$ and $S_{p_1+1 \cdots n+1}$ is the same as the distribution of the coverages of $[u_{(n-p_1+1)}, 1]$ and $[0, u_{(n-p_1+1)}]$ in sampling from the uniform distribution. Now from Theorem (3.1) the conditional distributions given these coverages, that is, given $F(\max(p_1) \ \phi(x_i)) = t$ and $u_{(n-p+1)} = t$, is for the first case that of samples of $p_1 - 1$ and $n - p_1$ from P restricted, respectively, to $S_{1 \cdots p_1}$ and to $S_{p_1+1 \cdots n+1}$, and for the uniform case is that of samples of $p_1 - 1$ and $n - p_1$ from the uniform distribution restricted to $[u_{(n-p_1+1)}, 1]$ and $[0, u_{(n-p_1+1)}]$. Also, for both the original case and the uniform case the coverages calculated using the restricted distribution to the coverages calculated using the original distribution will be in the ratio $1 - t$ to 1 for the sample of $p_1 - 1$, and t to 1 for the sample of $n - p_1$. The coverages of the sets $S_{1 \cdots p_1}, S_{p_1+1 \cdots n+1}$ have been related to corresponding coverages for the uniform distribution, and for each set the x's act as a sample from the restricted original distribution and correspond to u's from the restricted uniform distribution.

The above argument not only derived the necessary results for the first stage, but gave the additional argument necessary to show that for the second stage the proof will be a duplicate of the first-stage proof, only applied to the reduced space $S_{1 \cdots p_1}$ and $[u_{(n-p+1)}, 1]$ or $S_{p_1+1 \cdots n+1}$ and $[0, u_{(n-p+1)}]$ as the case may be.

After the final stage we obtain $P(S_1), \cdots, P(S_{n+1})$ with the same distribution as $c_{n+1}, \cdots, c_1$ for the uniform distribution. This completes the proof.

Note. The theorem can be generalized with little change in proof to permit the construction functions at any stage to depend on the value of the x's at previous cuts and not just on the values of the ϕ functions at those cuts (J. H. B. Kemperman).

A treatment of the discontinuous case is given in [6], [8], [9] and [10].

Distribution-free tolerance regions can be used to form β tolerance regions for a proportion p; for convenience we give again Definition 5.1 of Chapter 3:

$S(x_1, \cdots, x_n)$ *is a β tolerance region for a proportion p if*

$$\inf_{\theta \in \Omega} \mathrm{Pr}_\theta \{P_\theta(S(X_1, \cdots, X_n)) \geq p\} = \beta.$$

If $S(x_1, \cdots, x_n)$ is a distribution-free tolerance region, then we have that $P_\theta(S(X_1, \cdots, X_n))$ has a distribution on $[0, 1]$ which is independent of θ. Therefore, $S(x_1, \cdots, x_n)$ can be treated as a tolerance region for a proportion p if β is given by

$$\beta = \mathrm{Pr}_\theta \{P_\theta(S(X_1, \cdots, X_n)) \geq p\}.$$

Now for distribution-free tolerance regions obtained from Theorem 3.2, R. B. Murphy [11] has used the β distribution to construct graphs connecting β, p, n, r.

EXAMPLE 3.1. A sample of 59 observations is made from a continuous bivariate distribution known to have two modes; a 50% tolerance region in two parts centering on the two modes is desired. From Murphy's graphs [11] a region formed from 36 blocks† is seen to have a 90% probability of containing at least 50% of the population; that is, 90% confidence that the region contains at least 50% of the population. The following procedure is proposed as a solution to obtaining the required region.

The 59 points are plotted in Fig. 16. The function y is used to remove two blocks by the cut c_2; two further blocks using the function $-y$ are removed by the cut c_4. Similarly x and $-x$ are used to form cuts c_6 and c_8. The rectangle so formed now corresponds to 52 blocks.

† It is worth noticing that only 60% of the equivalent blocks yields 90% confidence in at least 50% of the population.

The rectangle is tentatively cut into eight sections formed by the two diagonals and the two lines through the center parallel to the x and y axis. For convenience, number these sections from 1 to 8 clockwise starting at top center.   In the first section, cut off one block from the outside, using a

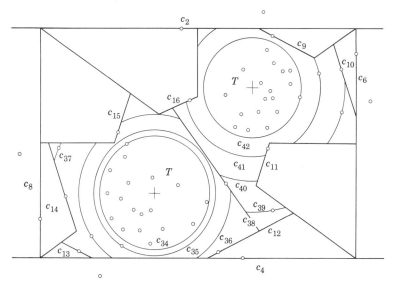

Figure 16.

line making an angle of $-22\frac{1}{2}°$ to the x axis; that is, use the function $y + x \tan 22\frac{1}{2}°$ to form the cut c_9.   For the second section, use the function $y + x \tan 67\frac{1}{2}°$ to remove one block by the cut c_{10}.   Apply a similar procedure to each of the 6 remaining sections, thus forming cuts c_{11}, c_{12}, c_{13}, c_{14}, c_{15}, and c_{16}.   The region now remaining corresponds to 44 blocks.

The 8 sections originally were of equal area.   Each section has had a block removed, thus reducing the areas to the values $a_1, \cdots, a_8$, say. Further cutting will depend on these areas, they being an indication of the relative positions of the two modes.   Consider the total area of an adjacent pair of reduced sections and of the opposite pair; for example, total area equals $a_1 + a_2 + a_5 + a_6$.   Do this for each of the four possible selections.   From the diagram it is easily seen that the group with minimum total area corresponds to Sections 3, 4, 7, 8.   These are the sections that presumably tend to separate the two modes; hence we divide the remaining region by a line with slope -1.   If the blocks had been 2, 3, 6, 7, we would have used a line with slope 0.   The reasoning behind this procedure is quite straightforward.

Using the function $y + x$, we divide the 44-block region into parts corresponding to 22 blocks and 22 blocks; that is, we choose the point giving the 22d largest value to the function $y + x$ and make the cut c_{38}. The two regions formed by this cut are further reduced with the objective being to form two circular regions each corresponding to 18 blocks.

Use the function $(y - \eta)^2 + (x - \xi)^2$ to remove four blocks from the right-hand region. As center of the circle (ξ, η) a reasonable choice would be the center, marked x, of the largest circle that can be inscribed in that region. Cuts c_{39}, c_{40}, c_{41}, and c_{42} are made by this function. We apply a similar procedure to the left-hand region.

The resultant two circles form a region T composed of 36 blocks and hence in repeated sampling have 90% confidence of being at least a 50% tolerance region. It should be noted that the two parts of T will not always be circular; they will be circular with perhaps indentations. See, for example, cut c_{41}.)

4. PROBLEMS FOR SOLUTION

1. By constructing a class of probability distributions contained in the absolutely continuous distributions on the real line, show that there does not exist an unbiased estimate of the median for any sample size.

2. By constructing a simple type of probability distribution, show that μ_x^2 is not of degree one with respect to the class of absolutely continuous distributions.

3. For the class of absolutely continuous distributions on the real line R^1, what are the degrees of the parameters

$$E(X^3),\ E^3(X),\ E\{[X - E(X)]^3\},\ E^4(X)?$$

Find the minimum variance unbiased estimators.

4. For the class of absolutely continuous distributions over R^2, what are the degrees of the parameters

$$E^2(X_1),\ \sigma_{X_1}^2,\ E(X_1X_2),\ \sigma_{X_2}^2,\ E^2(X_1)E^2(X_2)?$$

of the vector parameters

$$\begin{pmatrix} E(X_1^2) \\ E(X_1X_2) \\ E(X_2^2) \end{pmatrix} \quad \begin{pmatrix} \sigma_{X_1}^2 \\ \mathrm{Cov}\ \{X_1,\ X_2\} \\ \sigma_{X_2}^2 \end{pmatrix}\ ?$$

Find the minimum variance unbiased estimators.

5. If $(u_{(1)}, \cdots, u_{(n)})$ is the order statistic for a sample of n from the uniform distribution $[0, 1]$, find the marginal distribution of $(u_{(r)}, u_{(r+s)})$.

6. Find the joint distribution of $(P(\bigcup_R S_i), P(\bigcup_S S_i))$ where R, S are disjoint sets of r, s integers chosen from $1, \cdots, n + 1$, and where $S_1, \cdots, S_{n+1}$ are distribution-free tolerance regions as given by Theorem 3.2.

7. If $f_1(x)$, $f_2(x)$ are statistics over $\mathscr{X}(\mathscr{A})$ and $P(A)$ is a measure on $\mathscr{X}(\mathscr{A})$, show that the conditional measure $P(A|(f_1, f_2))$ is equal $P_{X|f_1}(A|f_2)$, the conditional measure given f_2, corresponding to $P(A|f_1)$. Assume the conditional probabilities are measures.

REFERENCES AND BIBLIOGRAPHY

1. P. R. Halmos, "The theory of unbiased estimation," *Ann. Math. Stat.*, Vol. 17 (1946), p. 34.
2. W. Hoeffding, "A class of statistics with asymptotically normal distribution," *Ann. Math. Stat.*, Vol. 19 (1948), p. 293.
3. E. L. Lehmann and H. Scheffé, "Completeness, similar regions, and unbiased estimation," *Sankhyā*, Vol. 10 (1950), p. 305.
4. S. S. Wilks, "Determination of sample sizes for setting tolerance limits," *Ann. Math. Stat.*, Vol. 12 (1941), p. 91.
5. A. Wald., "An extension of Wilks' method for setting tolerance limits," *Ann. Math. Stat.*, Vol. 14 (1943), p. 45.
6. H. Scheffé and J. W. Tukey, "Nonparametric estimation, I. Validation of order statistics," *Ann. Math. Stat.*, Vol. 16 (1945), p. 187.
7. J. W. Tukey, "Nonparametric estimation, II. Statistically equivalent blocks and tolerance regions—the continuous case," *Ann. Math. Stat.*, Vol. 18 (1947), p. 529.
8. J. W. Tukey, "Nonparametric Estimation, III. Statistically equivalent blocks and multivariate tolerance regions—the discontinuous case," *Ann. Math. Stat.*, Vol. 19 (1948), p. 30.
9. D. A. S. Fraser and R. Wormleighton, "Nonparametric estimation, IV," *Ann. Math. Stat.*, Vol. 22 (1951), p. 294.
10. D. A. S. Fraser, "Sequentially determined statistically equivalent blocks," *Ann. Math. Stat.*, Vol. 22 (1951), p. 372.
11. R. B. Murphy, "Nonparametric tolerance limits," *Ann. Math. Stat.*, Vol. 19 (1948), p. 581.
12. D. A. S. Fraser, "Nonparametric tolerance regions," *Ann. Math. Stat.*, Vol. 24 (1953), p. 44.
13. C. Gini, "Sulla misura della concentraziono e della variabilita doi carattori," *Atti reale ist. veneto sci. lettere ed arti*, Vol. 73 (1913–14), Part 2.

CHAPTER 5

The Theory of Hypothesis Testing

1. UNBIASEDNESS

Unbiasedness was defined in Section 3.6 of Chapter 2. Roughly, a test is unbiased if the probability of accepting the alternative is larger when the alternative is true than when the hypothesis is true. This is a reasonable property to require of a test. For nonparametric theory a general method of constructing unbiased tests would be of considerable value. However, we have only a technique which is capable, for some of the simpler problems, of producing *an* unbiased test. Also, for two of the simpler problems we have a criterion which can be used to check for unbiasedness. First we consider this criterion as it applies to the two-sample problem.

The two-sample problem was described by (3.1) in Chapter 3. For this let $X_1, \cdots, X_{n_1}$ be independent with distribution function $F(x)$ and $X_{n_1+1}, \cdots, X_{n_1+n_2}$ be independent with distribution function $G(x)$ where F and G are assumed continuous. The hypothesis is that $F(x) = G(x)$ for all x. We consider a one-sided alternative for which the second sample values tend to be larger than first sample values. Precisely, for the alternative we assume that

(1.1) $$F(x) > G(x)$$

for all x. This means that

$$\Pr_F \{X_1 \leq x\} > \Pr_G \{X_{n_1+1} \leq x\}$$

or

$$\Pr_F \{X_1 > x\} < \Pr_G \{X_{n_1+1} > x\}$$

for all x; in such a case we say that *the random variable X_{n_1+1} is stochastically larger than the random variable X_1*. The following criterion was given by Lehmann [1].

THEOREM 1.1. (LEHMANN). If the test function satisfies $\phi(x_1, \cdots,$
$x_{n_1}, x_{n_1+1}^* \cdots, x_{n_1+n_2}^*) \geq \phi(x_1, \cdots, x_{n_1}, x_{n_1+1}, \cdots, x_{n_1+n_2})$ whenever $x_i^* \geq x_i$
$(i = n_1 + 1, \cdots, n_1 + n_2)$, then the power function satisfies $\mathbf{P}_\phi(F, G) \geq$
$\mathbf{P}_\phi(F, F)$ for F, G satisfying (1.1). If, in addition ϕ is a similar test, then ϕ
is unbiased against the alternative given by (1.1).

Note. The criterion says that, if one outcome $(x_1, \cdots, x_{n_1}, x_{n_1+1}^*, \cdots,$
$x_{n_1+n_2}^*)$ is more "extreme" than another $(x_1, \cdots, x_{n_1+n_2})$, then the test
function for the first is at least as large as for the second, that is, more
likely to reject the hypothesis.

Proof. First we define a monotone function $f(x)$ so that, if X is a
random variable with distribution function $F(x)$, then $f(x)$ is a random
variable with distribution function $G(x)$. Let $G^{-1}(u)$ be the inverse
function to the continuous function $G(x)$. If $G(x)$ is strictly increasing,
then G^{-1} is well defined. Otherwise, there will be values for u such that
G^{-1} is multivalued. For each of these u we make G^{-1} single-valued by
choosing one of the possible values. Then we define a function $f(x)$ by
the equation

(1.2) $$f(x) = G^{-1}(F(x)).$$

This $f(x)$ satisfies the required property; for simplicity we give the proof
when $G(x)$ is strictly increasing. We must prove that $f(X) = G^{-1}(F(X))$
has the distribution function $G(x)$. By (3.7) in Chapter 4, $F(X)$ has the
uniform distribution $[0, 1]$. Designating by U a random variable with
this uniform distribution, we consider $G^{-1}(U)$:

$$\Pr\{G^{-1}(U) \leq x\} = \Pr\{U \leq G(x)\}$$
$$= G(x).$$

Thus $G^{-1}(U)$ has the distribution function $G(x)$, and the function $f(x)$ has
the desired property.

From (1.2) we obtain

(1.3) $$G(f(x)) = F(x),$$

and this with (1.1) implies that $f(x) > x$ for all x.

We now use the function $f(x)$ to establish the power-function inequality. Let E_{FG} designate an expectation taken with random variables
$X_1, \cdots, X_{n_1}$ having distribution function $F(x)$ and random variables
$X_{n_1+1}, \cdots, X_{n_1+n_2}$ having distribution function $G(x)$. We have

$$\mathbf{P}_\phi(F, G) = E_{FG}\{\phi(X_1, \cdots, X_{n_1}, X_{n_1+1}, \cdots, X_{n_1+n_2})\}$$
$$= E_{FF}\{\phi(X_1, \cdots, X_{n_1}, f(X_{n_1+1}), \cdots, f(X_{n_1+n_2}))\}$$
$$\geq E_{FF}\{\phi(X_1, \cdots, X_{n_1}, X_{n_1+1}, \cdots, X_{n_1+n_2})\}$$
$$= \mathbf{P}_\phi(F, F).$$

The inequality in the third line follows from the ϕ-function inequality in the statement of the theorem and from $f(x) > x$.

If the test function is similar of size α, then

$$\mathbf{P}_\phi(F, F) \equiv \alpha$$

for all F, and then it follows that

$$\mathbf{P}_\phi(F, G) \geq \alpha.$$

Therefore the test is unbiased for the alternative given by (1.1). This completes the proof.

The above theorem can also be used to extend the hypothesis for the two-sample problem. Let $\phi(x_1, \cdots, x_{n_1+n_2})$ be a test function which satisfies the criterion and which is similar of size α when $F(x) = G(x)$. The theorem states that ϕ is unbiased for

(1.4)

Hypothesis: $F(x) = G(x)$ for all x, F continuous,

Alternative: $F(x) > G(x)$ for all x, F, G continuous.

Consider two distribution functions satisfying $F(x) \leq G(x)$ for all x. We can define an $f(x)$ as in the first part of the proof; it will satisfy $f(x) \leq x$ for all x. Then, following the pattern of the remainder of the theorem, we obtain

$$\mathbf{P}_\phi(F, F) \geq \mathbf{P}_\phi(F, G).$$

But $\mathbf{P}_\phi(F, F) = \alpha$. Hence ϕ is a size-α test for the problem:

(1.5)

Hypothesis: $F(x) \leq G(x)$ for all x, F, G continuous,

Alternative: $F(x) > G(x)$ for all x, F, G continuous,

and by the theorem it is unbiased.

EXAMPLE 1.1.   We illustrate the theorem by the well known Mann–Whitney (Wilcoxon) test for the two-sample problem. The test is based on the statistic

$$V = \frac{1}{n_1 n_2} \text{ [number of pairs } (x_i, x_{n_1+j}) \text{ with } x_i < x_{n_1+j} \ (i = 1, \cdots, n_1;$$
$$j = 1, \cdots, n_2)],$$

and has

(1.6)

$$\phi(V) = 1 \quad \text{if} \quad V \geq V_\alpha$$
$$= 0 \quad\quad\quad < V_\alpha.$$

The number V_α is chosen to give the test size α and depends only on n_1 and n_2.

We see if the criterion is satisfied. If we increase any of the x_{n_1+j}, we can only increase the value of V; that is, only increase the value of ϕ. Now the value of the statistic V depends only on the permutation of the $n_1 + n_2$ numbers $x_{(1)}, \cdots, x_{(n_1+n_2)}$ which gives the numbers $x_1, \cdots, x_{n_1+n_2}$, and, when $F = G$, each permutation has the same probability $1/(n_1 + n_2)!$ Hence the distribution of V when $F = G$ does not depend on F, and the test is similar. Therefore, by Theorem 1.1 the Mann–Whitney test is unbiased for the problem (1.4) above.

By the argument following the theorem, it is easily seen that the Mann–Whitney test is an unbiased test of size α for the extended problem as given by (1.5).

For the two-sample scale problem (3.5) in Chapter 3 we have an analog of Theorem 1.1 above. Consider those tests based on the differences among the elements of the first sample and the differences among the elements of the second sample; that is, consider tests which can be written in the form

(1.7)　　$\phi(x_2 - x_1, \cdots, x_{n_1} - x_1; x_{n_1+2} - x_{n_1+1}, \cdots, x_{n_1+n_2} - x_{n_1+1}).$

Now, if an increase in the differences for the second sample results in at most an increase in ϕ, and if the test is similar for $F = G$, then the test is unbiased for the alternative of (3.5). There the second sample distribution was more spread out than the first sample distribution.

We now consider a procedure which is sometimes able to produce an unbiased test. For this, it is essential that we have repetitions of a component experiment; that is, a sample from a distribution over a component space. First, we try to find a real parameter which effectively distinguishes between the hypothesis and the alternative. Let θ be the parameter which indexes the probability measures in the problem, and let $\Delta(\theta)$ be a real parameter. We say that $\Delta(\theta)$ distinguishes between the hypothesis and the alternative if, on the basis of the value of $\Delta(\theta)$, we can say whether $\theta \in \omega$ (the hypothesis) or $\theta \in \Omega - \omega$ (the alternative). This would be the case if, for example, $\Delta(\theta) = \Delta_0$ when $\theta \in \omega$ and $\Delta(\theta) > \Delta_0$ when $\theta \in \Omega - \omega$. Second, we try to find an event for one, two, $\cdots$ repetitions of the component experiment which has as its probability of occurrence the real parameter $\Delta(\theta)$. This immediately restricts us to parameters $\Delta(\theta)$ which take their values in the interval $[0, 1]$. Then, depending on the number of such groups of repetitions that we can form in the over-all experiment, we can have that number of independent repetitions, on each of which we observe whether or not the event occurs. The problem can then be treated as one in terms of the binomial distribution. If $\Delta(\theta) = \Delta_0$ for the hypothesis and $\Delta(\theta) > \Delta_0$ for the alternative, there is certainly an unbiased test—it is the usual test based on the number of occurrences of the event. Also, if $\Delta(\theta) \neq \Delta_0$ corresponds to the alternative, a two-sided unbiased binomial test can be constructed. This procedure was developed by Lehmann in [1].

EXAMPLE 1.2.   Consider again the two-sample problem as given in Section 3.1 of Chapter 3.   Let $X_1, \cdots, X_{n_1}$ have a continuous distribution function $F(x)$ and $X_{n_1+1}, \cdots, X_{n_1+n_2}$ have a continuous distribution function $G(x)$.   We examine the general problem

(1.8)
$$\text{Hypothesis:}\quad F(x) = G(x),$$
$$\text{Alternative:}\quad F(x) \neq G(x).$$

As a real parameter which distinguishes between the hypothesis and alternative, consider

$$(1.9)\qquad \Delta(F, G) = \int_{-\infty}^{+\infty} [F(x) - G(x)]^2\, d\,\frac{F(x) + G(x)}{2},$$

the average squared difference with respect to the mean distribution function.   Obviously, for the hypothesis, $\Delta(F, F) = 0$.   By the following lemma we show that, for the alternative, $\Delta(F, G) > 0$.

LEMMA 1.1 $F(x) = G(x)$ if and only if

$$(1.10)\qquad \Delta(F, G) = \int_{-\infty}^{+\infty} (F - G)^2\, d\,\frac{F + G}{2} = 0.$$

Proof.   It is obvious that $F(x) = G(x)$ implies $\Delta(F, G) = 0$.   We therefore need only prove that $F(x) \not\equiv G(x)$ implies $\Delta(F, G) > 0$.   Let x_1 be such that $F(x_1) \neq G(x_1)$, and say $F(x_1) - G(x_1) = d > 0$.   But $F(-\infty) = G(-\infty) = 0$ and F, G are continuous; therefore there exists $x_0 < x_1$ such that $F(x_0) - G(x_0) = d/2$ and $F(x) - G(x) \geq d/2$ for $x_0 \leq x \leq x_1$.   Since neither $F(x)$ nor $G(x)$ can decrease, one of $F(x), G(x)$ must increase by at least $d/2$ when x goes from x_0 to x_1.   We have

$$\Delta(F, G) \geq \int_{x_0}^{x_1} (F - G)^2\, d\,\frac{F + G}{2}$$
$$\geq \left(\frac{d}{2}\right)^2 \frac{d/2}{2}$$
$$> 0.$$

This completes the proof.

From the lemma we have $\Delta(F, G) = 0, > 0$, according as (F, G) does or does not belong to the hypothesis. Δ is thus a real parameter which distinguishes between the hypothesis and alternative. We look for an event having Δ or a linear function of Δ as its probability.

Let X_1, X_2 be independent random variables with the distribution function $F(x)$, and let X_1', X_2' be independent random variables with the distribution function $G(x)$. For convenience we designate the relationship max $(x_1, x_2) <$ min (x_1', x_2') by $x_1, x_2 < x_1', x_2'$. Consider the event $X_1, X_2 < X_1', X_2'$ or $X_1', X_2' < X_1, X_2$. Designating its probability by p, we shall prove that

$$p = \Pr \{X_1, X_2 < X_1', X_2' \quad \text{or} \quad X_1', X_2' < X_1, X_2\}$$
$$= 1/3 + 2\Delta(F, G).$$

Noting for example that max (X_1, X_2) has distribution function $F^2(x)$ and remembering that F and G are continuous, we can write

$$p = \int (1 - G)^2 \, dF^2 + \int (1 - F)^2 \, dG^2$$

$$= 2 + \int (G^2 \, dF^2 + F^2 \, dG^2) - 2 \int G \, dF^2 - 2 \int F \, dG^2$$

$$= 2 + \int d(F^2 G^2) - 4 \int GF \, dF - 4 \int FG \, dG$$

$$= 3 - 4 \int GF \, d(F + G)$$

$$= 3 - 2 \int [(F + G)^2 - (F - G)^2] \, d\frac{F + G}{2}$$

$$= 3 - 8 \int \left(\frac{F + G}{2}\right)^2 d\frac{F + G}{2} + 2 \int (F - G)^2 \, d\frac{F + G}{2}$$

$$= 3 - 8/3 + 2\Delta(F, G)$$

$$= 1/3 + 2\Delta(F, G).$$

We thus have an event, $x_1, x_2 < x_1', x_2'$ or $x_1', x_2' < x_1, x_2$, based on two x's from the first sample and two x's from the second sample, and this event has probability $1/3 + 2\Delta(F, G)$, a parameter that distinguishes between the hypothesis and the alternative. This probability takes its minimum value $1/3$ for the hypothesis. Also, we are able to observe $m = \frac{1}{2} \min (n_1, n_2)$ independent repetitions, on each of which the event can or cannot occur.

Each repetition is formed from two x's from each sample.   Our problem is thus reduced to

$$\text{Hypothesis: } p = 1/3,$$

$$\text{Alternative: } p > 1/3,$$

for the binomial distribution with parameters m, p.   By Problem 26, in Chapter 1, the most powerful test is

$$\phi(y) = 1 \quad \text{if} \quad y > c$$

$$= a \qquad\qquad = c$$

$$= 0 \qquad\qquad < c,$$

where y is the number of occurrences of the event and a, c are chosen to give the test exact size α for the binomial distribution with parameters $m, 1/3$.   Since this binomial test is unbiased, we have obtained an unbiased test for the two-sample problem (1.8).

The test above has the satisfying property that its power is a strictly increasing function of p and hence of $\Delta(F, G)$ which is a measure of the difference between the distribution functions F, G.   However, from another point of view this test has a somewhat less satisfactory property.   We now discuss this.

We have expressed the problem in terms of the parameter $\Delta(F, G)$. Also, our test can be based on a statistic V, the proportion of times the pairwise inequality occurs:

$$V = \frac{2}{m} \left[\begin{array}{l} \text{number of pairs having } x_{2i}, x_{2i-1} < x_{n_1+2i}, x_{n_1+2i-1} \\ \text{or } x_{n_1+2i}, x_{n_1+2i-1} < x_{2i}, x_{2i-1} \quad (i = 1, \cdots, m) \end{array} \right]$$

From the properties of the binomial distribution, we have

$$E_{FG}\{V\} = \frac{1}{3} + 2\Delta(F, G);$$

thus the statistic V is an unbiased estimator of the parameter $1/3 + 2\Delta(F, G)$.   If we introduce a counter function $\psi(x_1, x_2; x_1', x_2')$ which records whether the pairwise inequality has occurred,

$$\psi(x_1, x_2; x_1', x_2') = 1 \quad \text{if} \quad x_1, x_2 < x_1', x_2' \quad \text{or} \quad x_1', x_2' < x_1, x_2$$

$$= 0 \qquad \text{otherwise,}$$

then the statistic V can be written

$$V = \frac{2}{m} \sum_{i=1}^{m} \psi(x_{2i}, x_{2i-1}; x_{n_1+2i}, x_{n_1+2i-1}).$$

It would seem that an improved test would be obtained if, instead of using the statistic V, we used the statistic having minimum variance among unbiased estimators of $1/3 + 2\Delta(F, G)$. By the technique used in Example 2.4 of Chapter 4, this better estimator will be a statistic V^* which is obtained from V by symmetrizing in the first sample x's and also in the second sample x's. We have

$$V^* = \frac{1}{\binom{n_1}{2}\binom{n_2}{2}} \sum_{i<i'} \sum_{j<j'} \psi(x_i, x_{i'} \; ; \; x_{n_1+j}, x_{n_1+j'});$$

V^* is the proportion of cases where a first sample pair is less than or greater than a second sample pair. The altered test would be to reject the hypothesis for large values of V^*:

$$\begin{aligned}
\phi'(V^*) &= 1 && \text{if} \quad V^* > c^* \\
&= a^* && \qquad = c^* \\
&= 0 && \qquad < c^*,
\end{aligned}$$

where a^*, c^* are chosen to give the test size α under the equal probability permutations of the hypothesis. Lehmann [1] has stated that this test is no longer unbiased. Nevertheless, the properties that V^* is of minimum variance and has a limiting normal distribution indicate that this is a good test for the two-sample problem (1.8).

2. MOST POWERFUL TESTS

2.1. Uniformly Most Powerful Tests. Even in parametric theory it is only the simplest problems that admit a uniformly most powerful test. In this section we consider one such nonparametric problem—the problem of location.

The problem of location was described in Section 2.2 of Chapter 3. Let $X_1, \cdots, X_n$ be independent and each have the same absolutely continuous distribution on the real line with density function $f_\theta(x)$; the problem is

(2.1)
$$\begin{aligned}
\text{Hypothesis:} & \quad \xi_p(f_\theta(x)) = \xi_0, \\
\text{Alternative:} & \quad \xi_p(f_\theta(x)) > \xi_0,
\end{aligned}$$

where $\xi_p(f_\theta(x))$ is the p percentile of the distribution as given by $f_\theta(x)$. For notational simplicity we assume $\xi_0 = 0$.

Let $f(x)$ be a typical density of the alternative. We write

(2.2)
$$f(x) = p^* f_-(x) + q^* f_+(x)$$

where $f_-(x), f_+(x)$ are positive only on the negative axis, the positive axis, respectively, and p^* is the probability to the left of the origin and q^* the probability to the right of the origin. (See Fig. 17.) Because of our choice of p^* and q^*, $f_-(x)$ and $f_+(x)$ will be density functions with probability only

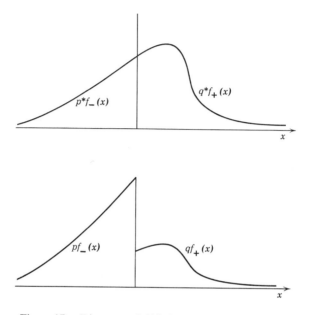

Figure 17.   Diagrams of $f(x)$ (top) and $f_0(x)$ (bottom).

on the negative and the positive axes, respectively. Since by assumption $\xi_p(f(x)) > 0$, if follows that $p^* \leq p$ and $q^* \geq q$ where $q = 1 - p$. If $p = p^*$, then $\xi_p(f(x)) = 0$, and $f(x)$ can be considered a density of the hypothesis. By assuming that $f(x)$ is strictly in the alternative, we obtain $p^* < p$. We now calculate the test that is most powerful for this density $f(x)$ of the alternative.

Following the method used in Section 3.3 of Chapter 2, we look for a hypothesis distribution which most resembles $f(x)$, which would be most difficult to test or distinguish from $f(x)$. Consider the density

(2.3) $$f_0(x) = p f_-(x) + q f_+(x).$$

Obviously $\xi_p(f_0(x)) = 0$, and $f_0(x)$ belongs to the hypothesis. Also, it resembles $f(x)$ in that the relative densities on the negative axis and on the positive axes are the same as for $f(x)$. For a sample of n, we find the most powerful test of the simple hypothesis that the density is $f_0(x)$ against the simple alternative that it is $f(x)$; applying the fundamental lemma, Theorem 3.1 in Chapter 2, we obtain

$$\phi(x_1, \cdots, x_n) = 1 \quad \text{if} \quad \frac{\prod\limits_{i=1}^{n} f(x_i)}{\prod\limits_{i=1}^{n} f_0(x_i)} > c$$

$$= a \qquad\qquad\qquad = c$$

$$= 0 \qquad\qquad\qquad < c.$$

Defining $i(x_1, \cdots, x_n)$ as the number of positive numbers $x_1, \cdots, x_n$, we can write the probability ratio

$$\frac{\prod\limits_{i=1}^{n} f(x_i)}{\prod\limits_{i=1}^{n} f_0(x_i)} = \frac{\prod\limits_{i=1}^{n} [p^* f_-(x_i) + q^* f_+(x_i)]}{\prod\limits_{i=1}^{n} [p f_-(x_i) + q f_+(x_i)]}$$

$$= \left(\frac{p^*}{p}\right)^{n - i(x_1, \cdots, x_n)} \left(\frac{q^*}{q}\right)^{i(x_1, \cdots, x_n)}$$

$$= \left(\frac{p q^*}{p^* q}\right)^{i(x_1, \cdots, x_n)} \left(\frac{p^*}{p}\right)^{n}.$$

Since $p q^*/p^* q$ is greater than 1, the probability ratio is a monotone-increasing function of $i(x_1, \cdots, x_n)$; hence the test function can be written

(2.4) $\qquad \phi(x_1, \cdots, x_n) = 1 \quad \text{if} \quad i(x_1, \cdots, x_n) > c$

$\qquad\qquad\qquad\qquad = a \qquad\qquad\qquad\qquad\qquad = c$

$\qquad\qquad\qquad\qquad = 0 \qquad\qquad\qquad\qquad\qquad < c,$

where a, c are chosen to give the test exact size α. Under the hypothesis the induced distribution of $i(x_1, \cdots, x_n)$ is binomial with parameters n, q; hence c is the α point from the right-hand tail of this distribution. This test is based on the signs of the x_i's and is usually referred to as the *sign test*.

The test is similar for the full hypothesis and hence is a size-α test. By the theory in Chapter 2 it is a most powerful test against $f(x)$. But the test does not depend on the form of $f(x)$. Therefore, it is a uniformly most powerful test for the problem (2.1). More generally, the sign test is based on the number of positive signs among $x_1 - \xi_0, \cdots, x_n - \xi_0$.

The sign test remains uniformly most powerful for the more general problem (2.5) in Chapter 3:

(2.5)
$$\text{Hypothesis:} \quad \xi_p(f_\theta(x)) \le \xi_0,$$
$$\text{Alternative:} \quad \xi_p(f_\theta(x)) > \xi_0.$$

The hypothesis has been enlarged; the alternative is the same. With respect to this enlarged hypothesis, the sign test is easily seen to remain of size α. For, given any one of the added distributions, it will have probability less than q to the right of the origin. Hence the probability for large values of $i(x_1, \cdots, x_n)$ is reduced; that is, the power function takes a value less than α. Then, by the theory of Section 3.3 in Chapter 2, the test remains uniformly most powerful for (2.5).

We mention another problem which has a uniformly most powerful test. Let $X_1, \cdots, X_n$ be independent and each have the same distribution on R^2 with density $f_\theta(x^{(1)}, x^{(2)})$; θ indexes the absolutely continuous distributions. Letting $G_\theta(z)$ stand for the induced distribution of $Z = X^{(2)} - X^{(1)}$, we consider briefly the problem

(2.6)
$$\text{Hypothesis:} \quad \xi_{0.5}(G_\theta) \le 0,$$
$$\text{Alternative:} \quad \xi_{0.5}(G_\theta) > 0.$$

This problem is concerned with the median of the random variable $Z = X^{(2)} - X^{(1)}$ where $X = (X^{(2)}, X^{(1)})$ has the density $f_\theta(x, y)$.

This problem could arise when two, say, treatments were applied to two "plots" in a block and a series of repetition of this basic experiment were made. The hypothesis and alternative (2.6) represent one attempt to describe treatment 2 being, respectively, no better and better than treatment 1.

By following the same methods, it is possible to show that the sign test based on the differences $x_1^{(2)} - x_1^{(1)}, \cdots, x_n^{(2)} - x_n^{(1)}$ is uniformly most powerful.

▶ For the problems above it is possible to find a generalized sufficient statistic as defined at the end of Section 5 in Chapter 1. For example, consider the first problem. We can represent any density function $f(x)$ by

(2.7)
$$f(x) = p_f f_-(x) + q_f f_+(x),$$

where p_f, q_f are, respectively, the probability to the left and the probability to the right of the origin, and $f_-(x), f_+(x)$ are the probability densities for the negative, the positive axes. Thus the density $f(x)$ can be equivalently described by three parameters $p_f, f_-(x), f_+(x)$. Also, by taking any $p_f, f_-(x), f_+(x)$ and combining them according to (2.7), a density for the problem will be obtained. Thus the parameter space is a product space of $[0, 1]$ for p_f, the space of densities on the negative axes, and the space of densities on the positive axes. It is straight-forward to show that $i(x_1, \cdots, x_n)$ is a sufficient statistic (p_f) for the problem. Then, since the hypothesis and alternative can be expressed in terms of the parameter p_f, we can apply Theorem 3.4 and obtain from the proof of that theorem the uniformly most powerful test—the sign test.

For the two-sided location parameter problem (2.6) in Chapter 3, a uniformly most powerful unbiased test exists. It is a sign test and is to reject for large or small values of the number of positive signs where the two critical values are chosen to make the test unbiased of the proper size. For the derivation see pages 59 and 60 in [2]. ◀

2.2. Most Powerful Tests for Simple Alternatives. Most of the hypothesis testing problems outlined in Chapter 3 are analogs of standard problems involving normal distributions. The nonparametric formulation may be preferred in cases where the statistician feels that the distributions are close to normality but where he wishes to protect himself by keeping the size of the test valid for the more general problem. In such a case it is reasonable to look among the nonparametric tests for ones that have maximum power for the alternatives which have an underlying normal distribution. In this section we consider a method of obtaining tests of maximum power for simple alternative hypotheses.

For most nonparametric problems we have no way of handling the full class of tests of a given size in order to find the test having maximum power. However, for some problems we can characterize rather simply those tests that are similar. We now discuss a technique outlined in Section 3.5 of Chapter 2.

Let the class of probability measures be $\{P_\theta \,|\, \theta \in \Omega\}$ over $\mathscr{X}(\mathscr{A})$ and the problem be

$$\text{Hypothesis:} \quad \theta \in \omega,$$

(2.8) $$\text{Alternative:} \quad \theta \in \Omega - \omega.$$

For this problem we consider a simple alternative:

(2.9) $$\text{Alternative*:} \quad \theta = \theta^*,$$

where $\theta^* \in \Omega - \omega$. If the problem possesses a statistic $t(x)$ which is both sufficient and boundedly complete for the measures of the hypothesis $\{P_\theta \,|\, \theta \in \omega\}$, then it is possible to describe simply the form of a similar size-α test. It must have conditional size α with respect to the statistic $t(x)$. That is, if $\phi(x)$ is a similar test of size α, then

(2.10) $$E_\omega\{\phi(X) \,|\, t(x) = t\} = \alpha$$

for almost all $(P_\theta^T \,|\, \theta \in \omega)$ values of t. The expectation has a subscript ω to indicate that the conditional measure is that of the hypothesis—there being only one because $t(x)$ was sufficient for $\theta \in \omega$. Thus, to examine similar tests of size α is to examine, for almost all $\{P_\theta^T \mid \theta \in \omega\}$ value of t, those tests that have size α in each of the subspaces of $\mathscr{X}$ given by $t(x) = t$. Of course, there is complete freedom of choice of test for values of t in any set having P_θ^T measure zero for each $\theta \in \omega$. Because $t(x)$ is a sufficient statistic, there is only one hypothesis distribution over each subspace, and hence in the subspace the hypothesis is simple. Thus, to find a most powerful similar test for $\theta = \theta^*$, we can apply the fundamental lemma to the simple hypothesis and alternative in each subspace. Of course, for values of t in a set having zero probability for each θ in the hypothesis but positive probability for $\theta = \theta^*$, we would choose $\phi(x) = 1$ to maximize the power. We summarize these ideas in the following theorem.

THEOREM 2.1. If $t(x)$ is sufficient and boundedly complete for the measures of the hypothesis, $\theta \in \omega$, then any similar test $\phi(x)$ of size α has for almost all $\{P_\theta^T \mid \theta \in \omega\}$ values of t conditional size α, given $t(x) = t$. The most powerful similar test against $\theta = \theta^*$ is obtained by finding for each t, the most powerful size-α test $\phi(x \mid t)$ of $P_\omega(A \mid t)$ against $P_{\theta^*}(A \mid t)$ but setting $\phi(x \mid t) = 1$ for t in the set B^* that has maximum $P_{\theta^*}^T$ probability, yet zero P_θ^T probability for $\theta \in \omega$.

Proof. Let $\mathscr{B}$ be the σ-algebra on the space of values of the statistic $t(x)$, and define $\mathscr{B}^*$ to consist of sets B for which

(2.11) $$P_{\theta^*}^T (B) > 0$$

and

$$P_\theta^T (B) = 0$$

for all $\theta \in \omega$. We first show there exists a $B \in \mathscr{B}^*$ for which (2.11) attains its supremum. In any case, we can find a B for which (2.11) is arbitrarily close to its supremum, and then we can add to it disjoint sets belonging to $\mathscr{B}^*$, each of which can be chosen to bring (2.11) more than halfway to its supremum. The result would be a monotone-increasing sequence of sets for which (2.11) approached its supremum. The limit set would also belong to $\mathscr{B}^*$ and have the limiting value for (2.11)—the supremum. Hence the B^* as required exists.

The remainder of the proof follows from Theorem 3.5 in Section 3.5, Chapter 2.

In a few nonparametric problems the method above gives a most powerful test without the restriction of similarity. For this we need the following extension of the concept of completeness.

A class of measures $\{P_\theta^T | \theta \in \omega\}$ is totally complete if

$$(2.12) \qquad\qquad E_\theta\{f(T)\} = \int_{\mathcal{T}} f(t)\, dP_\theta^T(t) \leq 0$$

for all $\theta \in \omega$, where $f(t)$ is a real-valued statistic, implies that $f(t) \leq 0$ almost everywhere $\{P_\theta^T\}$.

Frequently it will be convenient to say that a statistic is totally complete. When we do this it will be for a particular problem in which the statistic has a given class of measures, and we shall mean that the class of measures is totally complete. As with bounded completeness we have a theorem on the conditional size of tests, given a sufficient statistic which is totally complete.

THEOREM 2.2. If $t(x)$ is a sufficient and totally complete statistic for $\{P_\theta | \theta \in \omega\}$ over $\mathcal{X}(\mathcal{A})$, then a size-α test for $\theta \in \omega$ has for almost all $\{P_\theta^T | \theta \in \omega\}$ values of t conditional size α, given $t(x) = t$.

Proof. Let $\phi(x)$ be a size-α test. Then

$$E_\theta\{\phi(X)\} \leq \alpha$$

for $\theta \in \omega$. But this implies

$$E_\theta^T\{E_\omega\{\phi(X) | t(x) = T\} - \alpha\} \leq 0$$

for $\theta \in \omega$. Total completeness then gives

$$E_\omega\{\phi(X) | t(x) = t\} \leq \alpha$$

for almost all $\{P_\theta^T | \theta \in \omega\}$ values of t. This is the required result.

Thus, if we are interested in the size α-tests for the hypothesis, $\theta \in \omega$, and have a statistic sufficient and totally complete for $\theta \in \omega$, we can construct tests having conditional size α in each subspace, given $t(x) = t$. By the same type of argument used for Theorem 2.1, we obtain

THEOREM 2.3. If $t(x)$ is sufficient and totally complete for $\theta \in \omega$, then the most powerful size-α test against $\theta = \theta^*$ is obtained by finding for each t the most powerful size-α test $\phi(x | t)$ of $P_\omega(A | t)$ against $P_{\theta^*}(A | t)$ but setting $\phi(x \mid t) = 1$ for t in the set B^* having maximum $P_{\theta^*}^T$ probability, yet zero P_θ^T probability for $\theta \in \omega$.

In applying the above theory we need a statistic $t(x)$ for which the conditional distribution, given the statistic, is the same for all probability measures of the hypothesis. This is the requirement of sufficiency. The condition of total completeness would be satisfied if the induced distributions of the statistic $t(x)$ under the hypothesis were *all* probability distributions for the statistic. This is proved in the following theorem.

THEOREM 2.4. *If the class* $\{P_\theta^T | \theta \in \omega\}$ *is the class of all probability measures over* $\mathcal{T}(\mathcal{B})$, *then* $\{P_\theta^T | \theta \in \omega\}$ *is totally complete.*

Proof. Let $f(t)$ be a statistic over $\mathcal{T}(\mathcal{B})$ for which

$$(2.13) \qquad\qquad E_\theta\{f(T)\} \leq 0$$

for $\theta \in \omega$, and define B_+ by

$$(2.14) \qquad\qquad B_+ = \{t | f(t) > 0\}.$$

Let P_θ^T be any measure in $\{P_\theta^T | \theta \in \omega\}$, and assume that $P_\theta^T(B_+) > 0$. Then it is easily seen that the measure,

$$(2.15) \qquad\qquad \mu(B) = \frac{1}{P_\theta^T(B_+)} \int_B \phi_{B_+}(t) \, dP_\theta^T(t),$$

is a probability measure and hence also belongs to $\{P_\theta^T | \theta \in \omega\}$. $\phi_{B_+}(t)$ is the characteristic function of the set B_+.

But from (2.14) we have $f(t) > 0$, and this, together with our assumption that $P_\theta^T(B_+) > 0$, implies

$$(2.16) \qquad\qquad \int_{B_+} f(t) \, dP_\theta^T(t) > 0.$$

(2.13) and (2.16) provide a contradiction; hence our assumption was incorrect, and $P_\theta^T(B_+) = 0$. This means that the probability measure of $\{t | f(t) > 0\}$ is zero for all measures in $\{P_\theta^T | \theta \in \omega\}$ and therefore establishes total completeness.

▶   The following more general theorem can be proved in much the same way.

THEOREM 2.5. *If each measure in the class of probability measures* $\{P_\theta^T | \theta \in \omega\}$ *is dominated by a measure in* $\{\mu_\eta | \eta \in H\}$, *and if* $\{P_\theta^T | \theta \in \omega\}$ *contains at least the uniform distributions re each* μ_η *over the sets* B *of a basis* Bas $(\mathcal{B})$ *of* $\mathcal{B}$, *then* $\{P_\theta^T | \theta \in \omega\}$ *is totally complete.*

Note. For the definition of a basis see Section 7 of Chapter 1. By the uniform distribution over the set B^* re the measure μ_η we mean the probability measure

$$P_{B^*, \eta}(B) = \int_B \frac{\phi_{B^*}(t)}{\mu_\eta(B^*)} \, d\mu_\eta(t). \qquad ◀$$

EXAMPLE 2.1. THE TWO-SAMPLE PROBLEM. Let $X_1, \cdots, X_{n_1}$ be independent and each X_i have an absolutely continuous distribution over R^1 with density $f_{\theta_1}(x)$. Similarly let $X_{n_1+1}, \cdots, X_{n_1+n_2}$ be independent and each X_{n_1+j} have an absolutely continuous distribution over R^1 with density $f_{\theta_2}(x)$. $\theta \in \Omega$ indexes the density functions over R^1. Consider the problem of testing the

(2.17)   Hypothesis: $f_{\theta_1}(x) = f_{\theta_2}(x)$, $\theta_1 \in \Omega$,

against the simple

(2.18)   Alternative: $f_{\theta_1}(x) = \dfrac{1}{(2\pi)^{1/2}\sigma} \exp\left[-\dfrac{1}{2\sigma^2}(x - \mu_1)^2\right]$,

$$f_{\theta_2}(x) = \dfrac{1}{(2\pi)^{1/2}\sigma} \exp\left[-\dfrac{1}{2\sigma^2}(x - \mu_2)^2\right].$$

Without loss of generality, suppose $\mu_1 > \mu_2$.

Under the distributions of the hypothesis we have seen in Section 2 of Chapter 4 that the order statistic $t(\mathbf{x}) = \{x_1, \cdots, x_{n_1+n_2}\}$ is a sufficient statistic. By Theorems 7.1 and 6.1 in Chapter 1 we have that $t(\mathbf{x})$ is complete. Thus the assumptions of Theorem 2.1 are satisfied. We now consider the construction of a size-α test in a typical subspace $t(\mathbf{x}) = t$.

Under the hypothesis the conditional distribution of the outcome $(x_1, \cdots, x_{n_1+n_2})$, given $t(\mathbf{x})$, is equal probability $1/(n_1 + n_2)!$ to each permutation of the set of numbers in $t(\mathbf{x})$. The conditional distribution under the alternative can be derived in the same manner as the hypothesis conditional distribution was derived in Section 2 of Chapter 4. The result is that the probability to each permutation of the set of numbers in $t(\mathbf{x})$ is proportional to the values of the alternative density function at these points; that is, proportional to

$$p(\mathbf{x}) = \prod_{i=1}^{n_1} \frac{1}{(2\pi)^{1/2}\sigma} \exp\left[-\frac{1}{2\sigma^2}(x_i - \mu_1)^2\right] \prod_{j=1}^{n_2} \frac{1}{(2\pi)^{1/2}\sigma}$$

$$\times \exp\left[-\frac{1}{2\sigma^2}(x_{n_1+j} - \mu_2)^2\right].$$

We apply the fundamental lemma, Theorem 3.1, in Chapter 2, and obtain

$$\phi(\mathbf{x}) = 1 \quad \text{if} \quad \frac{p(\mathbf{x})}{1/(n_1 + n_2)!} > c$$

$$= a \qquad\qquad\qquad\quad = c$$

$$= 0 \qquad\qquad\qquad\quad < c.$$

Now, by remembering that there are at most $(n_1 + n_2)!$ points in the set, given $t(\mathbf{x})$, and that each of these points has the same set of coordinates which are just arrangements of the values in $t(\mathbf{x})$, we can see that, as a function of $\mathbf{x}$, given $t(\mathbf{x})$, each succeeding expression below is a monotone-increasing function of the previous expression.

$$\frac{p(\mathbf{x})}{1/(n_1 + n_2)!},$$

$$\exp\left[-\frac{1}{2\sigma^2}\sum_{i=1}^{n_1}(x_i - \mu_1)^2 - \frac{1}{2\sigma^2}\sum_{j=1}^{n_2}(x_{n_1+j} - \mu_2)^2\right],$$

$$-\sum_{i=1}^{n_1}(x_i - \mu_1)^2 - \sum_{j=1}^{n_2}(x_{n_1+j} - \mu_2)^2,$$

$$\mu_1\sum_{i=1}^{n_1}x_i + \mu_2\sum_{j=1}^{n_2}x_{n_1+j},$$

$$(\mu_1 - \mu_2)\sum_{i=1}^{n_1}x_i - \mu_2\sum_{k=1}^{n_1+n_2}x_k,$$

$$(\mu_1 - \mu_2)\sum_{i=1}^{n_1}x_i,$$

$$\sum_{i=1}^{n_1}x_i.$$

Thus the test function can be written

$$\phi(\mathbf{x}) = 1 \qquad \text{if} \quad \sum_{i=1}^{n_1}x_i > c$$
$$\qquad = a \qquad\qquad\qquad = c$$
$$\qquad = 0 \qquad\qquad\qquad < c,$$

where c, a are constants to be chosen to give the test size α. If we consider the test as being over R^n and not just in the subspace, given $t(\mathbf{x})$, then c, a will be functions of $t(\mathbf{x})$.

Using the alternative definition of the order statistic, $t'(\mathbf{x})=(x_{(1)}, \cdots, x_{(n_1+n_2)})$, we can describe quite simply how the choice of c and a is made. Under the hypothesis, the conditional distribution of $(x_1, \cdots, x_{n_1+n_2})$, given $(x_{(1)}, \cdots, x_{(n+n_2)})$, is equal probability to each permutation of $(x_{(1)}, \cdots, x_{(n_1+n_2)})$. For each such permutation we calculate $\sum_1^{n_1}x_i$. c is the largest number having a proportion less than α of permutations with

$\sum_{1}^{n_1} x_i > c.$ a is the probability of rejecting when $\sum_{1}^{n_1} x_i = c$ and is chosen

to bring the test up to exact size α.   By Theorem 2.1 this is the most powerful similar test against the simple alternative (2.18).   But the test does not
depend on σ^2, μ_1, μ_2 provided $\mu_1 > \mu_2$; therefore it is the similar test
uniformly most powerful against the normal

Alternative: $f_{\theta_1}(x) = \dfrac{1}{(2\pi)^{1/2}\sigma} \exp\left[-\dfrac{1}{2\sigma^2}(x - \mu_1)^2\right]$

$$\left(\begin{array}{c} \sigma^2 > 0 \\ \mu_1 > \mu_2 \end{array}\right).$$

$f_{\theta_2}(x) = \dfrac{1}{(2\pi)^{1/2}\sigma} \exp\left[-\dfrac{1}{2\sigma^2}(x - \mu_2)^2\right]$

For the two-sided normal alternative of common variance and means
μ_1, μ_2 with $\mu_1 \neq \mu_2$, the test that rejects for large values of the statistic

$\left| n_1^{-1} \sum_{1}^{n_1} x_i - n_2^{-1} \sum_{1}^{n_2} x_{n_1+j} \right|$ under permutations of the order statistic is a

most stringent similar test and has minimax risk with respect to any loss
function that depends on σ^2 and $\mu_1 - \mu_2$.   This is obtained by using
Theorems 3.9, 3.10, and 3.14 in Chapter 2.

The one- and two-sided tests described above can be exhibited in another
form.   Let $s(\mathbf{x})$ be the usual two-sample Student statistic for use when the
variances are assumed equal:

$$s(\mathbf{x}) = \frac{\bar{x} - \bar{x}'}{\left(\dfrac{1}{n_1} + \dfrac{1}{n_2}\right)^{1/2}\left[\dfrac{\displaystyle\sum_{1}^{n_1}(x_i - \bar{x})^2 + \displaystyle\sum_{1}^{n_2}(x_{n_1+j} - \bar{x}')^2}{n_1 + n_2 - 2}\right]},$$

where

$$\bar{x} = \frac{1}{n_1}\sum_{1}^{n_1} x_i,$$

$$\bar{x}' = \frac{1}{n_2}\sum_{1}^{n_2} x_{n_1+j}.$$

The tests are then to reject for large values, respectively, of $s(\mathbf{x})$ and of
$|s(\mathbf{x})|$ under the $(n_1 + n_2)!$ permutations of the coordinates of the order

statistic $t(\mathbf{x})$.   For this it is straightforward to show that $s(\mathbf{x})$ is a monotone-increasing function of $n_1^{-1} \sum_1^{n_1} x_i - n_2^{-1} \sum_1^{n_2} x_{n_1+j}$ for given $t(\mathbf{x}) = t$.

These two tests are usually referred to as the one- and two-sided Pitman tests.   The one-sided Pitman test is considered in Problem 1 in the previous section.

EXAMPLE 2.2.   PROBLEM OF INDEPENDENCE (2.4) IN CHAPTER 3.   Let $X_1, \cdots, X_n$ be independent and each have the same distribution function $F_\theta(x^{(1)}, x^{(2)})$, where θ indexes the absolutely continuous distributions on R^2.   Consider the independence

(2.19)   Hypothesis: $F_\theta(x^{(1)}, x^{(2)}) = F_\theta^{(1)} (x^{(1)}) F_\theta^{(2)} (x^{(2)})$,

against the simple

(2.20)   Alternative: $F_\theta(x^{(1)}, x^{(2)})$ is a bivariate normal with parameters

$$\mu_1, \mu_2, \sigma_1, \sigma_2, \rho.$$

Under the hypothesis there is a sample of n from $F_\theta^{(1)}$ and an independent sample of n from $F_\theta^{(2)}$.   By Example 2.4 in Chapter 4 we have the complete and sufficient statistic $t(\mathbf{x}) = (x_{(1)}^{(1)}, \cdots, x_{(n)}^{(1)}; x_{(1)}^{(2)}, \cdots, x_{(n)}^{(2)})$ which is just the combination of the order statistics for the two samples.   We construct a most powerful test in the subspace, given this statistic $t(\mathbf{x})$.

The fundamental lemma gives a test based on the probability ratio:

$$c \exp\left[-\frac{1}{2(1-\rho^2)}\left\{\frac{\Sigma (x_i^{(1)} - \mu_1)^2}{\sigma_1^2} - 2\rho \frac{\Sigma (x_i^{(1)} - \mu_1)(x_i^{(2)} - \mu_2)}{\sigma_1 \sigma_2} + \frac{\Sigma (x_i^{(2)} - \mu_2)^2}{\sigma_2^2}\right\}\right] \Big/ 1/(n!)^2 .$$

It is easily shown that, for given $t(\mathbf{x})$, each succeeding expression below is a monotone-increasing function of the previous expression:

$$-\frac{1}{2(1-\rho^2)}\left[\frac{\Sigma(x_i^{(1)} - \mu_1)^2}{\sigma_1^2} - 2\rho \frac{\Sigma(x_i^{(1)} - \mu_1)(x_i^{(2)} - \mu_2)}{\sigma_1 \sigma_2} + \frac{\Sigma(x_i^{(2)} - \mu_2)^2}{\sigma_2^2}\right],$$

$$\operatorname{sign} \rho \cdot \Sigma (x_i^{(1)} - \mu_1)(x_i^{(2)} - \mu_2),$$

$$\operatorname{sign} \rho \cdot \Sigma x_i^{(1)} x_i^{(2)},$$

$$\operatorname{sign} \rho \cdot \Sigma (x_i^{(1)} - \bar{x}^{(1)})(x_i^{(2)} - \bar{x}^{(2)}),$$

$$\operatorname{sign} \rho \cdot \frac{\Sigma (x_i^{(1)} - \bar{x}^{(1)})(x_i^{(2)} - \bar{x}^{(2)})}{[\Sigma (x_i^{(1)} - \bar{x}^{(1)})^2 \, \Sigma (x_j^{(2)} - \bar{x}_j^{(2)})^2]^{1/2}},$$

$$\operatorname{sign} \rho \cdot r.$$

r is the usual correlation statistic between $\mathbf{x}^{(1)}$ and $\mathbf{x}^{(2)}$. When $\rho > 0$, the test function can be written

$$\phi(\mathbf{x}) = 1 \quad \text{if} \quad \Sigma\, (x_i^{(1)} - \bar{x}^{(1)})(x_i^{(2)} - \bar{x}^{(2)}) > c$$

$$= a \qquad\qquad\qquad\qquad = c$$

$$= 0 \qquad\qquad\qquad\qquad < c.$$

The constants $c = c(t(x))$, $a = a(t(x))$ are chosen to give the test size α under the $n!$ equally likely pairings of $x^{(1)}$ values with $x^{(2)}$ values. This test does not depend on σ_1, σ_2 or ρ when $\rho > 0$; it is most powerful similar for the hypothesis of independence against the composite normal

(2.21)   Alternative: $F_\theta(x^{(1)}, x^{(2)})$ is the normal bivariate distribution with variances σ_1^2, σ_2^2, and correlation ρ; σ_1^2, $\sigma_2^2 \in \,]0, \infty[$, $\rho \in \,]0, 1[$.

The test can also be based on the statistic r, the sample correlation coefficient.

For the two-sided normal alternative with $\rho \neq 0$, the conditional test, given $t(\mathbf{x})$, which rejects for large values of $|\Sigma(x_i^{(1)} - \bar{x}^{(1)})(x_i^{(2)} - \bar{x}^{(2)})|$ or of $|r|$ is most stringent similar.

EXAMPLE 2.3. The one-sided location problem. We consider the general linear hypothesis formulation (4.7) in Chapter 3 as it applies to the one-sided location problem. Let $\mathbf{X} = (X_1, \cdots, X_n)$ have a distribution over R^n with density $f_\theta(x_1, \cdots, x_n)$; θ, belonging to Ω, indexes the absolutely continuous distribution over R^n. We consider the problem of testing the

Hypothesis: $f_\theta(x_1, \cdots, x_n) = h_\theta(x_1^2 + \cdots + x_n^2)$, $\theta \in \Omega$,

against the simple

Alternative: $X_1, \cdots, X_n$ are independent, and each is normal with mean $\mu > 0$ and variance σ^2.

The statistic $t(\mathbf{x}) = \sum_1^{n_1} x_i^2$ is sufficient under the hypothesis. For it can be easily shown that the conditional probability measure over the sphere $\sum_1^n x_i^2 = t$ is the uniform probability measure; that is, the measure of a set is proportioned to the 'area' of the set on the sphere. Also, under the hypothesis the statistic, $t(\mathbf{x})$ has an arbitrary absolutely continuous distribution. This can be seen by noting that an arbitrary absolutely continuous distribution for $t(\mathbf{x})$ combined with the uniform probability measure over the sphere $t(x) = t$ will produce a probability measure of our hypothesis. Then, by Theorem 2.4 in this section, $t(\mathbf{x})$ is totally complete.

Now, applying Theorem 2.3 in this section, we find the most powerful test by finding the most powerful test in each subspace $t(\mathbf{x}) = t$. The test obtained from the fundamental lemma is based on the following probability ratio:

$$\frac{c' \exp\left[-\frac{1}{2\sigma^2}\Sigma(x_i - \mu)^2\right]}{c''}.$$

But, given the value of the statistic $t(\mathbf{x}) = \Sigma x_i^2$, each succeeding expression below is a monotone-increasing function of the previous expression:

$$\frac{c' \exp\left[-\frac{1}{2\sigma^2}\Sigma(x_i - \mu)^2\right]}{c''},$$

$$-\frac{1}{2\sigma^2}\Sigma(x_i - \mu)^2,$$

$$\Sigma x_i \mu,$$

$$\Sigma x_i,$$

$$\bar{x},$$

$$\frac{n^{1/2}\bar{x}}{\left[\frac{1}{n-1}\Sigma(x_i - \bar{x})^2\right]^{1/2}}.$$

If we designate this last expression by $s(\mathbf{x})$, we find the conditional test to be

$$\phi(\mathbf{x}) = 1 \quad \text{if} \quad s(\mathbf{x}) > c$$
$$= a \qquad \qquad = c$$
$$= 0 \qquad \qquad < c.$$

But, under the hypothesis, the conditional distribution of $s(\mathbf{x})$ does not depend on the particular subspace $t(\mathbf{x}) = t$ and is in fact the Student distribution with $n - 1$ degrees of freedom. If we let s_α be the value exceeded with probability α according to this Student distribution, our test becomes

$$\phi(\mathbf{x}) = 1 \quad \text{if} \quad s(\mathbf{x}) > s_\alpha$$
$$= 0 \qquad \qquad < s_\alpha.$$

In this case the constant s_α obtained from the fundamental lemma does not depend on the statistic $t(\mathbf{x})$. This t test is the most powerful size-α test against the normal alternative with $\mu > 0$.

As in Example 2.1, we obtain that the most stringent test against the normal alternative $\mu \neq 0$ is the two-sided t test.

If we add to the assumptions of the hypothesis that the X_i's are independent, then it follows from probability theory that the X_i's are identically distributed according to a *normal distribution*. This is the 'parametric' location problem as given in normal theory. Example 3.5 in Chapter 2 applied the theory we have summarized in Theorem 2.1 to prove that the one-sided t test above was most powerful similar for that parametric problem.

3. MOST POWERFUL RANK TESTS. AN APPLICATION OF THE INVARIANCE METHOD

3.1. Introduction. Invariance theory for hypothesis testing was introduced in Section 3.7 of Chapter 2. We summarize briefly the ideas involved. Suppose there are transformations which can be applied to the outcome and which produce a transformed random variable having as its probability measures the given measures of the problem. If, in addition, the transform of a random variable always has its measure in the hypothesis or alternative, according as the random variable itself represents the hypothesis or alternative, then the transformations leave the hypothesis testing problem unchanged. The invariance principle then requires that attention be restricted to those test functions that are invariant under any of the transformations. In Section 3.2 we shall consider the application of the invariance method to nonparametric problems, treating in detail the problem of randomness. For a number of nonparametric problems the invariant tests are the tests based on ranks. In Section 3.3 we shall consider the use of ranks for a general type of nonparametric problem and discuss how to obtain rank tests most powerful for simple and composite alternatives.

3.2. The Invariance Method for Randomness and Other Problems. We consider the invariance method for the problem of randomness and indicate its application to the problem of independence.

Let $X_1, \cdots, X_n$ be independent, and let X_i have a distribution on R^1 with a continuous distribution function $F_{\theta_i}(x)$ where $\theta_i \in \Omega$ indexes the class of continuous distribution functions on the real line. The general problem of randomness is given by

Hypothesis: $\theta_1 = \cdots = \theta_n$,

Alternative: Not all θ_i equal; $\theta_1, \cdots, \theta_n \in \Omega$.

The special forms of the problem of randomness are obtained by substituting more restrictive alternatives.

We first define a class $\mathscr{G}$ of transformations of the real line into itself. As a typical transformation consider sx, a strictly increasing continuous function. Since s is strictly increasing, the inverse function s^{-1} is at most single valued, and since, in addition, s is continuous, s^{-1} is defined everywhere. Then it follows easily that s^{-1} is strictly increasing and continuous. Similarly, if s_1 and s_2 belong to $\mathscr{G}$, the product transformation $s_1 s_2$ is easily shown to be strictly increasing and continuous. The closure of $\mathscr{G}$ under multiplication and inverse then implies that $\mathscr{G}$ is a group.

If X is a random variable with the continuous distribution function F_θ, then the random variable sX has a distribution function, say $F_{\bar{s}\theta}$, given by the relation

$$
\begin{aligned}
F_{\bar{s}\theta}(x) &= \Pr_\theta \{sX \leq x\} \\
&= \Pr_\theta \{X \leq s^{-1}x\} \\
&= F_\theta(s^{-1}x).
\end{aligned}
$$
(3.1)

Now, since F_θ and s^{-1} are continuous, it follows that $F_\theta(s^{-1}x)$ is a continuous function of x. Hence, if $\theta \in \Omega$ and $s \in \mathscr{G}$, then $\bar{s}\theta \in \mathscr{G}$.

We now define for the problem of randomness a class $\mathscr{G}_n$ of transformations on the sample space R^n. A typical transformation $\mathbf{s}$ in $\mathscr{G}_n$ is given by

$$
\mathbf{s}(x_1, \cdots, x_n) = (sx_1, \cdots, sx_n),
$$
(3.2)

where s is a transformation in $\mathscr{G}$. $\mathbf{s}$ applies the same transformation s to each coordinate of the outcome. Obviously the class $\mathscr{G}_n$ is a group.

We now show that the transformations in $\mathscr{G}_n$ leave the problem of randomness unchanged. If we designate by $\bar{\mathbf{s}}$ the transformation on the parameter space Ω^n corresponding to the transformation $\mathbf{s}$ on R^n, then we have

$$
\bar{\mathbf{s}}(\theta_1, \cdots, \theta_n) = (\bar{s}\theta_1, \cdots, \bar{s}\theta_n).
$$
(3.3)

If $(\theta_1, \cdots, \theta_n)$ belongs to the hypothesis, then $\theta_1 = \cdots = \theta_n$. Then, for $\bar{\mathbf{s}}(\theta_1, \cdots, \theta_n)$, we have $\bar{s}\theta_1 = \cdots = \bar{s}\theta_n$, and hence $\bar{\mathbf{s}}(\theta_1, \cdots, \theta_n)$ also belongs to the hypothesis. Also, if $(\theta_1, \cdots, \theta_n)$ belongs to the alternative, then, for some $i, j, \theta_i \neq \theta_j$. Of course we use different θ's to designate different distribution functions; hence $F_{\theta_i}(x) \neq F_{\theta_j}(x)$ for some x. This immediately implies that $\bar{s}\theta_i \neq \bar{s}\theta_j$, and hence that $\bar{\mathbf{s}}(\theta_1, \cdots, \theta_n)$ belongs to the alternative.

Following the theory in Chapter 2, we now find the maximal invariant partition of the sample space R^n. This is simplified if we exclude from the sample space a set S having probability measure zero for all the probability measures of the problem:

$$
S = \{(x_1, \cdots, x_n) \mid x_i = x_j \text{ for some } i, j \text{ with } i \neq j\}.
$$
(3.4)

Obviously there is a transformation in $\mathscr{G}_n$ which transforms the point $(x_1, \cdots, x_n)$ into the point $(x'_1, \cdots, x'_n)$, provided the relative order of the magnitudes of the coordinates is the same, that is provided that, if $x_{i_1} < \cdots < x_{i_n}$, then $x'_{i_1} < \cdots < x'_{i_n}$. Alternatively, any transformation in $\mathscr{G}_n$ preserves the relative ordering among the coordinates. Therefore, the maximal invariant partition of $R^n - S$ divides it into $n!$ regions, each of which has a given relative ordering among the coordinates. A simple maximal invariant function is the set $r(\mathbf{x})$ of ranks of the coordinates:

$$(3.5) \qquad\qquad r(\mathbf{x}) = (r_1, \cdots, r_n),$$

where $(r_1, \cdots, r_n)$ is a permutation of $(1, \cdots, n)$, the same permutation that $(x_1, \cdots, x_n)$ is of $(x_{(1)}, \cdots, x_{(n)})$. It is easily seen that r_i is the number of coordinates smaller than or equal the coordinate x_i.

The natural thing to consider next is the maximal invariant partition on the parameter space. The real purpose of the maximal invariant partition is to define sets over which the distribution of any invariant statistic is constant. Therefore, instead of constructing the maximal sets, we define larger sets which are invariant but not maximal invariant. These sets have the property that the distribution of any invariant statistic remains constant within any set. However, these sets do not define a partition since they can overlap without being identical. For convenience we define the sets over the space of distribution functions corresponding to Ω^n. Consider the sets

$$(3.6) \qquad\qquad \{h_1(F_\theta(x)), \cdots, h_n(F_\theta(x)) \mid \theta \in \Omega\},$$

where the h_i are monotone-increasing continuous functions defined on $[0, 1]$.

First, any 'point' $(F_{\theta_1}(x), \cdots, F_{\theta_n}(x))$, belongs to one of these sets. For let $F_\theta(x)$ be any strictly increasing distribution function with $\theta \in \Omega$, and define

$$h_i(u) = F_{\theta_i}(F_\theta^{-1}(u)).$$

Then obviously

$$h_i(F_\theta(x)) = F_{\theta_i}(x),$$

and the point belongs to (3.6) with the above definition of the h_i. Second, the sets are invariant under any transformation $\bar{s}$. For, under this transformation, the transform of

$$(h_1(F_\theta), \cdots, h_n(F_\theta))$$

is

$$(h_1(F_\theta s^{-1}), \cdots, h_n(F_\theta s^{-1})),$$

and, since $F_\theta s^{-1}$ is a continuous distribution function, these points are in the same set.

THEOREM 3.1. Any invariant (rank) test for the problem of randomness has a power function which is constant-valued within any set $\{(h_1 F_\theta, \cdots, h_n F_\theta) \mid \theta \in \Omega\}$. For the hypothesis $\{(F_\theta, \cdots, F_\theta) \mid \theta \in \Omega\}$ against the alternative $\{(h_1^* F_\theta, \cdots, h_n^* F_\theta) \mid \theta \in \Omega\}$ with given $h_1^*, \cdots, h_n^*$, there is a most powerful invariant test.

Proof. We prove that the distribution of the maximal invariant statistic is constant within any set of the form (3.6). The two statements of the theorem then follow immediately. For this proof let s designate a typical strictly increasing transformation on the real line. Because of the strict monotonicity, the inverse function is at most single-valued, and its range may be extended to the entire real line by requiring that s^{-1} be nondecreasing. This insures that s^{-1} is always a continuous function. Hence, if X has a continuous distribution function $F_\theta(x)$, then the distribution function of sX, $F_\theta(s^{-1}x)$, is also continuous. Let $\bar{s}\theta$ be such that $F_{\bar{s}\theta}(x) = F_\theta(s^{-1}x)$.

If $F_{\theta_1}(x)$ and $F_{\theta_2}(x)$ are any continuous distribution functions, we now prove that there exist strictly increasing transformations s_1 and s_2 and a strictly increasing distribution function $F_\theta(x)$ such that $\theta_1 = \bar{s}_1\theta$ and $\theta_2 = \bar{s}_2\theta$. Let $F_\theta(x)$ be any strictly increasing distribution function. From the proof of Theorem 1.1 in this chapter we see that there exists a nondecreasing transformation s_1 such that, when X has distribution function $F_\theta(x)$, $s_1 X$ has distribution function $F_{\theta_1}(x)$. Then, since $F_{\theta_1}(x) = F_\theta(s^{-1}x)$, the strict monotonicity of F_θ and the continuity of $F_{\theta_1}(x)$ imply that s^{-1} is continuous, and hence s_1 is strictly increasing. s_2 can be similarly defined.

The rank function $r(\mathbf{x})$ is obviously invariant under any strictly increasing transformation s. We now show that the distribution of $r(\mathbf{x})$ is constant over each set (3.6). Let $(h_1 F_{\theta_1}, \cdots, h_n F_{\theta_1})$ and $(h_1 F_{\theta_2}, \cdots, h_n F_{\theta_2})$ be two points in a set (3.6), and let s_1, s_2, F_θ be defined as in the paragraph above. Then

$$\Pr\{r(\mathbf{X}) \in A \mid (h_1 F_{\theta_1}, \cdots, h_n F_{\theta_1})\} = \Pr\{r(\mathbf{s}_1 \mathbf{X}) \in A \mid (h_1 F_\theta, \cdots, h_n F_\theta)\}$$

$$= \Pr\{r(\mathbf{s}_2 \mathbf{X}) \in A \mid (h_1 F_\theta, \cdots, h_n F_\theta)\}$$

$$= \Pr\{r(\mathbf{X}) \in A \mid (h_1 F_{\theta_2}, \cdots, h_n F_{\theta_2})\}.$$

This proves the theorem.

We now consider briefly the problem of independence. Let $(X_1^{(1)}, X_1^{(2)}), \cdots, (X_n^{(1)}, X_n^{(2)})$ be independent, and let each $(X_i^{(1)}, X_i^{(2)})$ have the same continuous distribution function $F_\eta(x_i^{(1)}, x_i^{(2)})$ where $\eta \in \Omega^*$

indexes the continuous distribution functions on R^2. The problem of independence is given by

$$\text{Hypothesis:} \quad F_\eta(x^{(1)}, x^{(2)}) = F_\eta{}^{(1)}(x^{(1)})F_\eta{}^{(2)}(x^{(2)})$$
$$\text{for all } x^{(1)}, x^{(2)}; \quad \eta \in \Omega^*,$$

(3.7) $$\text{Alternative:} \quad F_\eta(x^{(1)}, x(^{(2)})) \neq F_\eta^{(1)}(x^{(1)})F_\eta^{(2)}(x^{(2)})$$
$$\text{for some } x^{(1)}, x^{(2)}; \quad \eta \in \Omega^*.$$

As a typical transformation of the outcome $(x_1^{(1)}, x_1^{(2)}; \cdots; x_n^{(1)}, x_n^{(2)})$, consider applying to each $x_i^{(1)}$ a transformation s belonging to the group $\mathscr{G}$ defined earlier and to each $x_i^{(2)}$ a transformation s' also belonging to $\mathscr{G}$. It is easily seen that such transformations leave the problem unchanged. The maximal invariant function for this class of transformations is the combination of the set of ranks for the $x_i^{(1)}$, say

$$r(\mathbf{x}^{(1)}) = (r_1^{(1)}, \cdots, r_n^{(1)}),$$

and the set of ranks for the $x_i^{(2)}$, say

$$r(\mathbf{x}^{(2)}) = (r_1^{(2)}, \cdots, r_n^{(2)}).$$

Let $h(u^{(1)}, u^{(2)})$ be any continuous distribution function defined over the unit square, $0 \leq u^{(1)}, u^{(2)} \leq 1$. We now define sets of distribution functions over R^2. As a typical set consider

(3.8) $$\{h(F_\theta(x^{(1)}), F_\theta(x^{(2)})) \big| \theta \in \Omega\},$$

where $\theta \in \Omega$ indexes the continuous distribution functions on R^1. Then we have

THEOREM 3.2.   Any rank test based on $(r(\mathbf{x}^{(1)}), r(\mathbf{x}^{(2)}))$ for the problem of independence has a power function which is constant-valued within each set (3.8). There is a most powerful rank test against the alternative $\{h^*(F_\theta(x^{(1)}), F_\theta(x^{(2)})) \big| \theta \in \Omega\}$ for given h^*.

Proof.   Similar to that for Theorem 3.1.

3.3 Most Powerful Rank Tests.   In Section 3.2 we showed how the invariance method reduced two general types of nonparametric problems to a consideration of tests based on ranks. Rank tests, however, have other properties which make them desirable, regardless of whether or not they have for any particular problem the justification of invariance. For example the consideration of rank tests has a certain mathematical simplicity in that, for the problem given in terms of the ranks, the sample space is finite. Also, rank tests are frequently easy to apply, and for many problems tables are available. In this section we consider a general type of problem for which rank tests can be applied and show how to obtain rank tests most powerful for a simple alternative.

Consider the sample space $\mathscr{X} = R^N$ with outcome

$$\mathbf{x} = (x_{11}, \cdots, x_{1n_1}; \cdots; x_{b1}, \cdots, x_{bn_b}),$$

where $N = \sum_1^b n_i$. Let $\mathbf{X}$ designate a random variable over R^N with

probability measure $P_\theta^\mathbf{X}$, $\theta \in \Omega$. We assume that, for each θ, the probability measure of the set S of diagonal points is zero:

$$S = \{\mathbf{x} \,|\, \text{for some } i, \quad x_{ij} = x_{ij'} \quad \text{for some } j \neq j'\}.$$

Thus we can in effect ignore the set S and use as our sample space $R^N - S$.

Assume that, for each $\theta \in \omega$, the probability measure $P_\theta^\mathbf{X}$ is invariant under any permutation of the coordinates $x_{i1}, \cdots, x_{in_i}$ for each i. Then consider the hypothesis testing problem

(3.9)

$$\text{Hypothesis:} \quad \theta \in \omega,$$

$$\text{Alternative:} \quad \theta \in \Omega - \omega,$$

and in particular the problem of obtaining a test which has maximum power for a simple

(3.10)   Alternative: $\theta = \theta^*$.

We are, of course, interested only in alternatives θ^* for which the probability measure $P_{\theta^*}^\mathbf{X}$ is not invariant under all the permutations mentioned above.

Consider the set of ranks

(3.11) $\mathbf{r}(\mathbf{x}) = (r(x_{11}, \cdots, x_{1n_1}); \cdots; r(x_{b1}, \cdots, x_{bn_b})).$

This set comprises the ranks for $x_{11}, \cdots, x_{1n_1}$ (a permutation of $1, \cdots, n_1$), the ranks for $x_{21}, \cdots, x_{2n_2}$ (a permutation of $1, \cdots, n_2$), and so on. Problem 14 is to construct a class of transformations and a parameter space Ω such that $\mathbf{r}(\mathbf{x})$ is a maximal invariant function. Because of the symmetry of the measures in the hypothesis (3.9) and the asymmetry of the alternative (3.10) and because of the inherent simplicity of ranks, we feel that the restriction to tests based on ranks has considerable merit.

Consider now the problem of obtaining a size-α rank test most powerful for the simple alternative (3.10). Under the hypothesis the probability measure is symmetric under the permutations within each group of coordinates $(x_{i1}, \cdots, x_{in_i})$. Thus the outcomes $\mathbf{x}$ producing any value of the statistic $\mathbf{r}(\mathbf{x})$ can be obtained from the outcomes producing any other value of $\mathbf{r}(\mathbf{x})$ by the permutations of the above form. Hence, each value of $\mathbf{r}(\mathbf{x})$ has the same probability, and this probability must therefore be

$$\frac{1}{n_1! \cdots n_b!}.$$

We have that, *under the hypothesis, the induced distribution of* $\mathbf{r(x)}$ *does not depend on* θ *and is equal probability to each of the* $n_1! \cdots n_b!$ *possibilities.* Under the simple alternative, there is of course a single induced distribution for the statistic $\mathbf{r(x)}$. Now, with a simple hypothesis and a simple alternative for the problem expressed in terms of $\mathbf{r(x)}$, we can apply the fundamental lemma of Chapter 2 and find the most powerful rank test. Since the density function under the hypothesis has a constant value, the most powerful test has the form

$$\phi(\mathbf{r}) = 1 \qquad \text{if} \quad P_{\theta*}^{\mathbf{R}}(\mathbf{r}) > c$$

$$= a \qquad\qquad\qquad = c$$

$$= 0 \qquad\qquad\qquad < c,$$

where $P_\theta^{\mathbf{R}}$ is the probability measure for $\mathbf{r(x)}$ induced from $P_\theta^{\mathbf{X}}$ over R^N. To conclude the theory in this section, we derive a theorem which can assist in the calculation of the probability distribution $P_{\theta*}^{\mathbf{R}}$ under the alternative θ^*.

Suppose that the alternative probability measure $P_{\theta*}^{\mathbf{R}}$ is absolutely continuous with respect to Lebesgue measure and has density function $f^*(\mathbf{x})$. Also suppose that under the hypothesis there is a probability measure $P_\theta^{\mathbf{R}}$ which has a density function $f(\mathbf{x})$ greater than 0 whenever $f^*(\mathbf{x})$ is greater than zero. Because of the symmetry of the hypothesis measures, we can always choose the density $f(\mathbf{x})$ to be symmetric under the permutations within blocks as defined above. We define an order statistic $\mathbf{x}^0$ for the outcome $\mathbf{x}$ considered in blocks,

$$\mathbf{x}^0 = (x_{1(1)}, \cdots, x_{1(n_1)}; \cdots, x_{b(1)}, \cdots, x_{b(n_b)})$$

where, for example, $(x_{1(1)}, \cdots, x_{1(n_1)})$ is the set $(x_{11}, \cdots, x_{1n_1})$ arranged in order of magnitude $x_{1(1)} < \cdots < x_{1(n_1)}$. By the same argument that produced the distribution of the order statistic for the uniform distribution (see Section 3 of Chapter 4), we obtain the probability density function for $\mathbf{x}^0$ as induced from the hypothesis density $f(\mathbf{x})$; it is

$$n_1! \cdots n_b! f(\mathbf{x}),$$

over the set $I = \{\mathbf{x} \,|\, x_{11} < \cdots < x_{1n_1}; \cdots; x_{b1} < \cdots < x_{bn_b}\}$ in R^N and zero elsewhere.

Designate by $\mathbf{r}'$ the operation that produces the permutations $\mathbf{r} = (r_{11}, \cdots, r_{1n_1}; \cdots; r_{b1}, \cdots, r_{bn_b})$ from $(1, \cdots, n_1; \cdots; 1, \cdots, n_b)$. Then let $\mathbf{x_{r'}}$ designate the vector obtained by applying the operation $\mathbf{r}'$ to the coordinates of **x**. Also let S_r designate the points **x** in R^N for which the rank statistic **r(x)** takes the value **r**. Then we have

$$\text{Pr}_{\theta*}^{\mathbf{X}}\{\mathbf{r}(\mathbf{X}) = \mathbf{r}\}$$

$$= \int_{S\mathbf{r}} f^*(\mathbf{x})\, d(\mathbf{x})$$

$$= \int_I f^*(\mathbf{x}_{r'})\, d\mathbf{x}$$

$$= \int_I \frac{f^*(\mathbf{x}_{r'})}{f(\mathbf{x}_{r'})} f(\mathbf{x}_{r'})\, d\mathbf{x}$$

$$= \frac{1}{n_1! \cdots n_b!} \int_I \frac{f^*(\mathbf{x}_{r'})}{f(\mathbf{x}_{r'})}\, n_1! \cdots n_b!\, f(\mathbf{x})\, d\mathbf{x}$$

$$= \frac{1}{n_1! \cdots n_b!}\, E_\theta^{\mathbf{X}}\left\{\frac{f^*(\mathbf{X}_{r'}^0)}{f(\mathbf{X}_{r'}^0)}\right\}.$$

Thus under the alternative the probability that the rank statistic takes the value **r** is a constant times the expectation under the hypothesis of a certain function of the order statistic—the function being the ratio of alternative to hypothesis density as calculated for the permutation **r**′ of the vector **x**. This proves the next theorem.

THEOREM 3.3 (HOEFFDING).   If $f(\mathbf{x})$ and $f^*(\mathbf{x})$ are probability densities of the hypothesis and alternative re Lebesgue measure and if $f(\mathbf{x}) > 0$ whenever $f^*(\mathbf{x}) > 0$, then the probability measure for the rank statistic under the alternative is given by

$$(3.12) \qquad n_1! \cdots n_b!\, \text{Pr}_{\theta*}\{\mathbf{r}(\mathbf{X}) = \mathbf{r}\} = E_\theta^{\mathbf{X}}\left\{\frac{f^*(\mathbf{X}_{r'}^0)}{f(\mathbf{X}_{r'}^0)}\right\}$$

where r' is the permutation of $(1, \cdots, n_1; \cdots; 1, \cdots, n_b)$ which produces **r** and is applied to the coordinates of the order statistic $\mathbf{X}^0$ to obtain the $\mathbf{X}_{r'}^0$ which occurs in the expectation.

EXAMPLE 3.1.   As a particular case of the problem of randomness we consider the two-sample problem.   Let $X_1, \cdots, X_{n_1}, X_{n_1+1}, \cdots, X_{n_1+n_2}$ be independent, each X_i ($i = 1, \cdots, n_1$) have a continuous distribution function $F_{\theta_1}(x)$, and each X_{n_1+j} ($j = 1, \cdots, n_2$) have a continuous distribution function $F_{\theta_2}(x)$, where θ_1, θ_2 ($\in \Omega$) index the continuous distributions on R^1.

Following the invariance method as applied to the randomness problem in Section 3.2, we restrict our attention to the tests based on the rank statistic $r(\mathbf{x}) = (r_1, \cdots, r_{n_1+n_2})$.   For the problem in terms of the induced distributions of $r(\mathbf{x})$ we have a sufficient statistic.   The distribution of the x's in the 'first sample' is symmetric.   From this it follows that the induced distribution of the ranks for the 'first sample' is also symmetric; that is, given any *set* of ranks for the first sample, the relative ordering within the sample is equal probability to each permutation of the elements of the set. Similarly for the second sample.   Hence a sufficient statistic is

$$\{r_1, \cdots, r_{n_1}\}, \quad \{r_{n_1+1}, \cdots, r_{n_1+n_2}\}.$$

But to know the set of ranks in the first sample is to know by elimination the ranks in the second sample, and conversely.   Hence either set by itself forms a sufficient statistic, and for later convenience we choose the second set.   Our sufficient statistic for the rank problem is

$$t'(\mathbf{r}) = \{r_{n_1+1}, \cdots, r_{n_1+n_2}\},$$

or more conveniently the ordered ranks

(3.13) $$t(\mathbf{r}) = (s_1, \cdots, s_{n_2}),$$

where $s_1, \cdots, s_{n_2}$ are the integers $r_{n_1+1}, \cdots, r_{n_1+n_2}$ arranged in order of magnitude $s_1 < \cdots < s_{n_2}$.   By Theorem 3.2, Chapter 2, we can confine our attention to tests based on the statistic $t(\mathbf{r})$.

We now consider the invariant sets of distribution functions (3.6), as defined for Theorem 3.1.   Since just two distribution functions $F_{\theta_1}(x)$, $F_{\theta_2}(x)$ completely specify a probability measure for the problem, we can simplify the description of a typical set (3.6).   Consider the set of pairs $(F_{\theta_1}(x), F_{\theta_2}(x))$ as given by

$$\{[h_1(F_\theta(x)), h_2(F_\theta(x))] \mid \theta \in \Omega\};$$

the two distribution functions in a pair refer, respectively, to the first and second samples.   It is straightforward to show that the sets having h_1 strictly increasing can be represented by

(3.14) $$\{(F_\theta, h(F_\theta)) \mid \theta \in \Omega\}.$$

We now consider the probability measure for $(s_1, \cdots, s_{n_2})$ corresponding to the distributions given by (3.14).   Assuming that F_θ and $h(F_\theta)$ are absolutely continuous with density functions, $f(x)$ and $f^*(x)$, we have

$$\frac{f^*(x)}{f(x)} = \frac{\dfrac{d}{dx} h(F_\theta(x))}{\dfrac{d}{dx} F_\theta(x)}$$

$$= h'(F_\theta(x)),$$

where

$$h'(u) = \frac{d}{du} h(u).$$

Then designating by $(S_1, \cdots, S_{n_2})$ the random variables with the induced distribution of $t(\mathbf{r}) = (s_1, \cdots, s_{n_2})$ and applying Hoeffding's Theorem 3.3, we obtain

$$\Pr_{F_\theta h(F_\theta)}\{S_1 = s_1, \cdots, S_{n_2} = s_{n_2}\}$$

$$= \frac{n_1! n_2!}{(n_1 + n_2)!} \, E_{F_\theta F_\theta} \, \{h'(F_\theta(X_{(s_1)})) \cdots h'(F_\theta(X_{(s_{n_2})}))\}.$$

The factor $n_1! n_2!$ takes account of the $n_1! n_2!$ different values of the rank statistic $(r_1, \cdots, r_{n_1+n_2})$ which produce a given *set* of ranks for the second sample $(s_1, \cdots, s_{n_2})$, and $X_{(s_1)}$, for example, is the s_1st order statistic in the set $X_1, \cdots, X_{n_1+n_2}$. Now, when X has the continuous distribution function $F_\theta(x)$, then $F_\theta(X)$ has the uniform distribution; therefore

$$(3.15) \qquad \Pr_{F_\theta h(F_\theta)} \{S_1 = s_1, \cdots, S_{n_2} = s_{n_2}\}$$

$$= \frac{1}{\binom{n_1 + n_2}{n_2}} \, E\{h'(U_{(s_1)}) \cdots h'(U_{(s_{n_2})})\},$$

where $(U_{(1)}, \cdots, U_{(n_1+n_2)})$ is the order statistic for a sample of $n_1 + n_2$ from the uniform distribution.

We now consider a simple function $h(u)$ and evaluate the probability measure of the ranks $s_1, \cdots, s_{n_2}$. Letting $h(u) = u^k$, we have the

$$(3.16) \qquad \text{Alternative:} \quad (F_1, F_2) \in \{(F_\theta, F_\theta^k) \mid \theta \in \Omega, \text{ fixed } k\}.$$

For this alternative a random variable in the second sample has the distribution function $F_\theta^k(x)$. If k is a positive integer, such a random variable is equivalent to the largest of k random variables having the distribution function F_θ associated with the first sample.

$$\Pr_{F_\theta^k} \{X \le x\} = F_\theta^k$$

$$= [\Pr_{F_\theta} \{X \le x\}]^k$$

$$= \Pr_{F_\theta} \{ \max_{i=1}^k X_i \le x\}.$$

The class of distributions in the alternative (3.16) corresponds to a mathematically simple example of the class (3.14) and has the easily visualized interpretation of a second sample value being equivalent to the largest of k from the first sample distribution.

For the alternative (3.16) with $h(u) = u^k$ we have $h'(u) = ku^{k-1}$. Then, substituting in (3.15), we obtain

$$\Pr_{F,F^k}\{S_1 = s_1, \cdots, S_{n_2} = s_{n_2}\}$$

(3.17)

$$= \frac{k^{n_2}}{\dbinom{n_1 + n_2}{n_1}} E\{[U_{(s_1)} \cdots U_{(s_{n_2})}]^{k-1}\}.$$

To evaluate this we need the joint distribution of $(U_{(s_1)}, \cdots, U_{(s_{n_2})})$. For a single order statistic $U_{(r)}$, this was obtained in formula (3.5) in Chapter 4. For two order statistics, see Problem 5, Chapter 4. In a similar manner it can be shown that the joint density function for $(U_{(s_1)}, \cdots, U_{(s_{n_2})})$ is equal to

(3.18)

$$\frac{\Gamma(n_1 + n_2 + 1)}{\prod\limits_{i=0}^{n_2} \Gamma(s_{i+1} - s_i)} \prod\limits_{j=0}^{n_2} (u_{j+1} - u_j)^{s_{j+1} - s_j - 1}$$

over the region $0 = u_0 \leq u_1 \cdots \leq u_{n_2+1} = 1$, where for convenience we define $s_0 = 0$, $s_{n_2+1} = n_1 + n_2 + 1$ and $u_0 = 0$, $u_{n_2+1} = 1$, and where we associate u_j with $U_{(s_j)}$. Now, making the change of variable

$$u_j = v_j v_{j+1} \cdots v_{n_2} \qquad (j = 1, \cdots, n_2),$$

and noting that the Jacobian has the value $v_1^0 v_2^1 \cdots v_{n_2}^{n_2-1}$, we obtain the joint density of the v's,

$$\frac{\Gamma(n_1 + n_2 + 1)}{\prod\limits_{j=0}^{n_2} \Gamma(s_{j+1} - s_j)} \prod\limits_{j=1}^{n_2} (1 - v_j)^{s_{j+1} - s_j - 1} \prod\limits_{j=0}^{n_2-1} (v_{j+1} \cdots v_{n_2})^{s_{j+1} - s_j - 1} (v_2^1 \cdots v_{n_2}^{n_2-1})$$

(3.19)

$$= \frac{\Gamma(n_1 + n_2 + 1)}{\prod\limits_{j=0}^{n_2} \Gamma(s_{j+1} - s_j)} \prod\limits_{j=1}^{n_2} (1 - v_j)^{s_{j+1} - s_j - 1} \prod\limits_{j=1}^{n_2} v_j^{s_j - 1}$$

$$= \prod\limits_{j=1}^{n_2} \frac{\Gamma(s_{j+1})}{\Gamma(s_j)\Gamma(s_{j+1} - s_j)} v_j^{s_j - 1} (1 - v_j)^{s_{j+1} - s_j - 1},$$

over the region $0 \leq v_j \leq 1$ $(j = 1, \cdots, n_2)$, where again for convenience we let $v_0 = 0$ and $v_{n_2+1} = 1$. From the factoring of the density function over the product set it is seen that $V_1, \cdots, V_{n_2}$ are independent and V_j has the β distribution with parameters $s_j, s_{j+1} - s_j$.

Now, since $u_1 \cdots u_{n_2} = v_1 v_2^2 \cdots v_{n_2}^{n_2}$, our formula (3.17) becomes

$$\Pr{}_{FF^k} \{S_1 = s_1, \cdots, S_{n_2} = s_{n_2}\}$$

(3.20)
$$= \frac{k^{n_2}}{\binom{n_1 + n_2}{n_2}} \prod_{j=1}^{n_2} E\{V_j^{j(k-1)}\}$$

$$= \frac{k^{n_2}}{\binom{n_1 + n_2}{n_1}} \prod_{j=1}^{n_2} \frac{\Gamma(s_j + jk - j)}{\Gamma(s_j)} \frac{\Gamma(s_{j+1})}{\Gamma(s_{j+1} + jk - j)}$$

This last step is obtained by noting that the rth moment of the β distribution with parameters p, q is

$$\frac{\Gamma(p + r)}{\Gamma(p)} \cdot \frac{\Gamma(p + q)}{\Gamma(p + q + r)} .$$

In the particular case when $k = 2$, formula (3.20) becomes

(3.21) $\Pr{}_{FF^2} \{S_1 = s_1, \cdots, S_{n_2} = s_{n_2}\}$

$$= \frac{2^{n_2}}{\binom{n_1 + n_2}{n_2}} \prod_{j=1}^{n_2} \frac{(s_j + j - 1) \cdots (s_j + 1)s_j}{(s_{j+1} + j - 1) \cdots (s_{j+1} + 1)s_{j+1}}$$

$$= \frac{2^{n_2}}{\binom{n_1 + n_2}{n_2}} \frac{s_1(s_2 + 1) \cdots (s_{n_2} + n_2 - 1)}{(n_1 + n_2 + 1)(n_1 + n_2 + 2) \cdots (n_1 + 2n_2)} .$$

These formulas, (3.20), (3.21), can be used to calculate the power of any rank test against the alternative given by (3.16). We use them now, however, in conjunction with Theorem 3.1 to obtain most powerful rank tests. Against the alternative (3.16) with $k = 2$, we order the values of the statistic $(s_1, \cdots, s_{n_2})$ according to their probability under the alternative and obtain the most powerful test

$\phi(s_1, \cdots, s_{n_2}) = 1$ if $s_1(s_2 + 1) \cdots (s_{n_2} + n_2 - 1) > c$

$\qquad\qquad\quad = a$ $= c$

$\qquad\qquad\quad = 0$ $< c,$

where a, c are chosen to give the test proper size.

We consider another alternative in which the function $h(u)$ takes the form

(3.22) $h_p(u) = qu + pu^2,$

where $0 < p \le 1$ and $p + q = 1$. We give an interpretation to this second sample distribution function, $qF + pF^2$. A random variable from this distribution is equivalent to a random variable chosen with probability q from the distribution F and p from the distribution F^2. We now show that the familiar one-sided Mann–Whitney test is the rank test maximizing the power when p is very close to zero, a *locally most powerful* test for the alternative (3.22).

Let $\mathbf{P}_\theta(p)$ designate the power function of a test ϕ against alternative (3.22). We wish to find the size-α test that maximizes $\mathbf{P}'_\theta(0)$, the slope of the power function at $p = 0$. From (3.15) we obtain

$$
(3.23) \quad
\begin{aligned}
&\frac{d}{dp} \Pr_{F h_p(F)} \{S_1 = s_1, \cdots, S_{n_2} = s_{n_2}\}\big|_{p=0} \\
&= \frac{1}{\binom{n_1 + n_2}{n_2}} E\left\{\frac{d}{dp} h'(U_{(s_1)}) \cdots h'(U_{(s_{n_2})})\right\}\bigg|_{p=0}
\end{aligned}
$$

Since $h'(u) = q + 2pu = 1 + p(2u - 1)$, (3.23) becomes

$$
\frac{1}{\binom{n_1 + n_2}{n_2}} E\left\{\sum_{j=1}^{n_2} (2U_{(s_j)} - 1)\right\}
$$

$$
= \frac{1}{\binom{n_1 + n_2}{n_2}} \left[\frac{2}{n_1 + n_2 + 1} \sum_{j=1}^{n_2} s_j - n_2\right].
$$

We wish to maximize $\mathbf{P}'_\phi(0)$; that is, to maximize the 'power' when calculated using the 'measure' given by (3.23). Noting that (3.23) is a strictly increasing function of $\sum_1^{n_2} s_j$ and applying the fundamental lemma of Chapter 2, we obtain the test

$$
\begin{aligned}
\phi(s_1, \cdots, s_{n_2}) &= 1 && \text{if } \sum_1^n s_j > c \\
&= a && = c \\
&= 0 && < c,
\end{aligned}
$$

where a, c are chosen to give the test size α. This is the one-sided Mann–Whitney test. However, when we introduced the test in Example 1.1 in Section 1 we based it on a statistic V. Problem 15 in Section 7 is to show that $\sum_1^{n_2} s_j$ is a strictly increasing function of V (actually a linear relationship). Thus the two definitions of the test are equivalent.

EXAMPLE 3.2.   We consider again the two-sample problem, but in this example we find a rank test most powerful against an alternative involving normal distributions.   Using the normal distribution having density function,

$$(3.24) \quad \frac{1}{(2\pi\sigma^2)^{\frac{n_1 + n_2}{2}}} \exp\left[-\frac{1}{2\sigma^2} \sum_{i=1}^{n_1} (x_i - \mu_1)^2 - \frac{1}{2\sigma^2} \sum_{j=1}^{n_2} (x_{n_1+j} - \mu_2)^2\right]$$

we consider the

(3.25)   Alternative: $\mu_2 > \mu_1$; $\mu_1, \mu_2 \in R^1$, $\sigma^2 \in \,]0, \infty[$.

Unfortunately there does not exist a rank test uniformly most powerful for this alternative.   However, the most powerful test for the alternative specifying μ_1, μ_2, σ^2 is found to depend only on the ratio $(\mu_2 - \mu_1)/\sigma$. Also, when the ratio is small, the test takes a particularly simple form and is called the c_1 test.   The c_1 test is the *locally most powerful* test against a one-sided normal alternative.

We now use Theorem 3.3 and the reductions made in the previous example to find the probability distribution of the rank statistic.   As hypothesis and alternative densities $f(x)$, $f^*(x)$, consider (3.24) with $\mu_2 = \mu_1$ and $\mu_2 = \mu_1 + \delta$, respectively.   Then we have

$$\frac{f^*(x)}{f(x)} = \exp\left[-\frac{1}{2\sigma^2} \sum_{j=1}^{n_2} (x_{n_1+j} - \mu_1 - \delta)^2 + \frac{1}{2\sigma^2} \sum_{j=1}^{n_2} (x_{n_1+j} - \mu_1)^2\right]$$

$$= \exp\left[\frac{1}{\sigma^2} \delta \sum_{j=1}^{n_2} x_{n_1+j} - \frac{n_2}{2\sigma^2} (2\mu_1 + \delta) \delta\right]$$

$$= \exp\left[-\frac{n_2}{2\sigma^2} (2\mu_1 + \delta) \delta\right] \sum_{\gamma=0}^{\infty} \frac{\left(\sum_1^{n_2} x_{n_1+j}\right)^\gamma \left(\frac{\delta}{\sigma^2}\right)^\gamma}{\gamma!}$$

We now apply Theorem 3.3 somewhat in the form of (3.15) and find that, under the alternative $u_2 - u_1 = \delta$,

$$(3.26) \quad \Pr_{*ff} \{S_1 = s_1, \cdots, S_{n_2} = s_{n_2}\}$$

$$= kE\left\{\sum_{\gamma=0}^{\infty} \left[\sum_1^{n_2} X_{(s_j)} \frac{\delta}{\sigma^2}\right] \frac{1}{\gamma!}\right\}$$

$$= k\left\{1 + c_1(s) \frac{\delta}{\sigma^2} + \cdots + c_\gamma(s) \left(\frac{\delta}{\sigma^2}\right)^\gamma \frac{1}{\gamma!} + 0(\delta^{\gamma+1})\right\},$$

where k is a positive constant re the s's,

$$c_\gamma(s) = E_{ff}\left\{\left[\sum_{j=1}^{n_2} X_{(s_j)}\right]^\gamma\right\},$$

and $(X_{(1)}, \cdots, X_{(n_1+n_2)})$ is the order-statistic random variable with its hypothesis distribution. The second step above is valid since the expression has continuous derivatives re δ of any order, and the conditions for differentiating under the sign of integration are fulfilled.

To find a most powerful test we order the possible values of $(s_1, \cdots, s_{n_2})$ by the alternative probability (3.26). However, this probability has an unwieldy form unless δ is small. By choosing δ sufficiently small we can order by the first term in (3.26) rather than by the whole expression (only a finite number of values for $(s_1, \cdots, s_{n_2})$. Thus for δ sufficiently small the most powerful rank test is given by

$$
\begin{aligned}
\phi(s_1, \cdots, s_{n_2}) &= 1 && \text{if} \quad c_1(\mathbf{s}) > c \\
&= a && \qquad\qquad = c \\
&= 0 && \qquad\qquad < c,
\end{aligned}
$$

where a, c are chosen to give the test size α. The statistic $c_1(\mathbf{s})$ can be evaluated:

$$
\begin{aligned}
c_1(\mathbf{s}) &= E\left\{\sum_{j=1}^{n_2} X_{(s_j)}\right\} \\
&= \sum_{j=1}^{n_2} E(X_{(s_j)}) \\
&= k_1^2 \sum_{j=1}^{n_2} E\{Z_{(s_j)}\} + k_2,
\end{aligned}
$$

where $(Z_{(1)}, \cdots, Z_{(n_1+n_2)})$ is the order-statistic random variable for the normal distribution with mean 0 and variance 1, and k_1, k_2 are constants re the s's. The statistic $c_1(\mathbf{s})$ is a monotone-increasing function of $\sum_1^{n_2} E\{Z_{(s_j)}\}$; therefore the test can be written

$$
\begin{aligned}
\phi(s_1, \cdots, s_{n_2}) &= 1 && \text{if} \quad \sum_{j=1}^{n_2} E\{Z_{(s_j)}\} > c \\
&= a && \qquad\qquad\qquad = c \\
&= 0 && \qquad\qquad\qquad < c.
\end{aligned}
$$

It is a uniformly most powerful test against one-sided normal alternatives having $(u_2 - u_1)/\delta$ small and positive. The method of applying the test is to replace each component of the order statistic $(x_{(1)}, \cdots, x_{(n_1+n_2)})$ that falls in the second sample by the expected value of the corresponding component of the order statistic for the unit normal and to reject if the sum of such values for the second sample is large. This test, derived by Terry [10], was proposed originally by Fisher and Yates in [11].

4. THE LIKELIHOOD-RATIO METHOD

The likelihood-ratio method was one of the earliest contributions to the theory of hypothesis testing; it was introduced by Neayman and E. S. Pearson in 1928. We outline briefly the method. Assume that the probability measures can be represented by a class of density functions $\{f_\theta(x)\,|\,\theta \in \Omega\}$ with respect to a fixed measure $\mu(A)$ over $\mathscr{X}(\mathscr{A})$. For the problem,

Hypothesis: $\theta \in \omega$,

Alternative: $\theta \in \Omega - \omega$,

the likelihood-ratio rest is given by

$$\phi(x) = 1 \quad \text{if} \quad L(x) > c$$
$$= a \qquad\qquad = c$$
$$= 0 \qquad\qquad < c,$$

where $L(x)$, called the likelihood ratio, is defined by

(4.1)
$$L(x) = \frac{\sup\limits_{\theta \in \Omega} f_\theta(x)}{\sup\limits_{\theta \in \omega} f_\theta(x)}.$$

In their original paper Neyman and Pearson used the reciprocal of $L(x)$ and considered only nonrandomized tests. In the case of a simple hypothesis and simple alternative the likelihood-ratio method usually produces the most powerful test. For consider the likelihood statistics:

$$L(x) = \frac{\max\{f_{\theta_0}(x), f_{\theta_1}(x)\}}{f_{\theta_0}(x)}$$
$$= \max\left\{1, \frac{f_{\theta_1}(x)}{f_{\theta_0}(x)}\right\}.$$

For large values of the likelihood ratio $L(x)$, there is a strictly increasing relationship (actuality equality) with the probability-ratio statistic, $f_{\theta_1}(x)/f_{\theta_0}(x)$, upon which the most powerful test is based. For other than this simple case, the success of the likelihood ratio in producing a good test is usually due to the fact that the likelihood test is always a function of a sufficient statistic for the problem; this fact follows from the factorization of the density as proved by the Halmos and Savage Theorem 5.2 in Chapter 1. The main justification for the method still remains its past success in producing workable tests often with good properties. However, an example has been given by Stein [13] where the likelihood-ratio test does *worse* than the simple randomized test which rejects with probability

α, regardless of the outcome. In the special case where the outcome is a sample of n from a distribution over a component space, the likelihood-ratio test has been shown to have asymptotically good properties as $n \to \infty$.

For the nonparametric problems of Chapter 3, a direct application of the likelihood-ratio method fails; both the numerator and the denominator equal infinity, and the statistic is indeterminate. If the sample space is R^n, one modification of the method would be to consider for each point $\mathbf{x}$ the ratio

$$(4.2) \qquad L^*(x) = \frac{\sup\limits_{\theta \in \Omega} P_\theta(C(\mathbf{x}))}{\sup\limits_{\theta \in \omega} P_\theta(C(\mathbf{x}))},$$

where $C(\mathbf{x})$ is a rectangular region with faces parallel to the coordinate planes and centered on the point $\mathbf{x}$. Unfortunately, this statistic, although determined, is usually equal to a constant. Problem 21 is to illustrate this. Another modification was proposed by Wolfowitz [7]. For the problems of randomness and independence he suggested that the invariance principle be used to reduce the problem to a consideration of rank tests and that then the likelihood-ratio method be used for the problem in terms of ranks. We illustrate his method for the two-sample problem.

Consider the two-sample problem, using the notation of Example 3.1 in the previous section. For the problem in terms of ranks we have the sufficient statistic, $t(\mathbf{r}) = (s_1, \cdots, s_{n_2})$, which is the ordered set of ranks for the x_i's falling in the second sample. To apply the Wolfowitz likelihood-ratio method, another statistic equivalent to $t(\mathbf{r})$ is more convenient. To define it, consider the order statistic for the combined samples: $(x_{(1)}, \cdots, x_{(n_1+n_2)})$. Replace each element of $(x_{(1)}, \cdots, x_{(n_1+n_2)})$ by a 1 or a 2, according as the element is equal to an x in the first sample or an x in the second sample. Let the statistic be

$$t^*(\mathbf{r}) = (v_1, \cdots, v_{n_1+n_2}),$$

where each v_i is either a 1 or a 2. Then clearly to know the ranks of the *set* of x's producing the second sample is equivalent to knowing which of the ordered sequence of x's came from the first sample and which from the second sample. We use the statistic $t^*(\mathbf{r})$.

The likelihood ratio for the problem in terms of ranks is

$$(4.3) \qquad \begin{aligned} L(t^*) &= \frac{\sup\limits_{\theta \in \Omega} \Pr_\theta \{t^*(\mathbf{r}(X)) = t^*\}}{\sup\limits_{\theta \in \omega} \Pr_\theta \{t^*(\mathbf{r}(X)) = t^*\}} \\ &= \binom{n_1 + n_2}{n_1} \sup\limits_{\theta \in \Omega} \Pr_\theta \{t^*(\mathbf{r}(X)) = t^*\}. \end{aligned}$$

To evaluate the supremum in this expression seems in general to be far too difficult. Wolfowitz therefore suggests an approximation. For each value of t^*, Wolfowitz replaces the full class of probability measures by a parametric class which depends on t^* and seems natural to the purpose of maximizing

$$\text{Pr}_\theta \{t^*(\mathbf{r}(\mathbf{X})) = t^*\}.$$

For the sequence $t^* = (v_1, \cdots, v_{n_1+n_2})$, let l_{ij} be the length of the jth run of 1's and let l_{2j} be the length of the jth run of 2's. Then if, for example,

Figure 18.   The relative position of the first and second sample x's when $n_1 = 4$, $n_2 = 3$, and $t^* = (1, 1, 2, 1, 2, 2, 1)$.

$t^* = (1, 1, 2, 1, 2, 2, 1)$, as is illustrated in Fig. 18, then $l_{11} = 2$, $l_{12} = 1$, $l_{13} = 1$ corresponding to the 1 runs, 11, 1, 1, and $l_{21} = 1$, $l_{22} = 2$ corresponding to the 2 runs, 2, 22. We now define a probability distribution for the first sample with parameters $p_{11}, p_{12}, \cdots$, and a probability distribution for the second sample with parameters $p_{21}, p_{22}, \cdots$. Take a set of x's

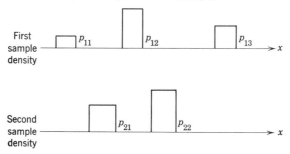

Figure 19.   Typical density functions for the first sample (parameters p_{11}, p_{12}, p_{13}) and for the second sample (parameters p_{21}, p_{22}).

which give rise to the chosen value of $t^*(\mathbf{r}(\mathbf{x}))$. Let the first probability distribution have probability p_{1j} over an interval containing the jth run of first-sample x's (for the $j_1 = 1, 2, \cdots$, which correspond to positive values of $l_{11}, l_{12}, \cdots$), and similarly for the second distribution using second-sample x's. The first- and second-sample intervals are chosen so that they do not overlap. (See Fig. 19.)

Now, to obtain $t^*(\mathbf{r}) = t^*$ for samples of n_1 and n_2 from these probability distributions, it is easily seen that the first- and second-sample x's must occur exactly in the pattern of the x's above for which the two parametric distributions were defined. Then we have

$$(4.4) \quad \Pr_{\{p_{ij}\}} \{t^*(\mathbf{r}(\mathbf{X})) = t^*\} = \frac{n_1!}{\prod_j l_{1j}!} \prod_j p_{1j}^{l_{1j}} \frac{n_2!}{\prod_{j'} l_{2j'}!} \prod_{j'} p_{2j'}^{l_{2j'}}$$

It is straightforward for fixed l_{ij} to maximize this expression as a function of p_{ij} subject to the restrictions $\sum_j p_{1j} = 1$, $\sum_j p_{2j} = 1$, and $p_{ij} \geq 0$ for all i, j. In fact, we have two multinomial distributions and the 'estimates',

$$\hat{p}_{1j} = \frac{l_{1j}}{n_1}, \qquad \hat{p}_{2j} = \frac{l_{2j}}{n_2},$$

are such as to maximize (4.4). The maximized value is then, of course,

$$\sup_{\{p_{ij}\}} \Pr_{\{p_{ij}\}} \{t^*(\mathbf{r}(\mathbf{X})) = t^*\} = \frac{n_1!}{\prod_j l_{1j}!} \frac{n_2!}{\prod_j l_{2j}!} \prod_j \left(\frac{l_{1j}}{n_1}\right)^{l_{1j}} \prod_{j'} \left(\frac{l_{2j'}}{n_2}\right)^{l_{2j'}}.$$

This is the statistic upon which Wolfowitz based his 'modified' likelihood-ratio test. An equivalent statistic is

$$T^* = \prod_j \frac{l_{1j}^{l_{1j}}}{l_{1j}!} \prod_{j'} \frac{l_{2j'}^{l_{2j'}}}{l_{2j'}!}$$

or, taking logarithms, the statistic

$$T = \sum_{i,j} \bar{l}_{ij},$$

where $\bar{l}_{ij}$ is defined by

$$\bar{l} = \ln \frac{l^l}{l!}$$

$$= l \ln l - \ln l!.$$

The Wolfowitz two sample test is then given by

$$\phi(\mathbf{r}) = 1 \quad \text{if} \quad \sum_{i,j} \bar{l}_{ij} > c$$
$$= a \qquad \qquad = c$$
$$= 0 \qquad \qquad < c.$$

5. DISCONTINUITIES

The theory developed in the earlier sections of this chapter has been concerned primarily with continuous and absolutely continuous distributions. However, in any application the numerical measurements are not free to take any value on the real line but must take values in a finite or countable set determined by the number of decimal places to which the numbers are recorded. Thus our models are only approximations to the correct models which are based on discrete distributions. Although in most cases we hope this approximation is quite good, we can no longer overlook the possibility that some of the measurements are equal. Most of the tests discussed earlier remain valid; that is, of the correct size. However, for the rank tests the problem arises of how to assign the ranks when there are 'ties'. One procedure is to use the average of the ranks that would have been assigned had there been no ties. An alternative† procedure is to randomly assign with equal probability the ranks that correspond to a set of tied measurements. If the hypothesis specifies symmetry, so that, in the continuous case, each permutation of the set of ranks has the same probability, then obviously, in the case of discrete probabilities, with an equal probability assignment of ranks in the case of ties, the different permutations of the set of ranks have equal probability under the hypothesis. Theorem 5.1 shows for the two-sample problem that properties of size and unbiasedness for rank tests derived under continuity assumptions remain valid when the continuity assumptions are dropped and tied ranks are assigned randomly.

For the theorem we assume that $X_1, \cdots, X_{n_1}, X_{n_1+1}, \cdots, X_{n_1+n_2}$ are independent, that each X_i $(i = 1, \cdots, n_1)$ has the distribution function $F_{\theta_1}(x)$ and that each X_{n_1+j} has the distribution function $F_{\theta_2}(x)$ $(j = 1, \cdots, n_2)$.

THEOREM 5.1. (LEHMANN). If $\mathscr{E}$ is an event whose occurrence depends only on the ranks $r_1, \cdots, r_{n_1+n_2}$ of the coordinates of the outcome $(x_1, \cdots, x_{n_1+n_2})$, and if in the cases of ties among the x's the different possible rankings are assigned at random, then for any $F_{\theta_1}, F_{\theta_2}$ with

† Putter [14] has shown that, for large samples using the Wilcoxon two-sample test or the sign test, the first procedure has a greater efficiency.

discontinuities there correspond $F^*_{\theta_1}, F^*_{\theta_2}$ which are continuous and for which

(5.1) $\Pr_{F^*_{\theta_1} F^*_{\theta_2}} \{\mathscr{E}\} = \Pr_{F_{\theta_1} F_{\theta_2}} \{\mathscr{E}\}$

and $F^*_{\theta_1} = F^*_{\theta_2}$ if and only if $F_{\theta_1} = F_{\theta_2}$.

Proof. We first give a construction for $F^*_{\theta_1}, F^*_{\theta_2}$. Let $a_1, a_2, \cdots$ be the countable set of points for which F_{θ_1} or F_{θ_2} has discontinuities. Construct from $F_{\theta_1}, F_{\theta_2}$ distribution functions $F^{(1)}_{\theta_1}, F^{(1)}_{\theta_2}$ by separating the probability measures at a_1 by an amount $1/2$ ($1/4$ in each direction) and replacing the probability discontinuity by the same probability uniformly distributed over the gap. Similarly define $F^{(2)}_1, F^{(2)}_2$ in terms of $F^{(1)}_1, F^{(1)}_2$ by separating the measures at a_2 by an amount $1/2^2$ and replacing the probability discontinuity by a uniform distribution over the gap. It is easily seen that the sequences $(F^{(1)}_1, F^{(2)}_1, \cdots)$, and $(F^{(1)}_2, F^{(2)}_2, \cdots)$, must converge to distribution functions, say F_1, F_2. The equal-probability assignment of ranks at discontinuities then is equivalent to the equal-probability assignment obtained from the corresponding uniform distributions. This establishes (5.1). The remainder of the theorem follows immediately from the construction procedure.

6. PROBLEMS FOR SOLUTION

1. For the two-sample problem as given for Theorem 1.1., show that the Pitman test for slippage of the second sample to the right is unbiased. This test can be described as a conditional test, given the order statistic for the combined sample $t(\mathbf{x}) = (x_{(1)}, \cdots, x_{(n_1 + n_2)})$. Under the hypothesis that $F(x) = G(x)$, each permutation of $(x_{(1)}, \cdots, x_{(n_1 + n_2)})$ has the same probability $1/(n_1 + n_2)!$ of being the outcome. Under this conditional distribution the Pitman statistic $f(\mathbf{x}) = \bar{x}'' - \bar{x}'$ where $\bar{x}' = n_2^{-1} \sum_1^{n_1} x_i$ and $\bar{x}'' = n_2^{-1} \sum_1^{n_2} x_{n_1 + j}$ has an induced distribution. Let f_α be the point exceeded with probability α according to this distribution; f_α will of course depend on the value of the order statistic $t(\mathbf{x})$. The test is obtained by rejecting the hypothesis if the observed value of $f(\mathbf{x})$ is greater than f_α. To get exact size, in general a randomized test is needed. Show that the Pitman test is a valid unbiased test for the extended problem as given by (1.3).

2. For the two-sample scale problem as given in Section (3.4) of Chapter 3, show that the following test proposed by Lehmann is unbiased (use the criterion given in Section 1 of this chapter). Let W be the proportion of quadruples $(x_i, x_{i'}; x_{n_1 + j}, x_{n_1 + j'})$ for which $|x_{n_1 + j'} - x_{n_1 + j}| > |x_{i'} - x_i|$, and let W_α be the value exceeded with probability α under the equally likely permutation distribution of $(x_{(1)}, \cdots, x_{(n_1 + n_2)})$ under the hypothesis. The test is to reject the hypothesis if the observed value of W exceeds W_α. A randomized test is needed in general to obtain exact size α.

3. Consider the two-sample problem (3.1) for k-variate distributions as given in Section 3.1 of Chapter 3. Construct an unbiased test on the basis of the following suggestions. As a parameter to discriminate between the hypothesis and alternative, consider

$$\int_{R^k} (F - G)^2 d\frac{F + G}{2}$$

$$= \int (F^2 + G^2)\, d\frac{F + G}{2} - 2\int FGd\frac{F + G}{2}$$

$$= 2\left[\int \frac{F^2 + G^2}{2}\, d\frac{F + G}{2} - \int FGd\frac{F + G}{2}\right]$$

$$= 2[p_1 - p_2],$$

where

$$p_1 = \int \frac{F^2 + G^2}{2}\, d\frac{F + G}{2},$$

$$p_2 = \int FGd\frac{F + G}{2}.$$

The problem is to test the hypothesis $p_1 = p_2$ against the alternative $p_1 > p_2$. If we can find events for p_1 and p_2, this binomial problem has of course an unbiased similar test. (See Problem 33 in Chapter 2.) For p_1 and p_2, consider, respectively, the events A and B. With probability $1/2$ observe either $\mathbf{x}_1$, $\mathbf{x}_2$ or $\mathbf{x}_{n_1+1}$, $\mathbf{x}_{n_1+2}$ and with probability $1/2$ observe either $\mathbf{x}_3$ or $\mathbf{x}_{n_1+3}$. Denote the three outcomes by $\mathbf{z}_1$, $\mathbf{z}_2$, $\mathbf{z}_3$ and define A as the event

$$z_{1s}, z_{2s}, \le z_{3s} \quad \text{for} \quad s = 1, \cdots, k.$$

Observe $\mathbf{x}_4$, $\mathbf{x}_{n_1+4}$ and with probability $\frac{1}{2}$ either $\mathbf{x}_5$ or $\mathbf{x}_{n_1+5}$. Designate this last outcome by $\mathbf{z}_5$, and define B as the event

$$x_{4s}, x_{n_1+4s} \le z_{5s} \quad \text{for} \quad s = 1, \cdots, k.$$

4. Consider the problem of independence, (2.4) in Chapter 3. The independence of the coordinates $X_1^{(1)}$, $X_1^{(2)}$ is equivalent to $(X_1^{(1)}, X_1^{(2)})$ having the same distribution as $X_2^{(1)}$, $X_3^{(2)}$. Using the two-sample unbiased test in the previous question, define an unbiased test based on a sample of n for the problem of independence.

5. Let $X_1, \cdots, X_n$ be independent and each have the distribution P_θ on R^1 where θ indexes the absolutely continuous distributions. Construct an unbiased test of the hypothesis that the distribution is symmetric about the origin against the alternative of asymmetry. (See Section 2.3 in Chapter 3.) Consider the following suggestions. For four x's, say x_1, x_2, x_3, x_4, define the events:

A: Exactly two of the x's are positive.

B: If A is satisfied and $x_i, x_j < 0 < x_k, x_l$, then B occurs if either $x_i, x_j < x_k, x_l$ or $x_i, x_j > x_k, x_l$.

Show that the maximum probability for AB is $1/4$ and corresponds to symmetry about the origin.

6. For the bivariate Problem 2.6 in Section 2.1 show that the sign test based on $x_1^{(2)} - x_1^{(1)}, \cdots, x_n^{(2)} - x_n^{(1)}$ is a uniformly most powerful test.

7. Show that the statistic $i(x_1, \cdots, x_n)$ is a sufficient statistic (p_t) for the two-sample location problem as formulated at the end of Section 2.1. By applying Theorem 3.4 in Chapter 2, prove that the sign test is uniformly most powerful for the one-sided location problem.

8. Prove that an unbiased test for the two-sided location problem, (2.6) in Chapter 3, is a similar test by using the method of proof found in Theorem 3.5 of Chapter 2. Then use the theorem in [2] to derive the uniformly most powerful unbiased test.

9. For the two-sided location parameter problem based on the median, show that the two-sided test is most stringent. Use Theorems 3.9 and 3.10 in Chapter 2 and the technique of Section 2.1 in this chapter.

10. Apply the theory of Section 2.2 to the problem of randomness with regression alternative, (3.3) in Chapter 3. Consider a simple alternative for which the 'error' has a normal distribution, and show that the most powerful similar test is to reject for large values of $\Sigma(x_i - \bar{x})(c_i - \bar{c})$ in each subspace $t(x_1, \cdots, x_n) = (x_{(1)}, \cdots, x_{(n)}) = t$. What is the most stringent similar test for the two-sided problem (3.4) with normal alternative?

11. Apply the theory of Section 2.2 to the problem of location as given with the assumption of symmetry, (2.7) with Assumption 2.a in Chapter 3. Consider a simple alternative for which each X_i has the same normal distribution with positive mean ξ, and show that the most powerful similar test is to reject for large values of Σx_i, given the statistic $t(\mathbf{x}) = \{|x_i|, \cdots, |x_n|\}$. What is the most stringent similar test for the two-sided problem with normal alternative, (2.8) of Chapter 3? To show completeness, note that $t(\mathbf{x})$ is the order statistic for an arbitrary absolutely continuous distribution on $]0, \infty[$. Theorems 7.1 and 7.3 in Chapter 1 extend to cover this case.

12. Apply the theory in Section 2.2 to the randomized-block problem, (4.3) in Chapter 3, with $r = 2$. Consider a simple alternative for which $X_{11}, X_{12}; \cdots; X_{c1}, X_{c2}$ are independent and each has a normal distribution with variance σ^2, the X_{i1} with mean μ_1, and the X_{i2} with mean μ_2 ($\mu_2 > \mu_1$, say). Show that the most powerful similar test is to reject for large values of $\Sigma(x_{i2} - x_{i1})$, given the statistic $t(\mathbf{x}) = \{\{x_{11}, x_{12}\}, \cdots, \{x_{c1}, x_{c2}\}\}$. What is the most stringent similar test for the two-sided problem ($\mu_1 \neq \mu_2$) with the normal alternative having the same variance for each coordinate?

13. Find the most powerful similar and most stringent similar tests for Problem 12 with formulation (4.3) replaced by (4.4) of Chapter 3. For this consider the statistic $t(\mathbf{x}) = (\{x_{11}, x_{12}\}, \cdots, \{x_{c1}, x_{c2}\})$.

14. Define a class $\{P_\theta | \theta \in \Omega\}$ of probability measures over R^N and a class of transformations such that the set of ranks $\mathbf{r}(\mathbf{x})$ defined by (3.10) in Section 3.3 is maximal-invariant.

15. For the two-sample problem the Mann–Whitney test in Section 1 was based on V, the proportion of pairs x_i, x_{n_1+j} having $x_i < x_{n_1+j}$ ($i = 1, \cdots, n_1; j = 1, \cdots, n_2$), and in Section (3.3) was based on $\sum_1^{n_2} s_j$, the sum of the ranks in the second sample. Prove that

$$V = \frac{1}{n_1 n_2}\left[\sum_1^{n_2} s_j - \frac{n_2(n_2 + 1)}{2}\right].$$

16. Consider the randomness problem with regression alternative (3.3) in Chapter 3. Show that, against a normal alternative, the rank test most powerful for ξ small and positive is to reject the hypothesis for large values of the statistic

$$c_1(r(\mathbf{x})) = \sum_{i=1}^n (c_i - \bar{c})E\{Z_{(r_i)}\},$$

where $Z_{(1)}, \cdots, Z_{(n)}$ are the order-statistic random variables for the unit normal.

17. Consider the single-sample problem of location and symmetry (2.9) in Chapter 3, and for simplicity take $\xi_0 = 0$. The problem is to test the hypothesis of symmetry about the origin. Let $F_\theta(0) = \rho_\theta$, and denote by F_θ' and F_θ'' the conditional distributions of $-X$, given that $X < 0$, and of X, given $X > 0$. Then the hypothesis is equivalent to $\rho_\theta = 1/2$, $F_\theta' = F_\theta''$. Let $n_1(\mathbf{x})$, $n_2(\mathbf{x})$ be the number of negative, positive x's in the sample and divide the sample of n x's into the n_1 x's originally negative with their signs changed to make them positive and the n_2 x's originally positive. The problem is treated as a binomial problem to test $\rho_\theta = 0$, combined with a two-sample problem to test $F_\theta' = F_\theta''$. In the notation of Example 3.1 with $F_\theta''(x) = g(F_\theta'(x))$, show that

Pr {The number of X's > 0 is n_2 and $S_1 = s_1, \cdots, S_{n_2} = s_{n_2}$}
$$= \rho_\theta^{n_1}(1 - \rho_\theta)^{n_2} E\{g'(U_{(s_1)}) \cdots g'(U_{(s_{n_2})})\}.$$

For the alternative for which $F'' = qF' + pF'^2$ $(0 < p < 1, p + q = 1)$, show that the rank test which maximizes the power for p small and $\rho_\theta = 1/2$ is to reject when $s_1 + \cdots + s_{n_2} > c$, and c is chosen to give the test size α under the hypothesis. This test was originally proposed by Wilcoxen [12]. The results in this example indicate that the test is sensitive toward slippage to the right of the positive axis distribution under the assumption the median remains at the origin.

18. For the problem of independence as formulated in Section 3.2 of this chapter, show by Hoeffding's theorem that, under the alternative (3.8), the probability for the rank statistic is given by

$$\mathrm{Pr}_h \{R_1^{(1)} = r_1^{(1)}, \cdots, R_n^{(1)} = r_n^{(1)};\ R_1^{(2)} = r_1^{(2)}, \cdots, R_n^{(2)} = r_n^{(2)}\}$$

$$= \frac{1}{(n!)^2} E\{h'(U_{(r_1^{(1)})}, V_{(r_1^{(2)})}) \cdots h'(U_{(r_n^{(1)})}, V_{(r_n^{(2)})})\},$$

where $h'(u, v) = (\partial^2/\partial u\,\partial v)\,h(u, v)$ and $U_1, \cdots, U_n$; $V_1, \cdots, V_n$ are two independent samples of n from the uniform distribution $[0, 1]$. Consider the alternatives for which $h(u, v) = quv + pu^2v^2$ $(0 < p \le 1, p + q = 1)$. Show that the rank test most powerful for p small rejects when the statistic $\Sigma_i r_i^{(1)} r_i^{(2)}$ is too large. This is the one-sided rank correlation test.

19. For the problem of independence (previous question), show that the rank test locally most powerful against the normal alternative with small positive ρ is to reject for large values of the statistic

$$\sum_{i=1}^{n} E\{Z_{(r_i^{(1)})}\}\, E\{Z_{(r_i^{(2)})}\},$$

where $Z_{(1)}, \cdots, Z_{(n)}$ are the order-statistic random variables for a sample of n from the normal distribution with mean 0 and variance 1. For the two-sided normal alternative with ρ small, find the rank test locally most stringent.

20. For Example 3.2 find the rank test that is locally most stringent.

21. Show that, for the two-sample problem (3.1) in Chapter 3, the modified likelihood-ratio statistic $L^*(\bar{x})$ is a constant equal to

$$\frac{(n_1 + n_2)^{n_1+n_2}}{n_1^{n_1} n_2^{n_2}}$$

22. Construct an example having a simple hypothesis and simple alternative for which the likelihood-ratio method does not produce the most powerful test. For simplicity choose two distributions on the real line.

23. Construct the Wolfowitz likelihood-ratio test for the problem of independence. For the parametric alternative, consider a distribution having a functional relationship between $x^{(1)}$ and $x^{(2)}$, a relationship that is one-to-one, and by sections linear, and that transforms the given ordering of $x^{(1)}$'s into the given ordering for the $x^{(2)}$'s.

REFERENCES AND BIBLIOGRAPHY

1. E. L. Lehmann, "Consistency and unbiasedness of certain nonparametric tests," *Ann. Math. Stat.*, Vol. 22 (1951), p. 165.

2. D. A. S. Fraser, "Nonparametric theory. Scale and location parameters," *Can. J. Math.*, Vol. 6 (1953), p. 46.

3. E. L. Lehmann and C. Stein, "On the theory of some nonparametric hypotheses," *Ann. Math. Stat.*, Vol. 20 (1949), p. 28.

4. E. L. Lehmann, "The power of rank tests," *Ann. Math. Stat.*, Vol. 24 (1953), p. 23.

5. W. Hoeffding, "Optimum nonparametric tests," *Proc. 2d Berkeley Symposium*, University of California Press, 1951.

6. H. Scheffé, "Statistical inference in the nonparametric case," *Ann. Math. Stat.*, Vol. 14 (1943), p. 305.

7. J. Wolfowitz, "Additive partition functions and a class of statistical hypotheses," *Ann. Math. Stat.*, Vol. 13 (1942), p. 247.

8. J. Wolfowitz, "Nonparametric statistical inference," *Proc. 2d Berkeley Symposium*, University of California Press, 1951.

9. P. R. Halmos, *Measure Theory*, D. Van Nostrand Co., 1950.

10. M. E. Terry, "Some rank-order tests which are most powerful against specific parametric alternatives," *Ann. Math. Stat.*, Vol. 23 (1952), p. 346.

11. R. A. Fisher and F. Yates, *Statistical Tables for Biological, Agricultural, and Medical Research*, 3d Ed., Hafner, 1949.

12. F. Wilcoxon, "Individual comparisons by ranking methods," *Biometrics*, Vol. 1 (1945), p. 80.

13. E. L. Lehmann, "Theory of testing hypotheses," Associated Students Store, University of California, Berkeley, 1949.

14. J. Putter, "On the treatment of ties in nonparametric tests," *Ann. Math. Stat.*, Vol. 24 (1953), p. 684.

CHAPTER 6

Limiting Distributions

1. INTRODUCTION

In Chapter 5 we developed methods for constructing nonparametric tests. For all the examples considered, the tests were or could be put in the form,

$$\phi(x) = 1 \quad \text{if} \quad t(x) > c$$

$$= a \qquad = c$$

$$= 0 \qquad < c,$$

where $t(x)$ is a real-valued statistic. In order to use such a test, the constants c, a must be chosen to give the test the correct size. This necessitates a knowledge of the induced distribution of the statistic $t(x)$ under the hypothesis. Also, to examine the power of the test we need the induced distribution of $t(x)$ corresponding to each parameter value of the alternative. For many problems these distributions are quite complicated and require excessive computation to tabulate them. However, in cases where the outcome corresponds to a sample of n from a distribution over a component space, it often happens that, as n becomes large, the distribution of the statistic $t(x)$ approaches some simple distribution such as the normal or χ^2 distribution. In this chapter we consider theorems concerning the approach of a distribution to a limiting form.

A number of theorems are standard theorems of probability theory with applications in many branches of statistics. We quote these theorems without proof, giving references where the proofs are available. However, others were developed primarily for nonparametric application, and we give the proofs for most of these.

2. GENERAL THEOREMS CONCERNING LIMITING DISTRIBUTIONS

As indicated above, we are interested in the distribution of a real-valued statistic and how it changes as a known parameter n, in most cases the sample size, becomes large. In particular, we are interested in the probability to one side of a real number. For this it is convenient to use distribution functions. Therefore, consider a sequence of distribution functions $\{F_n(x); n = 1, 2, \cdots\}$:

A sequence of distribution functions $\{F_n(x)\}$ is said to converge to a distribution function $F(x)$ if for each point x at which $F(x)$ is continuous

$$(2.1) \qquad \lim_{n \to \infty} F_n(x) = F(x)$$

If a random variable has the sequence of distribution functions $\{F_n(x)\}$ satisfying the definition, then we say the *random variable has asymptotically the distributions given by $F(x)$.*

The reason we require the limit to hold only at points of continuity is best illustrated by an example. Let $F_n(x)$ be the distribution function of the random variable which takes the value $1/n$ with probability one:

$$F_n(x) = 1 \qquad \text{if} \quad x \geq 1/n$$
$$= 0 \qquad \qquad < 1/n.$$

As $n \to \infty$, the probability distribution becomes close to the probability distribution having all probability at $x = 0$; it has distribution function

$$F(x) = 1 \qquad \text{if} \quad x \geq 0$$
$$= 0 \qquad \qquad < 0.$$

It is easily seen that $\lim F_n(x) = F(x)$ for all x other than 0, the point of discontinuity of $F(x)$; at that point we have

$$\lim_{n \to \infty} F_n(0) = 0 \neq F(0).$$

Thus, if we were to define convergence on the basis of the limit holding for all x, we would exclude this simple case. However, when the probability distribution has discrete probabilities, this is the sort of 'convergence' we want to consider, and hence we require the limit to hold only at points of continuity.

The definition of convergence does not in general imply that

$$\int_A dF_n(x) \xrightarrow[n \to \infty]{} \int_A dF(x).$$

To require that this limit hold for all Borel sets on the real line produces a much stronger definition of convergence than introduced above. For an interesting discussion of definitions of convergence and relations between them, see Scheffé [13].

An example of the convergence of distribution functions is obtained from the concept of convergence in probability of random variables. A sequence of independent random variables $\{X_n\}$ is said to *converge in probability to a constant c* and is written

(2.2) $$\text{p-lim}_{n \to \infty} X_n = c$$

if the probability in any neighborhood of c approaches 1 *as n approaches infinity*: that is, if, for all $\delta > 0$,

(2.3) $$\lim_{n \to \infty} \text{Pr} \{c - \delta \leq X_n \leq c + \delta\} = 1.$$

It is easy to show that this is equivalent to the convergence of the corresponding distribution functions to the distribution function of the random variable taking the value c with probability one (Problem 2). Also, it is easy to show by Tchebycheff's inequality that, if $E\{X_n\} \to c$ and $\sigma^2_{X_n} \to 0$, then p-lim $X_n = c$ (Problem 3).

Our first theorem relates the convergence of distribution functions to the convergence of the corresponding moments. The moments of the distribution functions $F_n(x)$ are defined by

(2.4) $$\mu_r^{(n)} = \int_{-\infty}^{+\infty} x^r \, dF_n(x)$$

for $r = 1, 2, \cdots$. When the integral does not converge, we say the corresponding moment does not exist.

THEOREM 2.1. (FRECHET AND SHOHAT). If for each n the moments $\{\mu_r^{(n)}; \ r = 1, 2, \cdots\}$ of $F_n(x)$ exist and if $\lim_{n \to \infty} \mu_r^{(n)} = \mu_r$ $(r = 1, 2, \cdots)$, then the μ_r are the moments of a distribution function. Also, if there is only one distribution function $F(x)$ having the moments μ_r, then the distribution function $F_n(x)$ converges to $F(x)$ as $n \to \infty$.

Proof. See Kendall [14], p. 110.

To apply this theorem we need to know whether a set of moments determines a distribution uniquely. The next theorem provides a criterion which, if satisfied, establishes the uniqueness of the distribution.

THEOREM (2.2). If $F(x)$ is a distribution function with moments $\{\mu_r;\ r = 1, 2, \cdots\}$, then the absolute convergence of the series

$$(2.5) \qquad \sum_{j=1}^{\infty} \mu_r \frac{t^r}{r!}$$

for some $t > 0$ implies that $F(x)$ is the only distribution function having moments $\{\mu_r\}$.

Proof. See Cramér [15], p. 176.

It is quite easy to show that the moments of any normal distribution satisfy this criterion and hence that the convergence of moments to normal moments implies a limiting normal distribution (Problem 1).

There is a multivariate analog to each of these theorems. Let $F_n(x_1, \cdots, x_k)$ be a distribution function over R^k. The moments are defined by

$$(2.6) \qquad \mu_{r_1 \cdots r_k}^{(n)} = \int_{R^k} x_1^{r_1} \cdots x_k^{r_k}\, dF(x_1, \cdots, x_k)$$

for $r_1, \cdots, r_k = 1, 2, \cdots$. If one of the integrals does not converge, we say that the corresponding moment does not exist. Theorem 2.1 using the set of moments $\{u_{r_1 \cdots r_k}^{(n)} \mid r_1, \cdots, r_k = 1, 2, \cdots\}$ can be shown to apply immediately to this more general case. There is an extension of Theorem 2.2, but for our purposes it suffices to note that the moments of a multivariate normal distribution satisfy the criterion and hence determine the distribution uniquely.

The next theorem relates the convergence of distributions to the convergence of the corresponding characteristic functions. The characteristic function of a distribution $F_n(x)$ is defined by

$$(2.7) \qquad \phi_n(t) = \int_{-\infty}^{+\infty} e^{ixt}\, dF_n(x)$$

for real t, and is in general a complex-valued function. The characteristic function always exists since the integrand is bounded: $|e^{ixt}| = 1$. We have the following uniqueness theorem for characteristic functions.

THEOREM 2.3. (LÉVY). If two distribution functions have the same characteristic function, then they are identical.

Proof. See Cramér [15], p. 93.

This theorem shows that there is a one-to-one correspondence between distribution functions and characteristic functions. The next theorem shows that in a certain sense this correspondence is continuous.

THEOREM 2.4 (LÉVY AND CRAMÉR). For the sequence of distribution functions $F_1(x)$, $F_2(x)$, $\cdots$ with corresponding characteristic functions $\phi_1(t)$, $\phi_2(t)$, $\cdots$, a necessary and sufficient condition that the distribution functions $F_n(x)$ converge to a distribution function $F(x)$ is that, for every real t, the sequence $\phi_n(t)$ converges to a limit $\phi(t)$ which is continuous at $t = 0$. $\phi(t)$ is the characteristic function of $F(x)$.

Proof. See Cramér [15], p. 96.

For multivariate distribution functions $F_n(x_1, \cdots, x_k)$ we can define a characteristic function,

$$(2.8) \qquad \phi_n(t_1, \cdots, t_k) = \int_{R^k} \exp\left(i \sum_{j=1}^{k} x_j t_j\right) dF_n(x_1, \cdots, x_k)$$

for $(t_1, \cdots, t_k) \in R^k$. With this definition Theorems 2.3 and 2.4 are valid for multivariate distributions.

We quote now a theorem which does not directly concern limiting distributions but which can frequently be used with earlier theorems in this section to find the form of a limiting distribution.

THEOREM 2.5. (CRAMÉR-WOLD). If the distribution of $\sum_{1}^{k} l_i X_i$ is identical to the distribution of $\sum_{1}^{k} l_i Y_i$ for all $(l_1, \cdots, l_k) \in R^k$, then the distribution of $(X_1, \cdots, X_k)$ is identical to the distribution of $(Y_1, \cdots, Y_k)$.

Proof. See Cramér [20], p. 105.

To complete this section we have three theorems which enable us to derive from the limiting distribution of one random variable the limiting distributions of related random variables. The first theorem is given for real-valued random variables, but it has an obvious multivariate analog.

THEOREM 2.6. If $(X_1, Y_1), (X_2, Y_2), \cdots$ is a sequence of random variables such that the sequence $X_1, \cdots, X_2, \cdots$ has limiting distribution $F(x)$ and the sequence $Y_1, Y_2, \cdots$ converges in probability to a constant c, then $X_n + Y_n$ has limiting distribution $F(x - c)$. Further, if $c > 0$, then $X_n Y_n$ has limiting distribution $F(x/c)$ and X_n/Y_n has limiting distribution $F(xc)$.

Proof. See Cramér [15], p. 254.

THEOREM 2.7. If $(X_1, Y_1), (X_2, Y_2), \cdots$ is a sequence of random variables over R^2 which has the limiting distribution of a random variable (X, Y) with mean $(0, 0)$, if d_n is a sequence of real numbers with $\lim_{n \to \infty} d_n = 0$, and if $h(x, y)$ is a real function having a total differential at $(0, 0)$, then, as $n \to \infty$, the distribution of

$$(2.9) \qquad d_n^{-1}[h(d_n X_n, d_n Y_n) - h(0, 0)]$$

converges to the distribution of $h_1 X + h_2 Y$ where

$$(2.10) \qquad h_1 = \frac{\partial h(0, 0)}{\partial x}, \qquad h_2 = \frac{\partial h(0, 0)}{\partial y}$$

Proof.   The proof is essentially that of Cramér's theorem on page 366 in [15].

THEOREM 2.8.   If $(X_1, Y_1), (X_2, Y_2), \cdots$ is a sequence of independent random variables which has the limiting distribution of a random variable (X, Y), and if $f(x, y)$ is a continuous function, then the limiting distribution of $f(X_n, Y_n)$ exists and is the distribution of $f(X, Y)$.

Proof.   Let b be a point of continuity for the distribution function of $f(X, Y)$. We shall prove that

$$(2.11) \qquad \lim_{n \to \infty} \Pr \{f(X_n, Y_n) \leq b\} = \Pr \{f(X, Y) \leq b\},$$

and this establishes the theorem.

Let $F_n(x, y)$ be the distribution function of (X_n, Y_n) and $F(x, y)$ be the distribution of (X, Y). Cramér's theorem (on page 74 [15]) establishes that

$$\lim_{n \to \infty} \int_{R^2} h(x, y) \, dF_n(x, y) = \int_{R^2} h(x, y) \, dF(x, y)$$

for bounded continuous functions $h(x, y)$. For positive ε, we define two functions $h_\varepsilon^+(x, y)$, $h_\varepsilon^-(x, y)$

$$
\begin{aligned}
h_\varepsilon^+(x, y) &= 1 & &\text{if } f(x, y) < b \\
&= \frac{b + \varepsilon - f(x, y)}{\varepsilon} & &\text{if } b \leq f(x, y) \leq b + \varepsilon \\
&= 0 & &\text{if } b + \varepsilon < f(x, y), \\
h^-(x, y) &= 1 & &\text{if } f(x, y) < b - \varepsilon \\
&= \frac{b - f(x, y)}{\varepsilon} & &\text{if } b - \varepsilon \leq f(x, y) \leq b \\
&= 0 & &\text{if } b < f(x, y).
\end{aligned}
$$

Since these functions are continuous and bounded, we have

(2.12) $\lim\limits_{n \to \infty} \int_{R^2} h_\varepsilon^+(x, y) \, dF_n(x, y) = \int_{R^2} h_\varepsilon^+(x, y) \, dF(x, y),$

(2.13) $\lim\limits_{n \to \infty} \int_{R^2} h_\varepsilon^-(x, y) \, dF_n(x, y) = \int_{R^2} h_\varepsilon^-(x, y) \, dF(x, y).$

But we have

$$\int_{R^2} h_\varepsilon^-(x, y) \, dF_n(x, y) \le \Pr\{f(X_n, Y_n) \le b\} \le \int_{R^2} h_\varepsilon^+(x, y) \, dF_n(x, y)$$

and

$$\int_{R^2} h_\varepsilon^-(x, y) \, dF(x, y) \le \Pr\{f(X, Y) \le b\} \le \int_{R^2} h_\varepsilon^+(x, y) \, dF(x, y).$$

Therefore the limit points of $\Pr\{f(X_n, Y_n) \le b\}$ are contained between the two values (2.12) and (2.13). However, by virtue of our choice of b as a continuity point of the distribution of $f(X, Y)$, it follows that (2.12) and (2.13) can be made arbitrarily close to $\Pr\{f(X, Y) \le b\}$ by choice of ε small. This establishes (2.12) and hence the theorem.

Theorem 2.7 and 2.8 are stated for bivariate distributions but they remain valid for multivariate distributions.

3. CENTRAL LIMIT THEOREMS

In this section we consider a number of theorems which are central to the theory on limiting distributions—central-limit theorems. However we first quote a related theorem mentioned in Chapter 2.

THEOREM 3.1. (KHINTCHINE). If $X_1, X_2, \cdots$ are independent random variables, each with the same distribution function $F(x)$, and if the mean μ' of $F(x)$ exists,

$$\mu' = \int x \, dF(x),$$

then $\bar{X} = n^{-1} \sum_1^n X_i$ converges in probability to μ' as $n \to \infty$.

Proof. See Cramér [15], p. 254.

This theorem states that, if we pick a sufficiently large value of n and examine probability statements, then most of the probability for $\bar{X}$ will be in a small neighborhood of μ. In such a case $\bar{X}$ is said to satisfy the *weak law of large numbers.* Also of interest is to inquire what happens in a probability sense to $\bar{X}$ as n increases, and in particular, what is the probability that

$$\lim_{n \to \infty} n^{-1} \sum_{1}^{n} X_i = \mu'.$$

A sequence for which the probability of convergence is one is said to obey the strong law of large numbers.   For this, we have a generalized form of Khintchine's theorem.

THEOREM 3.2 (KOLMOGOROV).   If $X_1, X_2, \cdots$ are independent random variables, each with the same distribution function $F(x)$, and if the mean μ' of $F(x)$ exists

$$\mu' = \int x \, dF(x),$$

then with probability one

$$\lim_{n \to \infty} n^{-1} \sum_{1}^{n} X_i = \mu'.$$

Proof.   See Feller [9], p. 208.

If in Theorem 3.1 we assume in addition that the second moment of the distribution exists, then a stronger statement can be made which gives the limiting distribution of $\bar{X}$ in the neighborhood of μ'.

THEOREM 3.3.   CENTRAL-LIMIT THEOREM (LINDEBERG AND LÉVY).   If $X_1, X_2, \cdots$ are independent random variables each with the same distribution having mean μ' and finite variance σ'^2, then

$$\frac{n^{-1} \sum_{1}^{n} X_i - \mu'}{n^{-1/2}}$$

is asymptotically normal with mean 0 and variance σ'^2.

Proof.   See Cramér [15], p. 214.

If we assume that third moments exist, then we can drop the assumption that the X_i have the same distribution; we have

THEOREM 3.4.   CENTRAL-LIMIT THEOREM (LIAPOUNOFF).   If $X_1, X_2, \cdots$ are independent random variables, if X_i has mean μ_i, variance σ_i^2, and third absolute central moment ρ_i^3,

$$\rho_i^3 = E\{|X_i - \mu_i|^3\},$$

and if $\lim \rho/\sigma = 0$ where

$$\rho^3 = \sum_{i=1}^{n} \rho_i^3,$$

$$\sigma^2 = \sum_{i=1}^{n} \sigma_i^2,$$

then

$$\frac{\sum_{i=1}^{n} X_i - \sum_{i=1}^{n} \mu_i}{\sigma}$$

is asymptotically normal with mean 0 and variance 1.

Proof. See Cramér [15], p. 216.

Note. Often we describe such a convergence by saying that ΣX_i is asymptotically normal with mean $\Sigma \mu_i$ and variance σ^2. (σ depends on n.)

These theorems remain valid if the random variables have a multivariate distribution over R^k. Also, the last theorem remains valid if, for each n, there is a fresh group of random variables rather than the first n from a given sequence. We illustrate these two extensions by the following bivariate form of the central-limit theorem.

THEOREM 3.5. CENTRAL-LIMIT THEOREM (BERNSTEIN). If, for each n, $\{(X_{n1}, Y_{n1}), \cdots, (X_{n\nu(n)}, Y_{n\nu(n)})\}$ is a set of independent random variables over R^2 for which

$$E(X_{ni}) = E(Y_{ni}) = 0 \qquad (i = 1, \cdots, \nu),$$

and

$$\lim_{n \to \infty} \nu(n) = \infty,$$

$$\lim_{n \to \infty} \nu^{-3/2}(n)\rho_n^3 = 0,$$

$$\lim_{n \to \infty} \nu^{-1}(n) \sum_{\alpha=1}^{\nu} \mu_{ij}^{(n\alpha)} = \mu_{ij}$$

for $(i, j) = (2, 0), (1,1), (0, 2)$ where

$$\mu_{ij}^{(n\alpha)} = E\{X_{n\alpha}^i Y_{n\alpha}^j\},$$

$$\rho_{n\alpha}^3 = \max \{E\{|X_{n\alpha}|^3\}, E\{|Y_{n\alpha}|^3\}\},$$

$$\rho_n^3 = \sum_{\alpha=1}^{\nu} \rho_{n\alpha}^3,$$

then

$$\left(\nu^{-1/2} \sum_{\alpha=1}^{\nu} X_{n\alpha}, \ \nu^{-1/2} \sum_{\alpha=1}^{\nu} Y_{n\alpha} \right)$$

has asymptotically the bivariate normal distribution with means 0 and covariances μ_{ij}.

Proof. See Hoeffding and Robbins [4].

For a version of these theorems having the existence of third absolute moments replaced by the existence of absolute moments of order $2 + \delta$ for some $\delta > 0$, see Uspensky [16].

4. CENTRAL-LIMIT THEOREM FOR DEPENDENT VARIABLES

In this section we consider two theorems which have somewhat the form of the central-limit theorems of the last section but which concern dependent random variables. These theorems were developed with a view toward nonparametric applications.

Let $X_1, X_2, \cdots$, be a sequence of random variables. We say *the sequence of random variables is m-dependent if* $(X_1, \cdots, X_r)$ *is always independent of* $(X_s, X_{s+1}, \cdots)$, provided $s - r > m$. In such a case, if m or more consecutive X's are removed, the two remaining portions of the sequence are independent. Also we define

$$A_i = 2 \sum_{j=0}^{m-1} \text{cov}\,\{X_{i+j}, X_{i+m}\} + \text{var}\,\{X_{i+m}\}$$

where var, cov, designate, respectively, variance, covariance. Then using this notation, we can state the first theorem.

THEOREM 4.1 (HOEFFDING AND ROBBINS). If (a) an m-dependent sequence $X_1, X_2, \cdots$ satisfies $E\{X_i\} = 0$, $E\{|X_i|^3\} \leq R^3 < \infty$ for $i = 1, 2, \cdots$ and (b) the limit

(4.1)
$$\lim_{p \to \infty} \frac{1}{p} \sum_{h=1}^{p} A_{i+h} = A$$

exists uniformly for all i, then $\sum_{1}^{n} X_i$ is asymptotically normal with mean 0 and variance nA.

Proof. Choose an α satisfying $0 < \alpha < 1/4$, and let $k = [n^\alpha]$, $\nu = [n/k]$ where the brackets designate the largest integer less than or equal to the bracketed number. Then we have $n = k\nu + r$ with $0 \leq r < k$. Our method of proof will be to break $\sum_1^n X_i$ into ν independent groups of $k - m$ X's and a remainder term, and then apply the univariate form of the central-limit Theorem 3.5. to show that the sum of these ν groups has a limiting normal distribution.

Let

$$S = X_1 + \cdots + X_n$$

(4.2) $$= S' + T,$$

where

(4.3) $$S' = U_1 + \cdots + U_\nu$$

and

$$U_i = X_{(i-1)k+1} + X_{(i-1)k+2} + \cdots + X_{ik-m}$$

$$T = \sum_{i=1}^{\nu-1} (X_{ik-m+1} + \cdots + X_{ik}) + (X_{\nu k-m+1} + \cdots + X_{\nu k+r})$$

We shall show that $n^{-1/2}S'$ has a limiting normal distribution with mean 0 and variance A and that $n^{-1/2}T$ approaches 0 in probability. The proof is then completed by applying Theorem 2.6 to show that

$$n^{-1/2}S = n^{-1/2}S' + n^{-1/2}T$$

is asymptotically normal with mean 0 and variance A.

First we consider $n^{-1/2}S'$. Since

$$n^{-1/2}S' = \left(\frac{\nu k}{n}\right)^{1/2} \nu^{-1/2} \sum_{i=1}^{\nu} k^{-1/2}U_i,$$

and $\nu k/n \to 1$ as $n \to \infty$, it is sufficient, again by Theorem 2.6, to show that

$$\nu^{-1/2} \sum_1^{\nu} k^{-1/2}U_i$$

has the limiting normal distribution. Now for $s > m$ we have

$$E\{(X_{i+1} + \cdots + X_{i+s})^2\} = E\{(X_{i+1} + \cdots + X_{i+s-1})^2\}$$

$$+ 2E\{(X_{i+1} + \cdots + X_{i+s-1})X_{i+s}\} + E\{X_{i+s}^2\}$$

$$= E\{(X_{i+1} + \cdots + X_{i+s-1})^2\} + A_{i+s-m},$$

where the second step follows from the fact that $E\{X_j X_{j+j'}\} = 0$ for $j' > m$; then by induction

$$E\{(X_{i+1} + \cdots + X_{i+s})^2\} = E\{(X_{i+1} + \cdots + X_{i+m})^2\} + \sum_{h=1}^{s-m} A_{i+h}.$$

Applying this to find the variance of U_i, we have

$$E\{U_i^2\} = E\{[X_{(i-1)k+1} + \cdots + X_{(i-1)k+m}]^2\} + \sum_{h=1}^{k-2m} A_{(i-1)k+h}.$$

But, since $y^{3/2}$ is a convex function, we have by Theorem 2.4 in Chapter 2,

$$E\{|X_i|^3\} = E\{[X_i^2]^{3/2}\} \geq [E\{X_i^2\}]^{3/2},$$

and hence

$$E\{X_i^2\} \leq [E\{|X_i|^3\}]^{2/3} \leq R^2.$$

Also by the Hölder inequality, page 238 in Monroe [17], we have

$$E\{|X_i X_j|\} \leq [E\{|X_i|^2\} \cdot E\{|X_j|^2\}]^{1/2}.$$
$$\leq R^2.$$

Therefore

$$E\{(X_{(i+1)k+1} + \cdots + X_{(i-1)k+m})^2\} \leq m^2 R^2,$$

and

$$\left| E\{U_i^2\} - \sum_{h=1}^{k-2m} A_{(i-1)k+h} \right| \leq m^2 R^2.$$

By summing for $i = 1, \cdots, \nu$ and dividing by ν and by k, we obtain

$$\left| \frac{1}{\nu} \sum_{i=1}^{\nu} E\{(k^{-1/2} U_i)^2\} - \frac{1}{k\nu}(k - 2m) \sum_{i=1}^{\nu} \frac{1}{k - 2m} \sum_{h=1}^{k-2m} A_{(i-1)k+h} \right| \leq k^{-1} m^2 R^2.$$

As $\nu \to \infty$, $k \to \infty$, and from (4.1) it follows that

$$\frac{1}{k - 2m} \sum_{h=1}^{k-2m} A_{(i-1)k+h}$$

approaches A uniformly; therefore

$$(4.4) \qquad \lim_{\nu \to \infty} \frac{1}{\nu} \sum_{i=1}^{\nu} E\{(k^{-1/2} U_i)^2\} = A \geq 0.$$

Now $k^{-1/2} U_1, \cdots, k^{-1/2} U_\nu$ are independent and have a distribution depending on n. For the application of Theorem 3.5 we have shown above that the average variance approaches a finite limit A.   The third absolute moment condition will be satisfied if we show that

(4.5) $\max [E\{|k^{-1/2}U_1|^3\}, \cdots, E\{|k^{-1/2}U_\nu|^3\}] = o(\nu^{1/2}).$

Applying Hölder's inequality again, we have

$$E\{|X_iX_jX_k|\} \leq [E\{|X_i|^3\}]^{1/3}[E\{|X_jX_k|^{3/2}\}]^{2/3}$$

$$\leq [E\{|X_i|^3\} \cdot E\{|X_j|^3\} \cdot E\{|X_k|^3\}]^{1/3}$$

$$\leq R^3.$$

Then

(4.6) $$E\{|k^{-1/2}U_i|^3\} = k^{-3/2}E\left\{\left|\sum_{h=1}^{k-m} X_{(i-1)k+h}\right|^3\right\}$$

$$\leq k^{-3/2}(k-m)^3R^3$$

$$\leq k^{3/2}R^3.$$

From our definition of k, we have

$$k \sim n^\alpha$$

$$\sim (\nu k)^\alpha;$$

therefore

$$k \sim \nu^{\alpha/(1-\alpha)}$$

$$= o(\nu^{1/3})$$

and

$$k^{2/3} = o(\nu^{1/2}).$$

This, with (4.6) proves that the third absolute moment condition (4.5). Theorem 3.5 then establishes that

$$\nu^{-1/2} \sum_{i=1}^\nu k^{-1/2}U_i,$$

and hence $n^{-1/2}S'$ are asymptotically normal with mean 0 and variance A.
    Next we consider $n^{-1/2}T$.   For $k > 2m$ the brackets in the definition of T are independent.   Therefore, for large n,

$$n^{-1}E\{T^2\} = \frac{1}{n}\left[\sum_{i=1}^\nu E\{[X_{ik-m+1} + \cdots + X_{ik}]^2\}\right.$$

$$\left. + E\{[X_{\nu k-m+1} + \cdots + X_{\nu k+r}]^2\}\right]$$

$$\leq n^{-1}[(\nu-1)m^2R^2 + (k+m)^2R^2].$$

From the definition of k and v,

$$k \sim n^{\alpha},$$

$$v \sim \frac{n}{k} \sim n^{1-\alpha};$$

hence

$$n^{-1}E\{T^2\} = O(n^{1-\alpha-1}) + O(n^{2\alpha-1})$$

$$= O(n^{-\alpha}) + O(n^{2\alpha-1})$$

$$= o(1).$$

The mean of $n^{-1/2}T$ is obviously zero.   The variance, $n^{-1}E(T^2)$, as we have just shown, approaches zero.   Hence $n^{-1/2}T$ approaches zero in probability. This completes the proof.

A sequence of random variables, $X_1, X_2, \cdots$, is called stationary if the joint distribution of $X_i, X_{i+1}, \cdots, X_{i+r}$ is independent of i for all r.   This gives the following simplification of Theorem 4.1.

THEOREM 4.2.   If $X_1, X_2, \cdots$ is a stationary m-dependent sequence of random variables with $E(X_1) = \mu$ and $E\{|X_1|^3\}$ existing, then, as $n \to \infty$, the limiting distribution of $n^{-1/2} \sum_{1}^{n} X_i$ is normal with mean $n^{1/2}\mu$ and variance

(4.7) $A = \text{var}(X_1^2) + 2[\text{cov}(X_1 X_2) + \cdots + \text{cov}(X_1 X_{m+1})].$

There are also multivariate extensions of these theorems and the method of proof is essentially that used above.   We quote the bivariate form of the theorem for a stationary sequence.

THEOREM 4.3.   If $(X_1, Y_1), (X_2, Y_2), \cdots$ is a stationary m-dependent sequence of random variables over R^2 which has $E\{X_1\} = 0$, $E\{Y_1\} = 0$ and $E\{|X_1|^3\}$, $E\{|Y_1|^3\}$ existing, then as $n \to \infty$, the limiting distribution of

$$\left(n^{-1/2} \sum_{1}^{n} X_i, n^{-1/2} \sum_{1}^{n} Y_i\right)$$

is normal with mean 0 and covariance matrix

$$\begin{pmatrix} A & B \\ B & C \end{pmatrix}$$

where

$$A = \text{var} \{X_1\} + 2 \sum_{j=1}^{m} \text{cov} \{X_1 X_{1+j}\},$$

(4.8) $$B = \text{cov} \{X_1 Y_1\} + \sum_{j=1}^{m} [\text{cov} \{X_1 Y_{1+j}\} + \text{cov} \{X_{1+j} Y_1\}],$$

$$C = \text{var} \{Y_1\} + 2 \sum_{j=1}^{m} \text{cov} \{Y_1 Y_{1+j}\}.$$

Example 4.1. Consider a sequence $Z_1, Z_2, \cdots$ of independent and identically distributed random variables having $E\{Z_1\} = 0$, var $\{Z_1\} = 1$, and $E\{|Z_1|^3\}$ finite. We can define a 1-dependent sequence $X_1, X_2, \cdots$ by the equation $X_i = Z_i Z_{i+1}$. Obviously this sequence is stationary, and we have $E\{X_1\} = 0$, var $\{X_1\} = 1$, and $E\{|X_1|^3\}$ finite. We calculate A:

$$\begin{aligned} A &= E\{X_1^2\} + 2E\{X_1 X_2\} \\ &= E\{Z_1^2 Z_2^2\} + 2E\{Z_1 Z_2^2 Z_3\} \\ &= 1. \end{aligned}$$

By Theorem (4.2) the random variable

$$n^{-1/2}(Z_1 Z_2 + Z_2 Z_3 + \cdots + Z_n Z_{n+1})$$

has a limiting normal distribution with mean 0 and variance 1.

If we assume further that $E\{Z_1^6\}$ is finite, then the bivariate sequence $(Z_1 Z_2, Z_1^2 - 1), (Z_2 Z_3, Z_2^2 - 1), \cdots$ satisfies the conditions of Theorem (4.3), and

$$n^{-1/2} \sum_{1}^{n} Z_i Z_{i+1}, \, n^{-1/2} \sum_{1}^{n} (Z_i^2 - 1)$$

has a bivariate normal limiting distribution. From this limiting distribution we can derive the limiting distribution of

$$W_n = n^{1/2} \frac{Z_1 Z_2 + \cdots + Z_n Z_{n+1}}{Z_1^2 + \cdots + Z_n^2},$$

by applying Theorem 2.7. Let $d_n = n^{-1/2}$ and $h(x, y) = x/(y + 1)$. Then $h_1 = 1$, $h_2 = 0$, and $h(0, 0) = 0$. As $n \to \infty$, the limiting distribution of

$$W_n = n^{1/2} \frac{n^{-1} \sum_{1}^{n} Z_i Z_{i+1}}{1 + n^{-1} \sum_{1}^{n} (Z_i^2 - 1)}$$

is the same as the limiting distribution of

$$h_1 n^{-1/2} \sum_1^n Z_i Z_{i+1} + h_2 n^{-1/2} \sum_1^n (Z_i^2 - 1) = n^{-1/2} \sum_1^n Z_i Z_{i+1},$$

which is the normal distribution with mean 0 and variance 1.

Problem 5 is to show that a serial correlation coefficient has a limiting normal distribution, and it illustrates the Hoeffding and Robbins theorem used in conjunction with a trivariate extension of Theorem 2.7.

m-dependent sequences of random variables often arise in the following manner. Let $Z_1, Z_2, \cdots$ be a sequence of independent and identically distributed random variables. If $f_i(x_1, \cdots, x_k)$ is a real-valued statistic defined for $i = 1, 2, \cdots$, then the sequence $f_1(Z_1, \cdots, Z_k), f_2(Z_2, \cdots, Z_{k+1}), \cdots$, is obviously $(k-1)$-dependent. The Hoeffding and Robbins theorem gives conditions under which the sum

$$\sum_{i=1}^n f_i(Z_i, \cdots, Z_{i+k-1})$$

has a limiting normal distribution. However, for some nonparametric applications we are interested in knowing the conditional distribution of the sum

$$\sum_{i=1}^n f_i(Z_i, \cdots, Z_{i+k-1}),$$

given the order statistic for the first n z's. This is the distribution of the sum under the $n!$ permutations of a given sequence of z's, $\{z_1, \cdots, z_n\}$. For this, we slightly alter the definition of the sum to put it in a 'circular' form, but the results derived apply equally to the form above. Any z having index greater than n, z_{n+j}, is taken to be z_j. A statistic of this form has been called a serial statistic by Ghosh.

To complete this section we quote a theorem by Ghosh. This theorem needs stronger assumptions than the Hoeffding and Robbins theorem and proves that, as $n \to \infty$, the distribution function of a serial statistic under equally likely permutations of the z_i converges in probability to a normal distribution function.

For this let $Z_1, Z_2, \cdots$ be a sequence of independent and identically distributed random variables, and let $f_1(z_1, \cdots, z_k), f_2(z_1, \cdots, z_k), \cdots$ be a sequence of real-value statistics such that

$$(4.9) \qquad E\{|f_i(Z_1, \cdots, Z_k)|^s\} < c_s$$

holds for all $i = 1, 2, \cdots$ and for each $s = 1, \cdots$. Ghosh defines a
serial statistic, $S(z_1, \cdots, z_n)$, by the equation

$$(4.10) \qquad S(z_1, \cdots, z_n) = \frac{1}{n} \sum_{i=1}^{n} f_i(z_i, \cdots, z_{i+k-1}),$$

where, for this sum $z_{n+j}(j > 0)$ is taken to be z_j, and we have the 'circular'
definition. We consider the distribution of $S(z_1, \cdots, z_n)$ under equally
likely permutations of the set $(z_1, \cdots, z_n)$. This is, of course, the conditional distribution of $S(Z_1, \cdots, Z_n)$, given that the order statistic
$\{Z_1, \cdots, Z_n\}$ takes the value $\{z_1, \cdots, z_n\}$. Expectations under this conditional distribution we designate by E'. Then for the mean and variance
of $S(z_1, \cdots, z_n)$ we have

$$M_1 = E'\{S(Z_1, \cdots, Z_n)\}$$

$$= \frac{1}{n} \sum_{i=1}^{n} \frac{1}{n(n-1)\cdots(n-k+1)} \sum_{P} f_i(z_{j_1}, \cdots, z_{j_k})$$

$$M_2 = E'\{(S(Z_1, \cdots, Z_n) - M_1)^2\},$$

where P denotes summation over all permutations $(j_1, \cdots, j_k)$ of k integers
selected from $(1, \cdots, n)$.

Also for the statement of the theorem we need to define two symbols
μ_{1n} and μ_{2n}. M_1 and M_2 are functions of $(z_1, \cdots, z_n)$ and hence have a
probability distribution corresponding to the random variable $(Z_1, \cdots, Z_n)$
μ_{1n} and μ_{2n} turn out to be related in a probability sense to M_1 and nM_2,
respectively.

$$\mu_{1n} = \frac{1}{n} \sum_{i=1}^{n} E\{f_i(Z_1, \cdots, Z_k)\},$$

$$\mu_{2n} = \frac{1}{n} \sum_{|i-j|<k} E\{f_i(Z_i, \cdots, Z_{i+k-1}) f_j(Z_j, \cdots, Z_{j+k-1})\}$$

$$- \frac{1}{n} \sum_{|i-j|<k} E\{f_i(Z_1, \cdots, Z_k) f_j(Z_{k+1}, \cdots, Z_{2k})$$

$$- \frac{1}{n^2} \sum_{i,j=1}^{n} \sum_{\alpha,\beta=1}^{k} E\{f_i(Z_1, \cdots, Z_k) f_j(Z_{\sigma_1}, \cdots, Z_{\sigma_k})\}$$

$$+ k^2 \left[\frac{1}{n} \sum_{i=1}^{n} E\{f_i(Z_1, \cdots, Z_k)\} \right]^2,$$

where again $Z_{n+j} = Z_j$ ($j > 0$), and where $\sigma_\beta = \alpha$ ($\alpha, \beta \leq k$), and σ_γ ($\gamma \neq \beta$) is greater than k. This last statement means that the suffix σ_β takes the value α and all other σ suffices in the expression take values greater than k.

THEOREM 4.4. (GHOSH). If $Z_1, Z_2, \cdots$ is a sequence of independent random variables, each having the same continuous distribution function, if (4.9) holds and if $\liminf\limits_{n \to \infty} \mu_{2n} > 0$, then, as $n \to \infty$, the probability approaches one that the permutation distribution function of

$$M^{-1/2} \left[\frac{1}{n} \sum_{i=1}^{n} f_i(z_i, \cdots, z_{i+k-1}) - M_1 \right]$$

differs by less than any preassigned amount from the normal distribution function with mean 0 and variance 1. Also $M_1 - \mu_{1n}$ and $nM_2 - \mu_{2n}$ converge in probability to zero as $n \to \infty$.

Proof. See Ghosh [12].

Note. The permutation distribution function for

$$M_2^{-1/2} \left[\frac{1}{n} \sum_{i=1}^{n} f_i(z_1, \cdots, z_{i+k-1}) - M_1 \right]$$

depends on the order statistic for $z_1, \cdots, z_n$ and hence is a random variable in terms of $Z_1, \cdots, Z_n$. This random distribution function converges in probability to the normal distribution function with mean 0 and variance 1.

Ghosh [12] has an extension of Theorem 4.4 to cover the case of vector functions $f_i(z_1, \cdots, z_n)$. Also he considers the distribution of $S(Z_1, \cdots, Z_n)$ when the Z's are not independent but have the distribution of a Markov process.

5. THE LIMITING DISTRIBUTION OF U STATISTICS

In Section 2 of Chapter 4 we defined U statistics and referred to a theorem by Hoeffding which gave the limiting distribution of U statistics. In this section we prove Hoeffding's theorem.

Let $\mathscr{X}(\mathscr{A})$ be a measurable space, and consider the sample space $\mathscr{X} = \mathscr{X}^n$. Corresponding to any statistic $f(x_1, \cdots, x_m)$ defined over $\mathscr{X}^m$ ($m \leq n$), we define a U statistic $U(x_1, \cdots, x_n)$ over $\mathscr{X}^n$,

$$(5.1) \quad U(x_1, \cdots, x_n) = \frac{1}{n(n-1) \cdots (n-m+1)} \sum_{P_n} f(x_{\alpha_1}, \cdots, x_{\alpha_m})$$

where P_n indicates that the summation is over all permutations $(\alpha_1, \cdots, \alpha_m)$ of m integers chosen from $(1, \cdots, n)$. As proved in Chapter 4, we can always write the U statistic in terms of a symmetric statistic $f^*(x_1, \cdots, x_m)$,

$$(5.2) \qquad U(x_1, \cdots, x_n) = \frac{1}{\binom{n}{m}} \sum_{C_n} f^*(x_{\alpha_1}, \cdots, x_{\alpha_m}),$$

where C_n indicates that the summation is over all combinations $(\alpha_1, \cdots, \alpha_m)$ of m integers chosen from $(1, \cdots, n)$ and where

$$f^*(x_1, \cdots, x_m) = \frac{1}{m!} \sum_{P_m} f(x_{\alpha_1}, \cdots, x_{\alpha_m}).$$

Let $X_1, \cdots, X_n$ be n independent random variables having the same probability measure P over $\mathscr{X}(\mathscr{A})$. We first consider the variance of a U statistic. Assume that $E\{(f^*(X_1, \cdots, X_m))^2\}$ exists. Then, of course, the first moment also exists, and we let

$$(5.3) \qquad E\{f^*(X_1, \cdots, X_m)\} = \eta.$$

From the theory of Chapter 4 it follows then that

$$E\{U(X_1, \cdots, X_n)\} = \eta.$$

We define a function $f_c^*(x_1, \cdots, x_c)$ by taking the conditional expectation of $f^*(x_1, \cdots, x_m)$, given $x_1, \cdots, x_c$:

$$(5.4) \qquad f_c^*(x_1, \cdots, x_c) = E\{f^*(x_1, \cdots, x_c, X_{c+1}, \cdots, X_m)\}$$

for $c = 1, \cdots, m$. To obtain a simple expression for the variance of U, we need the variances of these functions f_c^*; let

$$(5.5) \qquad \begin{aligned} \zeta_0 &= 0 \\ \zeta_c &= \operatorname{var}\{f_c^*(X_1, \cdots, X_c)\} \qquad (c = 1, \cdots, m). \end{aligned}$$

The variance ζ_m is the variance of $f(X_1, \cdots, X_m)$ and exists by reason of our assumption above. By Theorem 2.4 in Chapter 2 it can be shown that the other variances satisfy $\zeta_c \le \zeta_m$ and hence are finite (Problem 7).

Let $\alpha_1, \cdots, \alpha_m$ and $\beta_1, \cdots, \beta_m$ be two sets of m different integers chosen from $1, \cdots, n$, and let c be the number of integers common to the two sets. Then, using the symmetry of the function $f^*(x_1, \cdots, x_m)$, we find the covariance of $f^*(X_{\alpha_1}, \cdots, X_{\alpha_m})$ and $f^*(X_{\beta_1}, \cdots, X_{\beta_m})$:

$$\begin{aligned} \operatorname{cov}\{f^*(X_{\alpha_1}, \cdots, X_{\alpha_m}), f^*(X_{\beta_1}, \cdots, X_{\beta_m})\} \\ = E\{[f^*(X_{\alpha_1}, \cdots, X_{\alpha_m}) - \eta][f^*(X_{\beta_1}, \cdots, X_{\beta_m}) - \eta]\} \\ = E\{[f_c^*(X_1, \cdots, X_c) - \eta][f_c^*(X_1, \cdots, X_c) - \eta]\} \\ = \zeta_c. \end{aligned}$$

Then, for the variance of U, we have

$$\operatorname{var}\{U(X_1, \cdots, X_n)\} = \binom{n}{m}^{-2} \sum \operatorname{cov} f^*(X_{\alpha_1}, \cdots, X_{\alpha_m}) f^*(X_{\beta_1}, \cdots, X_{\beta_m}),$$

where the summation is over all combinations $(\alpha_1, \cdots, \alpha_m)$ of m integers from $(1, \cdots, n)$ and all combinations $(\beta_1, \cdots, \beta_m)$ of m integers from $(1, \cdots, n)$. We have

$$\operatorname{Var}\{U(X_1, \cdots, X_n)\}$$

(5.6)
$$= \binom{n}{m}^{-2} \sum_{c=0}^{m} \binom{n}{m}\binom{m}{c}\binom{n-m}{m-c} \zeta_c$$

$$= \binom{n}{m}^{-2} \sum_{c=1}^{m} \binom{n}{m}\binom{m}{c}\binom{n-m}{m-c} \zeta_c$$

$$= \binom{n}{m}^{-1} \sum_{c=1}^{m} \binom{m}{c}\binom{n-m}{m-c} \zeta_c,$$

where $\binom{n}{m}\binom{m}{c}\binom{n-m}{m-c}$ gives the number of pairs of sets $(\alpha_1, \cdots, \alpha_m)$ $(\beta_1, \cdots, \beta_m)$ having exactly c common integers.

Using the notation introduced above, we now give Hoeffding's theorem.

THEOREM 5.1. (HOEFFDING). If $X_1, \cdots, X_n$ are independent random variables having the same distribution over $\mathscr{X}(\mathscr{A})$, and if $f^*(x_1, \cdots, x_m)$ is a real-valued symmetric statistic over $\mathscr{X}^m$ and has expectation η, and finite second moment $E\{[f^*(X_1, \cdots, X_m)]^2\} < \infty$, then as $n \to \infty$, the limiting distribution $n^{1/2}[U(X_1, \cdots, X_n) - \eta]$, where

(5.7)
$$U(x_1, \cdots, x_n) = \frac{1}{\binom{n}{m}} \sum_{C_n} f^*(x_{\alpha_1}, \cdots, x_{\alpha_m})$$

is normal with mean 0 and variance $m^2 \zeta_1$ [ζ_1 is defined by (5.5)].

Proof. By the introduction to this theorem we know that $E\{[f^*(X_1, \cdots, X_m)]^2\} < \infty$ implies that $\zeta_1, \cdots, \zeta_m$ exist finite. Our method of proof is to show that the random variable $Z_n = n^{1/2}[U(X_1, \cdots, X_n) - \eta]$ is asymptotically equivalent to the random variable Y defined by

(5.8)
$$Y_n = mn^{-1/2} \sum_{\alpha=1}^{n} [f_1^*(X_\alpha) - \eta].$$

First we show that Y_n has asymptotically the normal distribution with mean 0 and variance $m^2\zeta_1$. By our introduction we know $E\{f_1^*(X_\alpha)\} = \eta$ and var $\{f_1^*(X_\alpha)\} = \zeta_1$. Also $f_1(X_1), f_1(X_2), \cdots$ is a sequence of real-valued, independent, and identically distributed random variables. By the central-limit Theorem 3.3, Y_n is asymptotically normal with mean 0 and variance $m^2\zeta_1$.

Now we show that p-lim $\underset{n \to \infty}{}(Y_n - Z_n) = 0$. For this it suffices to show that $E\{(Y_n - Z_n)^2\} \to 0$ (See Problem 3 and remarks on p-lim in Section 2.)

$$(5.9) \qquad E\{(Y_n - Z_n)^2\} = E\{Y_n^2\} + E\{Z_n^2\} - 2E\{Y_nZ_n\}$$

By our results above we have

$$(5.10) \qquad E\{Y_n^2\} = m^2\zeta_1.$$

From (5.6) we obtain

$$\text{var } \{U(X_1, \cdots, X_n)\}$$

$$= \frac{1}{\binom{n}{m}} \left\{ \binom{m}{1}\binom{n-m}{m-1}\zeta_1 + \binom{m}{2}\binom{n-m}{m-2}\zeta_2 + \cdots \right\}$$

$$= \frac{m^2}{n}\zeta_1 + 0\left(\frac{1}{n^2}\right);$$

therefore

$$E\{Z_n^2\} = n \text{ var } \{U(X_1, \cdots, X_n)\}$$

$$(5.11) \qquad\qquad = m^2\zeta_1 + 0\left(\frac{1}{n}\right).$$

We evaluate $E\{Y_nZ_n\}$.

$$E\{Y_nZ_n\} = mE\left\{[U(X_1, \cdots, X_n) - \eta]\sum_{\alpha=1}^{n}[f_1^*(X_\alpha) - \eta]\right\}$$

$$= \frac{m}{\binom{n}{m}}E\left\{\sum_{C_n}[f^*(X_{\alpha_1}, \cdots, X_{\alpha_m}) - \eta]\sum_{\alpha=1}^{n}[f_1^*(X_\alpha) - \eta]\right\}$$

$$= \frac{m}{\binom{n}{m}}\sum_{C_n}\sum_{\alpha=1}^{n}E\{[f^*(X_{\alpha_1}, \cdots, X_{\alpha_m}) - \eta][f_1(X_\alpha) - \eta]\}.$$

The expectation in the expression above is zero if α is not equal any α_i, and is ζ_1 if α is equal one of the α_i. For a fixed α the number of sets $\{\alpha_1, \cdots, \alpha_m\}$ containing α is $\binom{n-1}{m-1}$. Therefore,

(5.12)
$$E\{Y_n Z_n\} = \frac{m}{\binom{n}{m}} n \binom{n-1}{m-1} \zeta_1$$

$$= m^2 \zeta_1.$$

Equations (5.10), (5.11), (5.12) imply that the expression (5.9) has limit zero. Therefore p-lim $(Y_n - Z_n) = 0$.

We have $Z_n = Y_n + (Z_n - Y_n)$. By Theorem 2.6 and our results above, it follows that Z_n is asymptotically normal with mean 0 and variance $m^2 \zeta_1$. This completes the proof.

Hoeffding also proves some inequalities among var $\{U\}$ and the ζ's. These can be useful for the application of the theorem, and we quote them without proof.

THEOREM 5.2. The variances $\zeta_1, \zeta_2, \cdots, \zeta_m$ defined by (5.5) satisfy the inequalities

(5.13)
$$\zeta_c \leq \frac{c}{d} \zeta_d$$

where

$$1 \leq c \leq d \leq m.$$

THEOREM 5.3. If $X_1, \cdots, X_n$ are independent and identically distributed, then the variance of a U statistic satisfies

(5.14)
$$\frac{m^2}{n} \zeta_1 \leq \text{var } \{U_n\} \leq \frac{m}{n} \zeta_m.$$

n var $\{U_n\}$ is a decreasing function of n,

(5.15)
$$(n+1) \text{ var } \{U_{n+1}\} \leq n \text{ var } \{U_n\},$$

which takes its upper bounded $m\zeta_m$ for $n = m$ and tends to its lower bound $m^2 \zeta_1$ as n increases:

(5.16)
$$\lim_{n \to \infty} n \text{ var } \{U_n\} = m^2 \zeta_1.$$

Using this last theorem with Theorem (2.6) we obtain immediately

THEOREM 5.4. If the conditions of Theorem 5.1 are fulfilled and if $\zeta_1 > 0$, then the limiting distribution of

$$\frac{U_n - \eta}{\sigma_{U_n}}$$

is normal with mean 0 and variance 1.

In [5] Hoeffding generalizes the results above to obtain the limiting distribution of a vector U statistic. We indicate the form of these results. Let $\mathbf{U} = (U^{(1)}, \cdots, U^{(g)})$ be based on the symmetric statistics $f^{*(1)}(x_1, \cdots, x_{m_1}), \cdots, f^{*(g)}(x_1, \cdots, x_{m_g})$. If $\zeta_1(i,j)$ is the covariance between $f_1^{*(i)}(X)$ and $f_1^{*(j)}(X)$, using the previous notation, then $n^{1/2}(\mathbf{U} - \mathbf{\eta})$ has a limiting multivariate normal distributions with means 0 and covariance matrix $\| m_i m_j \zeta^{(ij)} \|$. (Assuming of course that second moments of the $f^{*(i)}(X_1, \cdots, X_{m_i})$ exist). To derive the covariance of two U statistics is given as Problem 10.

Also Hoeffding treats the case of X's not identically distributed and obtains for U statistics a generalization which corresponds to the Liapounoff form of the central-limit theorem. We quote this second generalization after developing some necessary notation.

Let $X_1, \cdots, X_n$ be independent random variables over $\mathcal{X}(\mathcal{A})$, and suppose they do not necessarily have the same probability distributions. Corresponding to a U statistic,

$$(5.17) \qquad U(x_1, \cdots, x_n) = \frac{1}{\binom{n}{m}} \sum_{P_n} f^*(x_{\alpha_1}, \cdots, x_{\alpha_m}),$$

with f^* symmetric, we define

$$\eta_{\alpha_1 \cdots \alpha_m} = E\{f^*(X_{\alpha_1}, \cdots, X_{\alpha_m})\},$$

$$f^*_{c \, \beta_1 \cdots \beta_{m-c}}(x_1, \cdots, x_c) = E\{f^*(x_1, \cdots, x_c, X_{\beta_1}, \cdots, X_{\beta_{m-c}})\},$$

$$\zeta_{c(\alpha_1 \cdots \alpha_c) \, \beta_1 \cdots \beta_{m-c}; \, \gamma_1 \cdots \gamma_{m-c}}$$
$$= \text{cov} \{f^*_{c\beta_1 \cdots \beta_{m-c}}(X_{\alpha_1}, \cdots, X_{\alpha_c}) f^*_{c; \gamma_1 \cdots \gamma_{m-c}}(X_{\alpha_1}, \cdots, X_{\alpha_c}),$$

$$\zeta_{c,n} = \frac{c!(m-c)!(m-c)!}{n(n-1) \cdots (n-2m+c+1)}$$

$$\Sigma \, \zeta_{c \, (\alpha_1 \cdots \alpha_c) \, \beta_1 \cdots \beta_{m-c}; \, \gamma_1 \cdots \gamma_{m-c}},$$

where the sum is extended over all disjoint sets $\{\alpha_1, \cdots, \alpha_c\}$, $\{\beta_1, \cdots, \beta_{m-c}\}$, $\{\gamma_1, \cdots, \gamma_{m-c}\}$ chosen from $(1, \cdots, n)$. Then it is straightforward to show that

$$(5.18) \qquad \text{var} \{U\} = \frac{1}{\binom{n}{m}} \sum_{c=1}^{m} \binom{m}{c} \binom{n-m}{m-c} \zeta_{c,n}.$$

We also define a function $g_{1(\nu)}(x)$

$$(5.19) \quad g_{1(\nu)}(x) = \frac{1}{\binom{n-1}{m-1}} \sum_{\neq \nu} [f^*_{1;\beta_1\cdots\beta_{m-1}}(x) - \eta_{\gamma\beta_1\cdots\beta_{m-1}}],$$

where the summation is over all sets $(\beta_1, \cdots, \beta_{m-1})$ chosen from the first n integers excluding the integer ν. We now quote Hoeffding's theorem for the case of X's not necessarily identically distributed.

THEOREM 5.5. If $X_1, \cdots, X_n$ are n independent random variables, if

$$E\{[f^*(X_{\alpha_1}, \cdots, X_{\alpha_m})]^2\} < A$$

for all $\alpha_1, \cdots, \alpha_n$, if

$$E\{|g_{1(\nu)}(X_\nu)|^3\} < \infty$$

for $\nu = 1, \cdots, n$ and if

$$\lim_{n\to\infty} \frac{\sum_{\nu=1}^{n} E\{|g_{1\nu}(X_\nu)|^3\}}{\sum_{\nu=1}^{n} E\{[g_{1\nu}(X_\nu)]^2\}^{3/2}} = 0,$$

then, as $n \to \infty$, the limiting distribution of

$$\frac{U - E\{U\}}{[\text{var }\{U\}]^{1/2}}$$

is normal with mean 0 and variance 1.

Another extension of Hoeffding's theorem has been proposed by E. L. Lehmann. Problem 8 suggests a method of proof following the pattern of proof for Theorem 5.1. Let $X_1, \cdots, X_{n_1}$ be independent and have the same distribution over $\mathscr{X}(\mathscr{A})$, and let $Y_1, \cdots, Y_{n_2}$ be independent and have the same distribution over $\mathscr{Y}(\mathscr{B})$. Then we have

THEOREM 5.6. If $f^*(x_1, \cdots, x_{m_1}; y_1, \cdots, y_{m_2})$ is a real-valued statistic symmetric in the x's, symmetric in the y's with expectation η and with finite second moment, and if $n_1 \leq n_2$ and $n_1 \to \infty$ such that $\lim \dfrac{n_1}{n_2}$ exists, then $n_1^{1/2}(U - \eta)$, where U is given by

$$(5.20) \quad U = \frac{1}{\binom{n_1}{m_1}\binom{n_2}{m_2}} \sum_C f^*(x_{\alpha_1}, \cdots, x_{\alpha_m}; y_{\beta_1}, \cdots, y_{\beta_m}),$$

and the summation is over all combinations $(\alpha_1, \cdots, \alpha_{m_1})$ from $(1, \cdots, n_1)$ and all combinations $(\beta_1, \cdots, \beta_{m_2})$ from $(1, \cdots, n_2)$, has a limiting normal distribution with mean 0.

Note. The variance of the limiting distribution together with suggestions for a proof are given in Problem 8.

EXAMPLE 5.1. In Chapter 4 we considered the estimation of moments and cumulants by means of U statistics. By Hoeffding's theorem we now know that, if the second moment of a symmetric kernel exists, then

$$n^{1/2}(U - E(U))$$

has a limiting normal distribution. Actually, as is easily seen, it is sufficient to have a finite second moment for any kernel. By Theorem 2.7 we can then infer that many functions of moments and k statistics have a limiting normal distribution.

Also in Chapter 4 we defined Gini's mean difference for n real variables, $y_1, \cdots, y_n$:

(5.21)
$$d = \frac{1}{n(n-1)} \sum_{\alpha \neq \beta} |y_\alpha - y_\beta|.$$

If $Y_1, \cdots, Y_n$ are independent and identically distributed random variables having distribution function $F(x)$, then the mean of the induced distribution of d is

(5.22)
$$\Delta = \int \int |y_1 - y_2| \, dF(y_1) \, dF(y_2),$$

and the variance by (5.6) is

$$\operatorname{var}\{d\} = \frac{2}{n(n-1)} [2\zeta_1(n-2) + \zeta_2],$$

where

$$\zeta_1 = \int [\int (y_1 - y_2) \, dF(y_2)]^2 \, dF(y_1) - \Delta^2$$

(5.23)
$$\zeta_2 = \int \int (y_1 - y_2)^2 \, dF(y_1) \, dF(y_2) - \Delta^2$$

$$= 2 \operatorname{var}\{Y\} - \Delta^2.$$

Values of var $\{d\}$ for several distributions have been tabulated by U. S. Nair [18]. By Hoeffding's theorem, $\sqrt{n}(d - \Delta)$ has a limiting normal distribution provided the variance exists.

EXAMPLE 5.2. Some interesting applications of Hoeffding's theorem are obtained for statistics based on ranks. First we introduce some notation which simplifies the use of ranks. The sign function $s(x)$ is given by

$$s(x) = -1 \quad \text{if} \quad x < 0$$
$$(5.24) \qquad\qquad = 0 \qquad\qquad = 0$$
$$= 1 \qquad\qquad > 0.$$

Also let

$$c(u) = 0 \qquad \text{if} \quad x < 0$$
$$(5.25) \qquad\qquad = \frac{1}{2} \qquad\qquad = 0$$
$$= 1 \qquad\qquad > 0$$
$$= \frac{1}{2}[1 + s(x)].$$

For a sequence of numbers, $x_1, \cdots, x_n$, the rank r_α of the α-th number x_α is of course one more than the number of smaller x's; therefore

$$r_\alpha = \frac{1}{2} + \sum_{\beta=1}^{n} c(x_\alpha - x_\beta)$$
$$(5.26)$$
$$= \frac{n+1}{2} + \frac{1}{2} \sum_{\beta=1}^{n} s(x_\alpha - x_\beta).$$

If some of the x's are equal, this definition for r gives what is known as the midrank. For a set of equal x's, each has the same rank, the average of the ranks that would have been assigned had the x's been all different. From the above it is seen that any function of ranks can be represented as a function of the $\binom{n}{2}$ signs of differences, and of course any functions of the signs of differences can be represented as functions of ranks.

For a sequence of n vectors, $\mathbf{x}_1, \cdots, \mathbf{x}_n$, where $\mathbf{x}_\alpha = (x_\alpha^{(1)}, \cdots, x_\alpha^{(r)})$, we can define for each vector coordinate a set of n ranks, $r_1^{(i)}, \cdots, r_n^{(i)}$. $r_\alpha^{(i)}$ is the rank of $x_\alpha^{(i)}$ in $\{x_1^{(i)}, \cdots, x_n^{(i)}\}$. Consider a kernel $f(\mathbf{x}_1, \cdots, \mathbf{x}_m)$ of a U statistic, and suppose that $f(\mathbf{x}_1, \cdots, \mathbf{x}_m)$ is a function only of signs of differences, $s(x_\alpha^{(i)} - x_\beta^{(i)})$, for $\alpha, \beta = 1, \cdots, m$ and $i = 1, \cdots, r$. The corresponding U statistic can then be expressed as a function of the ranks, $r_\alpha^{(i)}$.

Let $\mathbf{X}_1, \cdots, \mathbf{X}_n$ be independent and each have the same distribution over R^r. The kernel $f(\mathbf{x}_1, \cdots, \mathbf{x}_m)$ defined above will automatically satisfy the conditions of the Theorem 3.1. For this we need only show that it has finite variance. From its definition $f(\mathbf{x}_1, \cdots, \mathbf{x}_m)$ can take on only a finite number of real values, and therefore the induced distribution of $f(\mathbf{X}_1, \cdots, \mathbf{X}_m)$ will have finite second moment (in fact, the induced distribution will have bounded second moment, regardless of the distribution for the X's). Then, if U is the U statistic corresponding to f, and η is its expected value, we have by Theorem 5.1 that $n^{1/2}(U - \eta)$ has a limiting normal distribution with mean 0.

For the remainder of this example we consider the application of the above ideas to the difference sign correlation. The application to the rank correlation coefficient, the grade correlation coefficient, the partial-difference-sign correlation coefficient, and a statistic used by Mann for detecting trend will be considered in Problems 10 to 17.

Consider the sequence $(x_1^{(1)}, x_1^{(2)}), \cdots, (x_n^{(1)}, x_n^{(2)})$, where the $x_\alpha^{(i)}$ are real. For each coordinate we can form $n(n - 1)$ signs of difference, $s(x_\alpha^{(i)} - x_\beta^{(i)})$, for $\alpha, \beta = 1, \cdots, n$ ($\alpha \neq \beta$). These $n(n - 1)$ numbers satisfy

$$\sum_{\alpha \neq \beta} s(x_\alpha^{(i)} - x_\beta^{(i)}) = 0$$

for $i = 1, 2$. Hence, if we define t to be the covariance between the $n(n - 1)$ values for the first coordinate and the corresponding $n(n - 1)$ values for the second coordinate, we have

(5.27)
$$t = \frac{1}{n(n - 1)} \sum_{\alpha \neq \beta} s(x_\alpha^{(1)} - x_\beta^{(1)})\, s(x_\alpha^{(2)} - x_\beta^{(2)}).$$

t is called the *difference-sign covariance* of the n pairs $(x_\alpha^{(1)}, x_\alpha^{(2)})$.
If all the $x^{(1)}$'s and all the $x^{(2)}$'s are different, then

$$\sum_{\alpha \neq \beta} s^2(x_\alpha^{(i)} - x_\beta^{(i)}) = n(n - 1),$$

and t is the product-moment correlation of the difference signs.

t is a U statistic with the symmetric kernel $s(x_1^{(1)} - x_2^{(1)})\, s(x_1^{(2)} - x_2^{(2)})$. Let $(X_1^{(1)}, X_1^{(2)}), \cdots, (X_n^{(1)}, X_n^{(2)})$ be independent and identically distributed over R^2 with distribution function $F(\mathbf{x})$. From our theory in Chapter 4 we know that t is an unbiased estimate of the parameter

(5.28)
$$\tau = \int_{R^2} \int_{R^2} s(x_1^{(1)} - x_2^{(1)}) s(x_1^{(2)} - x_2^{(2)})\, dF(\mathbf{x}_1)\, dF(\mathbf{x}_2),$$

and for a sufficiently large class of F's it has minimum variance among unbiased estimates of τ. For $\mathbf{X}_1$ and $\mathbf{X}_2$ independent with distribution function $F(\mathbf{x})$, τ is the covariance of the sign of the difference between the first coordinates with the sign of the difference between the second coordinates. If τ^+, τ^- are the probabilities that the two signs are the same, different, then of course

$$(5.29) \qquad \tau = \tau^+ - \tau^-$$

and, if $F(\mathbf{x})$ is continuous, $\tau^+ + \tau^- = 1$ and $\tau = 2\tau^+ - 1 = 1 - 2\tau^-$.

Assume now that $F(\mathbf{x})$ is a continuous distribution function. Using the notation of Theorem 5.1, we have

$$
\begin{aligned}
f_1^*(\mathbf{x}) &= E\{s(x^{(1)} - X_2^{(1)})s(x^{(2)} - X_2^{(2)}\} \\
&= F(x^{(1)}, x^{(2)}) - [F(x^{(1)}, \infty) - F(x^{(1)}, x^{(2)})] \\
&\quad - [F(\infty, x^{(2)}) - F(x^{(1)}, x^{(2)})] \\
&\quad + [1 - F(x^{(1)}, \infty) - F(\infty, x^{(2)}) + F(x^{(1)}, x^{(2)})] \\
&= 1 - 2F(x^{(1)}, \infty) - 2F(\infty, x^{(2)}) + 4F(x^{(1)}, x^{(2)}).
\end{aligned}
$$

(5.30)

The variance of t is

$$(5.31) \qquad \operatorname{var}\{t\} = \frac{2}{n(n-1)}[2(n-2)\zeta_1 + \zeta_2],$$

where

$$
\begin{aligned}
\zeta_1 &= E\{[f_1^*(X)]^2\} - \tau^2 \\
\zeta_2 &= E\{s^2(X_1^{(1)} - X_2^{(1)})s^2(X_1^{(2)} - X_2^{(2)})\} - \tau^2 \\
&= 1 - \tau^2.
\end{aligned}
$$

If $X^{(1)}$ and $X^{(2)}$ are independent and continuous, then the induced distributions of $F(x^{(1)}, \infty)$ and $F(\infty, x^{(2)})$ are uniform on the interval $[0, 1]$. Designating by U_1, U_2 two independent random variables with this uniform distribution, we have

$$(5.32) \qquad \tau = E\{s(X_1^{(1)} - X_2^{(1)})\}\, E\{s(X_1^{(2)} - X_2^{(2)})\}$$

$$= 0,$$

$$(5.33) \qquad \zeta_1 = E\{(1 - 2U_1 - 2U_2 + 4U_1U_2)^2\} - 0$$

$$= \frac{1}{9},$$

$$(5.34) \qquad \zeta_2 = 1,$$

and hence

$$(5.35) \qquad \operatorname{var}\{t\} = \frac{2(2n+5)}{9n(n-1)}.$$

If, however, we have a discontinuous distribution function, then in the case of independence the var $\{t\}$ will depend on the probabilities at the discontinuities.

Theorem 5.1 says that $n^{1/2}$ $(t - \tau)$ has a limiting normal distribution with mean 0. The variance of the limiting distribution is 4/9 when the distribution function is continuous and the coordinates are independent. If with probability one $X^{(2)}$ is an increasing function of $X^{(1)}$, then it can be shown that $\zeta_1 = 0$, and hence $n^{1/2}(t - \tau)$ converges to zero in probability.

EXAMPLE 5.3. Consider the problem of independence, Section 2.2 in Chapter 3. $(X_1^{(1)}, X_1^{(2)}), \cdots, (X_n^{(1)}, X_n^{(2)})$ are independent and have the same distribution function $F_\theta(x^{(1)}, x^{(2)})$ where θ indexes the absolutely continuous distributions over R^2. The problem is

Hypothesis: $F_\theta(x^{(1)}, x^{(2)}) = F_\theta^{(1)}(x^{(1)})F_\theta^{(2)}(x^{(2)})$ for all $(x^{(1)}, x^{(2)})$, $\theta \in \Omega$,

Alternative: $F_\theta(x^{(1)}, x^{(2)}) \neq F_\theta^{(1)}(x^{(1)})F_\theta^{(2)}(x^{(2)})$ for some $(x^{(1)}, x^{(2)})$, $\theta \in \Omega$.

According to the theory at the end of Section 3.2 in Chapter 5, any invariant test function for this problem can be represented by a function of ranks and hence of difference signs. Also we have the simplicity that any statistic based on difference signs has a single distribution under the hypothesis. Two statistics frequently used to form such tests are the difference-sign correlation t defined in Example 5.2 and the rank correlation k' defined in Problem 10. Theorem 5.1 enables us to choose the constants to give the test correct size for large n and also enables us to find the power function for large n.

For the difference-sign correlation t, we have $E\{t\} = 0$ under the hypothesis. Hence a natural test is to reject when $|t| > c_n$. For a size-α test Theorem 5.1 and formula (5.35) show that, for large n,

$$c_n \sim \frac{2}{3n^{1/2}} z_\alpha',$$

where $[-z_\alpha', z_\alpha']$ is the interval containing probability $1 - \alpha$ for the normal distribution with mean 0 and variance 1.

For large n the power function is given by

$$\mathbf{P}_n = \Pr\{|t| \geq c_n\}.$$

Since var $\{t\} = O(n^{-1})$ and $c_n \to 0$, the power approaches one for any alternative distribution having $\tau \neq 0$; and, if $\tau = 0$, the limit of the power will be less than one.

For the rank correlation we have similar results. The test is to reject if $|k'| > c_n'$ where c_n' is chosen to give the test correct size. Again for any alternative distribution we can find an approximate value for the power when n is large. Also if $\kappa \neq 0$, the limiting value of the power as n increases will be one.

Thus the two tests are consistent against alternatives for which, respectively, $\tau \neq 0$ and $\kappa \neq 0$.

EXAMPLE 5.4. In Example 1.1 we introduced the Mann–Whitney test for the two-sample problem. Let $X_1, \cdots, X_{n_1}$ be independent with continuous distribution function $F(x)$, and $X_{n_1+1}, \cdots, X_{n_1+n_2}$ be independent with continuous distribution function $G(x)$. The Mann–Whitney test is based on the statistic

$$v = \frac{1}{n_1 n_2} \sum_{i=1}^{n_1} \sum_{j=1}^{n_2} c(x_{n_1+j} - x_i),$$

where $c(u)$ was defined by (5.25). We consider the application of Theorem 5.6 to obtain the limiting distribution of v as the sample size increases.

Without loss of generality let $n_1 \leq n_2$. v is a symmetric function of $x_1, \cdots, x_{n_1}$ and a symmetric function of $x_{n_1+1}, \cdots, x_{n_1+n_2}$. Also, since v takes on only a finite number of values, its second moment exists. Then, if $n_1, n_2 \to \infty$ such that n_1/n_2 has a limit, then by Theorem 5.6

$$n^{1/2}(V - E(V))$$

has a limiting normal with mean 0 and finite variance. For large samples the limiting distribution under the hypothesis can be used to give a test size α. Also, for large samples the limiting distribution under an alternative $(F(x), G(x))$ gives the power function of the test.

6. THE WALD–WOLFOWITZ LIMIT THEOREM

In Section 2 of Chapter 5 we developed a method for constructing tests having maximum power for a particular parameter value of the alternative. The tests were conditional tests. For each example considered, the test statistic was a linear function of the coordinates of the outcome, and the hypothesis conditional distribution gave equal probability to each of a finite number of permutations of the coordinates of the outcome. In this section we consider a theorem by Wald and Wolfowitz and a number of extensions which give the large-sample hypothesis distribution of such test statistics.

Let $\mathcal{H}_n = (h_{1n}, \cdots, h_{nn})$ for $n = 1, 2, \cdots$ be sequences of real numbers.

In their theorem, Wald and Wolfowitz considered sequences that satisfy a condition which we designate by W:

Condition W.   For all $r = 3, 4, \cdots$,

(6.1)
$$\frac{\dfrac{1}{n}\sum_{1}^{n}(h_{in} - \bar{h}_n)^r}{\left[\dfrac{1}{n}\sum_{1}^{n}(h_{in} - \bar{h}_n)^2\right]^{r/2}} = O(1),$$

where $\bar{h}_n = n^{-1}\sum_{1}^{n} h_{in}$.

The condition says that, as n increases, the rth central moment standardized with respect to the variance should be bounded. Another condition was introduced by Noether and we designate it by N.

Condition N.   For all $r = 3, 4, \cdots$,

(6.2)
$$\frac{\sum_{i=1}^{n}(h_{in} - \bar{h}_n)^r}{\left[\sum_{i=1}^{n}(h_{in} - \bar{h}_n)^2\right]^{r/2}} = o(1),$$

where $\bar{h}_n = n^{-1}\sum_{1}^{n} h_{in}$.

Corresponding to a sequence $\mathscr{A}_n$, we define a random variable $\mathbf{X}_n = (X_1, \cdots, X_n)$ which takes each permutation of $(a_{1n}, \cdots, a_{1n})$ with the same probability $1/n!$. Then, corresponding to sequences $\mathscr{A}_n$ and $\mathscr{C}_n$, we investigate the limiting distribution as $n \to \infty$ of the linear expression

(6.3)
$$L_n = c_{in}X_i + \cdots + c_{nn}X_n.$$

It is straightforward to prove

(6.4)
$$E\{L_n\} = \frac{\sum_{1}^{n} c_{in} \sum_{1}^{n} a_{jn}}{n}$$

and

(6.5)
$$\operatorname{var}\{L_n\} = \frac{1}{n-1}\sum_{i=1}^{n}(c_{in} - \bar{c}_n)^2 \sum_{j=1}^{n}(a_{jn} - \bar{a}_n)^2.$$

(See Problem 18.)

The original theorem concerning the distribution of L_n was proved by Wald and Wolfowitz and was a generalization of a limit theorem for the rank correlation coefficient derived by Hotelling and Pabst. Our first theorem is an extension of the Wald–Wolfowitz theorem and was proved by Noether.

THEOREM 6.1. (WALD–WOLFOWITZ–NOETHER). If $\mathscr{C}_n$ satisfies condition W (6.1), and $\mathscr{A}_n$ satisfies condition N (6.2), then

$$(6.6) \qquad L_n^0 = \frac{L_n - E\{L_n\}}{\sigma_{L_n}},$$

where L_n is defined by (6.3), has a limiting normal distribution with mean 0 and variance 1.

Proof. Let $C_{e_1 \cdots e_m}$ be a symmetric function generated by $c_1^{e_1} \cdots c_m^{e_m}$, that is

$$(6.7) \qquad C_{e_1 \cdots e_m} = \sum_P c_{i_1}^{e_1} \cdots c_{i_m}^{e_m},$$

where the summation is over all permutations $(i_1, \cdots, i_m)$ of m integers chosen from $(1, \cdots, n)$. Similarly let $A_{e_1 \cdots e_m}$ designate the corresponding symmetric function for the $\mathscr{A}_n$ sequence.

If we multiply each element of a sequence by a constant, or if we add a constant to each element, we do not alter L_n^0. Hence it suffices to prove the theorem when $\sum_1^n a_{in} = \sum_1^n c_{in} = 0$ and $\sum_1^n a_{in}^2 = \sum_1^n c_{in}^2 = n$. These relations together with the conditions W and N establish that

$$(8.6) \qquad \begin{array}{llll} C_1 = 0, & C_2 = n, & C_r = O(n), & r = 3, 4, \cdots; \\ A_1 = 0, & A_2 = n, & A_r = o(n^{r/2}), & r = 3, 4, \cdots. \end{array}$$

Then we have

$$
\begin{aligned}
E\{L_n\} &= C_1 E\{X_1\} = 0, \\
\mathrm{var}\,\{L_n\} &= E\{L_n^2\} \\
&= C_2 E(X_1^2) + C_{11} E(X_1 X_2) \\
&= \frac{1}{n} C_2 A_2 + \frac{1}{n(n-1)} (C_1^2 - C_1)(A_1^2 - A_2) \\
&= \frac{1}{n} C_2 A_2 = \frac{1}{n(n-1)} C_2 A_2 \\
&= \frac{1}{n-1} C_2 A_2 \\
&\sim n.
\end{aligned}
$$

By Theorem 2.6 it is equivalent to prove that $n^{-1/2}L_n$ has a limiting normal distribution, and we shall do this by the method of moments, using Theorems 2.1 and 2.2. We now prove that the rth moment of $n^{-1/2}L_n$ approaches the rth moments of the standardized normal distribution.

We have

(6.9) $\mu_r = n^{-r/2}E\{L_n^r\}$

$$= n^{-r/2}\sum_{i_1=1}^{n}\cdots\sum_{i_r=1}^{n}E\{c_{i_1}X_{i_1}\cdots c_{i_r}X_{i_r}\}$$

$$= n^{-r/2}[C_rE(X_1^r) + \cdots + c(r, e_1, \cdots, e_m)C_{e_1\cdots e_m}E\{X_1^{e_1}\cdots X_m^{e_m}\}$$

$$+ \cdots + C_1\ldots{}_1E\{X_1\cdots X_r\}],$$

where $e_1 + \cdots + e_m = r$, e_k for $k = 1, \cdots, m$ is a positive integer, and the coefficient $c(r, e_1, \cdots, e_m)$ is the number of ways that the r indices $i_1, \cdots, i_r$ can be tied into m groups so that the m groups in the order in which their first element occurs in the sequence $i_1, \cdots, i_r$ are, respectively, of size $e_1, \cdots, e_m$.

Since $E\{X_1^{e_1}\cdots X_m^{e_m}\} \sim n^{-m}A_{e_1\cdots e_m}$, we have

(6.10) $n^{-r/2}C_{e_1\cdots e_m}E\{X_1^{e_1}\cdots X_m^{e_m}\} \sim n^{-(r/2+m)}C_{e_1\cdots e_m}A_{e_1\cdots e_m}$,

and we designate by $B(r, e_1, \cdots, e_m)$ the right-hand side of this relation. To complete the proof of the theorem we need a lemma which we shall prove later.

LEMMA 6.1. $B(r, e_1, \cdots, e_m) \sim 0$ unless

(6.11) $m = \dfrac{r}{2}, \qquad e_1 = \cdots = e_m = 2,$

in which case $B(r, 2, \cdots, 2) \sim 1$.

By (6.9) μ_r is the sum of a finite number of expressions $B(r, e_1, \cdots, e_m)$. Therefore, if $r = 2s + 1$ ($s = 1, 2, \cdots$), $\mu_{2r+1} \sim 0$ since at least one of the e's in each B must be odd. If $r = 2s$, $\mu_{2s} \sim c(2s, 2, \cdots, 2)$. Since the first index of the expression being summed in (6.9) can be tied with any of the $2s - 1$ others, the next free index with any of $2s - 3$ others, etc., it is seen that $\mu_{2s} \sim (2s - 1)\cdots 3$. But these are the moments of the normal distribution with mean 0 and variance 1, and hence the theorem follows.

Proof of Lemma. Let $A(j_1, \cdots, j_h) = A_{j_1}\cdots A_{j_h}$. Then by the theory of symmetric functions $A_{e_1\cdots e_m}$ can be expressed uniquely as a linear combination of a finite number of $A(j_1, \cdots, j_h)$, where

(6.12) $j_1 + \cdots + j_h = e_1 + \cdots + e_m = r,$

and the j's correspond to sums of e's. Since $A_1 = 0$, we need only consider $A(j_1, \cdots, j_h)$ having $j_g \geq 2$ $(g = 1, \cdots, h)$. If some $j_g > 2$, then (6.8) with (6.12) implies that

$$A(j_1, \cdots, j_h) = o(n^{r/2}).$$

If all $j_g = 2$, then

$$A(2, \cdots, 2) = A_2^{r/2}$$

(6.13) $$= n^{r/2},$$

r is even, and, from the remark following (6.12), all the e's must be 1's or 2's; therefore $m > r/2$ unless (6.11). From this we have

$$A_{e_1 \cdots e_m} = o(n^{r/2}) \qquad m < r/2,$$

and certainly

$$A_{e_1 \cdots e_m} = o(n^m) \qquad m > r/2,$$

unless $m = r/2$ and $e_1 = \cdots = e_m$, in which case

$$A_{2 \cdots 2} \sim A(2, \cdots, 2) = n^{r/2}.$$

Similarly, writing $C_{e_1 \cdots e_m}$ as a sum of products of the form $C_{j_1 \cdots j_h}$, we obtain the relations

$$C_{e_1 \cdots e_m} = O(n^m) \qquad m < r/2$$
$$= O(n^{r/2}) \qquad m > r/2.$$

Combining these results, we have

$$A_{e_1 \cdots e_m} C_{e_i \cdots e_m} = o(n^{m+r/2}),$$

unless r is even and all the e's are equal 2, in which case

$$A_2 \ldots {}_2 C_2 \ldots {}_2 \sim n^r.$$

This proves the lemma.

The condition N introduced by Noether can be given in two simpler forms, both of which are more convenient for application. We have

THEOREM 6.2.   (HOEFFDING).   The condition N for $\mathcal{H}_n$ is equivalent to either of the following two conditions:

(6.14) $$\lim_{n \to \infty} \frac{\sum_{1}^{n} |h_{in} - \bar{h}_n|^r}{\left[\sum_{1}^{n} (h_{in} - \bar{h}_n)^2 \right]^{r/2}} = 0 \quad \text{for some} \quad r > 2;$$

(6.15) $$\frac{\max_{1}^{n} (h_{in} - \bar{h}_n)^2}{\sum_{1}^{n} (h_{in} - \bar{h}_n)^2} \to 0.$$

Hence, if $\mathscr{C}_n$ satisfies condition W (6.1), and $\mathscr{A}_n$ satisfies any one of conditions (6.2), (6.14), (6.15), then L_n^0 given by (6.4) has a limiting normal distribution with mean 0 and variance 1.

Proof. Let

$$g_i = \frac{h_{in} - \bar{h}_n}{\left[\sum_1^n (h_{in} - \bar{h}_n)^2\right]^{1/2}}.$$

and

$$G_n = \max \{g_1, \cdots, g_n\}.$$

We must prove the equivalence of the three conditions:

(6.16) $$\lim_{n \to \infty} \sum_{i=1}^n g_i^r = 0 \qquad r = 3, 4, \cdots;$$

(6.17) $$\lim_{n \to \infty} \sum_{i=1}^n |g_i|^r = 0 \qquad \text{for some } r > 2;$$

(6.18) $$\lim_{n \to \infty} G_n = 0.$$

Since we have

$$\sum_{i=1}^n g_i^2 = 1,$$

then, for $r > 2$,

$$G_n^r < \sum_{i=1}^n |g_1|^r \le G_n^{r-2} \sum_{i=1}^n g_i^2 = G_n^{r-2}.$$

These inequalities imply the equivalence of the three conditions.

There are extensions of Theorem 6.1 which give the joint limiting distribution of a number of L_N statistics. We consider one such extension giving the limiting joint distribution of two L_N statistics.

THEOREM 6.3. If $\mathscr{A}_N$ satisfies condition N (6.2), if $\mathscr{C}_n$, and $\mathscr{D}_n$ satisfy condition W, and if the correlation between $\mathscr{C}_n$ and $\mathscr{D}_n$,

(6.19) $$\rho_n = \frac{\sum_1^n (c_{in} - \bar{c}_n)(d_{in} - \bar{d}_n)}{\left[\sum_1^n (c_{in} - \bar{c}_n)^2 \sum_1^n (d_{in} - \bar{d}_n)^2\right]^{1/2}},$$

has a limit ρ, then the limiting distribution of

(6.20) $$L_n^0 = \frac{L_n - E(L_n)}{\sigma(L_n)}, \qquad L_n^{'0} = \frac{L_n' - E(L_n')}{\sigma(L_n')},$$

where $L_n = \sum_1^n c_{in} X_i$, $L_n' = \sum_1^n d_{in} X_i$ [see (6.3)], is bivariate normal with means 0, variance 1 and correlation ρ.

Proof. By the same argument used in the proof of Theorem 6.1, it suffices to consider the case when $\sum_1^n a_{in} = \sum_1^n c_{in} = \sum_1^n d_{in} = 0$ and $\sum_1^n a_{in}^2 = \sum_1^n c_{in}^2 = \sum_1^n d_{in}^2 = n^{1/2}$. Then it is easily seen that L_n^0 is asymptotically equivalent to L_n and has a limiting normal distribution with mean 0 and variance 1, and similarly for $L_n^{'0}$ and L_n'. As a first step we shall prove that, if $\rho \neq \pm 1$, then, for any δ_1, δ_2, the linear combination $\delta_1 L_n + \delta_2 L_n'$ has a limiting normal distribution with mean 0 and variance $\delta_1^2 + \delta_2^2 + 2\delta_1\delta_2\rho$.

To apply Theorem 6.1 to the linear combination,

(6.21) $$\delta_1 L_n + \delta_2 L_n' = \sum_1^n (\delta_1 c_{in} + \delta_2 d_{in}) X_i,$$

we need only show that $\delta_1 \mathscr{C}_n + \delta_2 \mathscr{D}_n$ satisfies the condition W. For this we take n large enough that $1 > \rho' > |\rho_n|$ and consider the second moment of the elements $\delta_1 c_{in} + \delta_2 d_{in}$:

$$\frac{1}{n} \sum_1^n (\delta_1 c_{in} + \delta_2 d_{in})^2 \geq \frac{1}{n} \delta_1^2 \sum_1^n c_{in}^2 + \frac{1}{n} \delta_2^2 \sum_1^n d_{in}^2 - 2\delta_1\delta_2 \left| \sum_1^n c_{in} d_{in} \right|$$

$$= \delta_1^2 + \delta_2^2 - 2\delta_1\delta_2 |\rho_n|$$

$$\geq \delta_1^2 + \delta_2^2 - 2\delta_1\delta_2\rho'.$$

Hence the denominator of the condition W expression for $\delta_1 \mathscr{C}_n + \delta_2 \mathscr{D}_n$ is bounded from zero. We now show that the numerator is bounded. The numerator is the rth moment of a sum, $\delta_1 c_{in} + \delta_2 d_{in}$. This rth moment is bounded by

(6.22) $$\delta_1^r \frac{2^r}{n} \sum_1^n |c_{in}|^r + \delta_2^r \frac{2^r}{n} \sum_1^n |d_{in}|^r$$

by virtue of the inequality $|x + y|^r \leq |2x|^r + |2y|^r$; (6.22) is easily seen to be bounded because from condition W all the moments of $\mathscr{C}_n$ and $\mathscr{D}_n$ are bounded. Thus the sequence $\delta_1 \mathscr{C}_n + \delta_2 \mathscr{D}_n$ satisfies condition W.

Applying Theorem 6.1, we find that the limiting distributiom of $\delta_1 L_n + \delta_2 L'_n$ is normal with mean 0 and variance

(6.23) $\delta_1^2 + \delta_2^2 - 2\delta_1\delta_2\rho.$

Let (Y, Y') designate a random variable having a bivariate normal distribution with means 0, variances 1, and correlation ρ. Then we can say that the limiting distribution of $\delta_1 L_n + \delta_2 L'_n$ is the distribution of $\delta_1 Y + \delta_2 Y'$. If we knew that the joint distribution of (L_n, L'_n) approached a limiting distribution, say of (Z, Z'), we could apply Theorem 2.8 and state that $\delta_1 L_n + \delta_2 L'_n$ had the limiting distribution of $\delta_1 Z + \delta_2 Z'$. Theorem 2.5 would then imply that (Z, Z') had the same distribution as (Y, Y'). However, if the distribution function of (L_n, L'_n) does not approach a limit, it is easily seen (cf. Cramér [15], p. 60) that two subsequences can be extracted which converge to different limiting distributions. This contradicts the result above that the limiting distribution must be identical to that of (Y, Y').

If $\rho = +1$, then it is easily seen that $L_n + L'_n$ has a limiting normal distribution with mean 0 and variance 2 and that $L_n - L'_n$ approaches zero in probability. This proves that (L_n, L'_n) has the limiting bivariate distribution (degenerate) as stated in the theorem. A similar result is obtained if $\rho = -1$. This completes the proof.

The conditions of Theorem 6.1 have been modified by Hoeffding, who at the same time has considered the limiting distribution of a more general statistic. We shall quote his theorem, but first we introduce some necessary notation.

Let $b_n(i, j)$ $(i, j = 1, \cdots, n)$ be n^2 real numbers defined for every positive integer n, and let $(R_1, \cdots, R_n)$ designate the random variable which takes each permutation of $(1, \cdots, n)$ with the same probability $1/n!$. Theorem 6.4 is concerned with the limiting distribution of the random variable.

(6.24) $L_n = \sum_{i=1}^{n} b_n(i, R_i).$

We define

$$d_n(i, j) = b_n(i, j) - \frac{1}{n}\sum_{g=1}^{n} b_n(g, j) - \frac{1}{n}\sum_{h=1}^{n} b_n(i, h) + \frac{1}{n^2}\sum_{g,h=1}^{n} b_n(g, h).$$

Then it is straightforward to prove that

(6.25) $E\{L_n\} = \frac{1}{n}\sum_{i,j=1}^{n} b_n(i, j)$

and

(6.26) $\text{var}\,\{L_n\} = \frac{1}{n-1}\sum_{i,j=1}^{n} d_n^2(i, j).$

Problem 19 is to prove these relations.

THEOREM 6.4.   (HOEFFDING).   If

$$(6.27) \qquad \lim_{n \to \infty} \frac{\dfrac{1}{n}\sum_{i=1}^{n}\sum_{j=1}^{n} d_n^r(i,j)}{\left[\dfrac{1}{n}\sum_{i=1}^{n}\sum_{j=1}^{n} d_n^2(i,j)\right]^{r/2}} = 0, \qquad r = 3, 4, \cdots,$$

then L_n (6.24) is asymptotically normally distributed with mean and variance given by (6.25) and (6.26).   Condition (6.27) is satisfied if

$$(6.28) \qquad \lim_{n \to \infty} \frac{\max_{1 \le i, j \le n} d_n^2(i,j)}{\dfrac{1}{n}\sum_{i=1}^{n}\sum_{j=1}^{n} d_n^2(i,j)} = 0.$$

Proof.   See Hoeffding [7].

In the particular case having $L_n = \sum_{1}^{n} c_{in} a_{R_i n}$ we obtain more general conditions under which Theorem 6.1 remains valid; we have

Theorem 6.5.   If

$$(6.29) \qquad \lim_{n \to \infty} n^{r/2-1} \frac{\sum_{1}^{n}(c_{in} - \bar{c}_n)^r \sum_{1}^{n}(a_{in} - \bar{a}_n)^r}{\left[\sum_{1}^{n}(c_{in} - \bar{c}_n)^2 \sum_{1}^{n}(a_{in} - \bar{a}_n)^2\right]^{r/2}} = 0, \qquad r = 3, 4, \cdots,$$

then $L_n = \sum_{1}^{n} c_{in} a_{R_i n}$ is asymptotically normally distributed with mean and variance given by (6.4) and (6.5).   Condition (6.29) is satisfied if

$$(6.30) \qquad \lim_{n \to \infty} n \frac{\max_{n}(c_{in} - \bar{c}_n)^2 \; \max_{n}(a_{in} - \bar{a}_n)^2}{\sum_{1}^{n}(c_{in} - \bar{c}_n)^2 \sum_{1}^{n}(a_{in} - \bar{a}_n)^2} = 0.$$

Proof.   This is an immediate corollary of Theorem 6.4.

Dwass [11] has also obtained an extension of Theorem 6.1.   Let $X_1, \cdots, X_n$ be independent and each have the continuous distribution function $F(x)$.   Designating by $(x_{(1)}, \cdots, x_{(n)})$ the order statistic over R^n, we define a sequence $(b_{in}, \cdots, b_{nn})$:

$$b_{in} = E\{X_{(i)}^k\} - \frac{1}{n}\sum_{j=1}^{n} E\{X_{(j)}^k\}$$

THEOREM 6.6. (DWASS). If $k \geq 1$, if $\int |x|^{3k} \, dF(x) < \infty$, and if either X_i^k has a normal distribution or

$$(6.31) \qquad \lim_{n \to \infty} \frac{\max_{1}^{n} (c_{in} - \bar{c}_n)^2}{\sum_{1}^{n} (c_{in} - \bar{c}_n)^2} = 0,$$

then $L_n = \sum_{1}^{n} c_{in} b_{Rin}$ is asymptotically normally distributed with mean

and variance given by (6.4) and (6.5) (with a's replaced by b's).

Proof. See Dwass [11]. The method of proof is to show that asymptotically the random variable L_n is equivalent to the random variable

$$(6.32) \qquad L_n^* = \sum_{i=1}^{n} c_{in} X_i^k,$$

which can be shown by the central-limit theorem to have a limiting normal distribution.

In many applications of the theorems a sequence will be the observed value of a sequence of random variables. It is then of interest to inquire whether the conditions of a theorem are fulfilled with probability one for large samples. We have

THEOREM 6.7. If $X_1, \cdots, X_n$ are independent and identically distributed and if var $\{X_i\} > 0$ and $E\{|X_i|^3\} < \infty$, then with probability one the sequence $(X_1, \cdots, X_n)$ satisfies Noether's condition N (6.2), (6.14) or (6.15).

Proof. By Kolmogorov's Theorem 3.2 (strong law of large numbers), it follows that with probability one each of the following limits holds:

$$\lim_{n \to \infty} n^{-1} \sum_{1}^{n} X_i = E(X)$$

$$\lim_{n \to \infty} n^{-1} \sum_{1}^{n} X_i^2 = E(X^2)$$

$$\lim_{n \to \infty} n^{-1} \sum_{1}^{n} |X_i|^3 = E(|X|^3),$$

where X designates a random variable with the distribution of the X_i. From this it follows simply that with probability one

$$\lim_{n \to \infty} n^{-1} \Sigma (X_i - \bar{X})^2 = E\{[X - E(X)]^2\}$$

$$\lim_{n \to \infty} n^{-1} \Sigma |X_i - \bar{X}|^3 = E\{|X - E(X)|^3\}.$$

Then, since var $\{X_i\} > 0$, we have with probability one that

$$\lim_{n \to} \frac{n^{-1} \sum_1^n |X_i - \bar{X}|^3}{[n^{-1}\Sigma(X_i - \bar{X})^2]^{3/2}} = \frac{E\{|X - E(X)|^3\}}{[E\{[X - E(X)]^2\}]^{3/2}}$$

But this implies that with probability one that condition (6.14) is fulfilled. This with Theorem 6.2 completes the proof.

If $\mathscr{C}_n = (c_{in}, \cdots, c_{nn})$ is a sequence satisfying condition W (6.1), and if $X_1, \cdots, X_n$ are independent random variables satisfying the conditions of Theorem 6.7, then with probability one the sequence $(X_1, \cdots, X_n)$ produces an outcome $(x_1, \cdots, x_n)$ for which the limiting distribution of

$$(6.33) \qquad\qquad L_n = \sum_1^n c_{in} x_{R_i}$$

is normal.

As a related result we have a theorem proved by Hoeffding in [8]. Let $X_1, \cdots, X_n$ be identically distributed according to a distribution having $E\{|X|^3\} < \infty$ and var $\{X\} > 0$.

THEOREM 6.8. (HOEFFDING). The condition X is normally distributed or the condition

$$(6.34) \qquad\qquad \lim_{n \to \infty} \frac{\max_n (c_{in} - \bar{c}_n)^2}{\sum_1^n (c_{in} - \bar{c}_n)^2} = 0$$

is a necessary and sufficient condition that, as $n \to \infty$, the probability approaches one that the random variable $(X_1, \cdots, X_n)$ produces outcomes $(x_1, \cdots, x_n)$ for which the limiting distribution function of

$$(6.35) \qquad s(\mathbf{x}_R) = \frac{\sum_1^n (c_{in} - \bar{c}_n) x_{R_i}}{\left[\sum_1^n (c_{in} - \bar{c}_n)^2 (n-1)^{-1} \sum_1^n (x_i - \bar{x})^2\right]^{1/2}}$$

is within any preassigned amount of the normal distribution function with mean 0 and variance 1.

Proof. See Hoeffding [8].

Note. If $F(s; \mathbf{x})$ is the distribution function of $s(\mathbf{x}_R)$, the theorem gives a necessary and sufficient condition that $F(s; \mathbf{X}) \to \Phi(s)$ stochastically as $n \to \infty$ where $\Phi(s)$ is the standardized normal distribution function.

We complete this section by quoting a related theorem also proved by Hoeffding [8]. Let $X_1, \cdots, X_n$ be independent and identically distributed according to a distribution having $E\{|X|^3\} < \infty$ and var $\{X\} > 0$. Also, let the random variables $Z_1, \cdots, Z_n$ be defined by

$$(6.36) \qquad Z_i = X_i + d_{in},$$

where $\mathscr{D}_n = (d_{in}, \cdots, d_{nn})$ is a sequence of real numbers.

THEOREM 6.9. (HOEFFDING). In order that, as $n \to \infty$ the probability approach one that the random variable $(Z_1, \cdots, Z_n)$ defined above produce outcomes $(z_1, \cdots, z_n)$, for which the limiting distribution function of

$$(6.37) \qquad s(z_R) = \frac{\displaystyle\sum_1^n (c_{in} - \bar{c}_n) z_{R_i}}{\left[\displaystyle\sum_1^n (c_{in} - \bar{c}_n)^2 (n-1)^{-1} \sum_1^n (z_i - \bar{z})^2 \right]^{1/2}}$$

is within any preassigned amount of the normal distribution function with mean 0 and variance 1, a sufficient condition is that

$$(6.38) \qquad \text{either } X \text{ is normally distributed} \\ \text{or} \qquad \lim_{n \to \infty} \frac{\max\limits_1^n (c_{in} - \bar{c}_n)^2}{\displaystyle\sum_1^n (c_{in} - \bar{c}_n)^2} = 0$$

and

$$(6.39) \lim_{n \to \infty} n^{p/2-1} \frac{\displaystyle\sum_1^n (c_{in} - \bar{c}_n)^p}{\left[\displaystyle\sum_1^n (c_{in} - \bar{c}_n)^2 \right]^{p/2}} \frac{\displaystyle\sum_1^n (d_{in} - \bar{d}_n)^p}{\left[\displaystyle\sum_1^n (d_{in} - \bar{d}_n)^2 \right]^{p/2}}, \quad p = 3, 4, \cdots,$$

the latter condition being satisfied if

$$(6.40) \qquad \lim_{n \to \infty} n \frac{\max\limits_1^n (c_{in} - \bar{c}_n)^2}{\displaystyle\sum_1^n (c_{in} - \bar{c}_n)^2} \frac{\max\limits_1^n (d_{in} - \bar{d}_n)^2}{\displaystyle\sum_1^n (d_{in} - \bar{d}_n)^2} = 0.$$

Condition (6.39) can be replaced by

$$(6.41) \qquad \lim n^{-1} \sum_1^n (d_{in} - \bar{d}_n)^2 = 0.$$

Condition (6.38) can be replaced by

$$(6.42) \qquad \lim n^{-1} \sum_1^n (d_{in} - \bar{d}_n)^2 = \infty.$$

Proof. We merely sketch the main idea of the proof; for the details, see Hoeffding [8]. By using (6.36) the numerator of (6.37) can be broken into $\sum_1^n (c_{in} - \bar{c}_n) x_{R_i}$ and $\sum_1^n (c_{in} - \bar{c}_n) d_{R_i n}$. Then condition (6.38) with Theorem 6.8 gives the first expression a limiting normal distribution, and condition (6.39) with Theorem 6.5 gives the second expression a limiting normal distribution.

EXAMPLE 6.1.   The rank correlation coefficient is defined in Problem 11. In Example 5.3 we considered its use for making a test of independence. Let $(X_1^{(1)}, X_1^{(2)}), \cdots, (X_n^{(1)}, X_n^{(2)})$ be independent and each have the same continuous distribution function over R^2. The problem of independence is to test the hypothesis that the coordinates of the bivariate distribution are independent. Letting $r_1^{(1)}, \cdots, r_n^{(1)}$ designate the ranks of $x_1^{(1)}, \cdots, x_n^{(1)}$ and similarly $r_1^{(2)}, \cdots, r_n^{(2)}$ designate the ranks of $x_1^{(2)}, \cdots, x_n^{(2)}$, then we can write the rank correlation statistic

$$(6.43) \qquad \begin{aligned} k' &= \frac{12}{n^3 - n} \sum_{\alpha=1}^n \left(r_\alpha^{(1)} - \frac{n+1}{2} \right) \left(r_\alpha^{(2)} - \frac{n+1}{2} \right) \\ &= \frac{12}{n^3 - n} \sum_{\alpha=1}^n r_\alpha^{(1)} r_\alpha^{(2)} - \frac{3(n+1)^2}{n^3 - n}. \end{aligned}$$

An equivalent statistic is $\sum_1^n r_\alpha^{(1)} r_\alpha^{(2)}$. To construct an independence test based on k' or $\sum_1^n r_\alpha^{(1)} r_\alpha^{(2)}$, we need to know the distribution of the statistic under the hypothesis. This has been tabulated for small n, but, as n increases, the numerical work to obtain the distribution becomes excessive. However, the Wald–Wolfowitz theorem gives the limiting distribution, and it has been observed that the approximation is good even for n of the order of 10. For the statistic $\Sigma r_\alpha^{(1)} r_\alpha^{(2)}$ we can describe the hypothesis distribution by the random variable

$$\sum_{i=1}^{n} iR_i,$$

where $(R_1, \cdots, R_n)$ is a random permutation of $(1, \cdots, n)$. We apply Theorem 6.1:

$$\frac{1}{n}\Sigma\left(i - \frac{n+1}{2}\right)^2 = \frac{(n+1)(2n+1)}{6} - \frac{(n+1)^2}{4}$$

$$= \frac{n^2-1}{12},$$

$$\frac{1}{n}\sum_{1}^{n} i^r = O(n^r).$$

From these two relations it is easily seen that the conditions of Theorem 6.1 or 6.5 are fulfilled. Hence $\sum_{1}^{n} iR_i$ has a limiting normal distribution with mean given by (6.4),

$$(6.44) \qquad E\left\{\sum_{1}^{n} iR_i\right\} = n\,\frac{(n+1)^2}{4} \sim \frac{n^3}{4},$$

and variance given by (6.5)

$$(6.45) \qquad \text{var}\left\{\sum_{1}^{n} iR_i\right\} = \frac{n^2(n^2-1)^2}{144(n-1)} \sim \frac{n^5}{144}$$

In Chapter 5, Section 3, we developed a method for finding rank tests having maximum power at a particular distribution in the alternative or having locally maximum power for a parametric class of alternatives. A test (Problem 19, Chapter 5) of independence having locally maximum power against normal alternatives involving dependence is based on the statistic

$$(6.46) \qquad \sum_{i=1}^{n} c_{r_i^{(1)}} b_{r_i^{(2)}},$$

where

$$(6.47) \qquad c_i = \left[\sum_{j=1}^{n} [E\{Z_{(j)}\}]^2\right]^{-1/2},$$

$$b_i = E\{Z_{(i)}\},$$

and $E(Z_{(1)}), \cdots, E(Z_{(n)})$ are the expected values of the order statistics for a sample of n from the normal distribution with mean 0 and variance 1. The statistic's limiting distribution under the hypothesis of independence can be proved normal by the use of Theorem 6.6 (see Problem 20).

The similar test most powerful against normal alternatives was developed in Chapter 5, Example 2.2. It is a conditional test, given the order statistics $(x_{(1)}^{(1)}, \cdots, x_{(n)}^{(1)}), (x_{(1)}^{(2)}, \cdots, x_{(n)}^{(2)})$ and is based on the statistic

$$(6.48) \qquad \sum x_\alpha^{(1)} x_\alpha^{(2)}.$$

Under the independence hypothesis we consider the limiting form of the distribution of this statistic as the sample size n increases. Assume that var $\{X^{(1)}\} > 0$, var $\{X^{(2)}\} > 0$ and that the third absolute moments are finite. By Theorem 6.7 it is seen that with probability one the set $(x_1^{(1)}, \cdots, x_n^{(1)})$ will satisfy condition N. Then by Theorem 6.8 it is seen that, as $n \to \infty$, the probability approaches one that the conditional distribution of $\sum_1^n X_\alpha^{(1)} X_\alpha^{(2)}$, given $(x_{(1)}^{(1)}, \cdots, x_{(n)}^{(1)})$, and $(x_{(1)}^{(2)}, \cdots, x_{(n)}^{(2)})$, is within any preassigned amount of the normal distribution function having the same mean and variance.

EXAMPLE 6.2. In Chapter 5, Example 2.1, we showed that Pitman's two-sample test was the similar test most powerful for normal alternatives. Let $(x_1, \cdots, x_{n_1})$ and $(x_{n_1+1}, \cdots, x_{n_1+n_2})$ be outcomes for the 'first' and 'second' samples. The Pitman test is a conditional test, given the order statistic $(x_{(1)}, \cdots, x_{(n_1+n_2)})$ for the combined sample and can be based on the statistic

$$(6.49) \qquad \frac{\sum_1^{n_2} x_{n_1+j}}{n_2} - \frac{\sum_1^{n_1} x_i}{n_1}.$$

To perform the test we need to know the hypothesis distribution of this statistic, given the order statistic. The limiting form of this distribution can be found by using Theorem 6.8 or Theorem 6.1 with Theorem 6.7. For we can describe the hypothesis distribution by the random variable:

$$\sum_{j=1}^{n_2} \frac{1}{n_2} x_{(R_{n_1+j})} + \sum_{i=1}^{n_1} \left(-\frac{1}{n_1}\right) x_{(R_i)}.$$

The coefficients, $1/n_2, - 1/n_1$, obviously satisfy (6.34) as the sample sizes approach infinity in a given ratio. Then, if $E\{|X_1|^3\}$ and var $\{X_1\} > 0$, we have that the conditional distribution of (6.48) under the hypothesis approaches in probability the normal distribution as the sample sizes approach infinity in a given ratio.

The rank test locally most powerful against normal alternatives is based on the statistic

$$\sum_{j=1}^{n_2} E\{Z_{(r_{n_1+j})}\}\left(\frac{1}{n_2}\right) + \sum_{i=1}^{n_1} E\{Z_{(R_i)}\}\left(\frac{-1}{n_1}\right)$$

where the Z's were defined in the previous problem with $n = n_1 + n_2$ and $r_1, \cdots, r_{n_1+n_2}$ are the ranks of $x_1, \cdots, x_{n_1+n_2}$ in the combined sample. By Theorem 6.6 the statistic has a limiting normal distribution under the hypothesis.

7. THE LIMITING DISTRIBUTION OF RUNS AND ADDITIVE PARTITION FUNCTIONS

In this section we quote some limiting distributions which can be used in the construction of two-sample tests. Let $V = (V_1, \cdots, V_{n_1+n_2})$ be a random variable which takes each different permutation of n_1 1's and n_2 2's with the same probability,

$$\binom{n_1 + n_2}{n_1}^{-1}$$

Let $v = (v_1, \cdots, v_{n_1+n_2})$ designate a typical permutation. Then we define a *run of* 1's to be a set of consecutive 1's in $(v_1, \cdots, v_{n_1+n_2})$ preceded by 2's or the beginning and succeeded by 2's or the end. A run of 2's is defined analogously. We now consider some statistics which are functions of v; let

r_{1j} = number of runs of 1's of length j,

r_{2j} = number of runs of 2's of length j,

r'_{1j} = number of runs of 1's of length j or more,

r'_{2j} = number of runs of 2's of length j or more,

r_1 = number of runs of 1's,

r_2 = number of runs of 2's,

r = number of runs.

There are relations among these statistics, for example:

$$r'_{1j} = r_{1j} + r_{1j+1} + \cdots,$$
$$r_1 = r_{11} + r_{12} + \cdots,$$
$$r = r_1 + r_2.$$

Corresponding to the random variable $V = (V_1, \cdots, V_{n_1+n_2})$, we now find the induced probability distribution of the r_{1j}'s and r_{2j}'s. First we note that the number of runs of 1's can differ from the number of runs of 2's by at most 1, since the two types of runs alternate in the sequence. Also, a given sequence of 1 runs and a given sequence of 2 runs can be put together to form a V sequence in only one way if $r_1 - r_2 = 1$ and in two ways if $r_1 = r_2$. For this it is convenient to define a function,

(7.1)
$$\begin{aligned} F(r_1, r_2) &= 0 && \text{if } |r_1 - r_2| > 1 \\ &= 1 && \text{if } |r_1 - r_2| = 1 \\ &= 2 && \text{if } r_1 = r_2. \end{aligned}$$

Consider the runs of 1's. There are r_{11} of length 1, r_{12} of length 2, and so on. The number of ways of arranging these to form different sequences is

$$\frac{r_1!}{r_{11}!\, r_{12}! \cdots}.$$

Similarly, for the 2's the number of ways of arranging r_{21} runs of length 1, r_{22} of length 2, and so on, is

$$\frac{r_2!}{r_{21}!\, r_{22}! \cdots}.$$

Also, a sequence of 1 runs can be put with a sequence of 2 runs to form a V sequence in $F(r_1, r_2)$ ways. Hence we have

(7.2)
$$P(r_{11}, r_{12}, \cdots ; r_{21}, r_{22}, \cdots) = \frac{r_1!}{\prod r_{1j}!} \frac{r_2!}{\prod r_{2j}!} \frac{F(r_1, r_2)}{\binom{n_1 + n_2}{n_1}}.$$

The number of ways of forming r_2 runs from a sequence of n_2 2's is the number of ways that $r_2 - 1$ dividing places may be chosen from the $n_2 - 1$ spaces between 2's in the sequence. Hence we have the marginal distribution for $r_{11}, r_{12}, \cdots ; r_2$.

(7.3)
$$P(r_{11}, r_{12}, \cdots ; r_2) = \frac{r_1!}{\prod r_{1j}!} \binom{n_2 - 1}{r_2 - 1} \frac{F(r_1, r_2)}{\binom{n_1 + n_2}{n_1}}.$$

Then, summing this over r_2, we obtain

$$P(r_{11}, r_{12}, \cdots)$$

(7.4)
$$= \frac{r_1!}{\prod r_{1j}!} \left[\binom{n_2 - 1}{r_1 - 2} + 2\binom{n_2 - 1}{r_1 - 1} + \binom{n_2 - 1}{r_1} \right] \frac{1}{\binom{n_1 + n_2}{n_1}}$$

$$= \frac{r_1!}{r_{1j}!} \binom{n_2 - 1}{r_1 - 2} \left[1 + 2\,\frac{n_2 - r_1 + 1}{r_1 - 1} + \frac{(n_2 - r_1 + 1)(n_2 - r_1)}{r_1(r_1 - 1)} \right] \frac{1}{\binom{n_1 + n_2}{n_1}}$$

$$= \frac{r_1!}{\prod r_{1j}!} \frac{\binom{n_2 + 1}{r_1}}{\binom{n_1 + n_2}{n_1}}$$

By the argument that produced (7.3) we find the distribution for r_1, r_2 to be

(7.5)
$$P(r_1, r_2) = \binom{n_1 - 1}{r_1 - 1}\binom{n_2 - 1}{r_2 - 1} \frac{F(r_1, r_2)}{\binom{n_1 + n_2}{n_1}}$$

and the distribution for r to be

$$P(r) = \binom{n_1 - 1}{\frac{r}{2} - 1}\binom{n_2 - 1}{\frac{r}{2} - 1} \frac{2}{\binom{n_1 + n_2}{n_1}} \quad \text{if } r \text{ is even}$$

(7.6)

$$= \left[\binom{n_1 - 1}{\frac{r+1}{2} - 1}\binom{n_2 - 1}{\frac{r-1}{2} - 1} + \binom{n_1 - 1}{\frac{r-1}{2} - 1}\binom{n_2 - 1}{\frac{r+1}{2} - 1}\right] \frac{1}{\binom{n_1 + n_2}{n_1}}$$

$$\text{if } r \text{ is odd.}$$

We now consider the problem of finding the means, variances, and covariances for the $r_{11}, r_{12}, \cdots$ and $r_{21}, r_{22}, \cdots$. As is the case with most discrete distributions involving integers the factorial moments are the natural moments to calculate. If we define

$$x^{(a)} = x(x - 1) \cdots (x - a + 1),$$

then the ath factorial moment of a real random variable X is defined to be

$$E\{X^{(a)}\}.$$

From the first and second factorial moments it is straightforward to calculate the ordinary means and variance:

$$E(X) = E(X^{(1)})$$

$$\text{var}(X) = E(X^{(2)}) + E(X) - [E(X)]^2.$$

We illustrate the method of calculating factorial moments by evaluating $E\{r_{1j}\}$, and then we quote the formulas for the other means and for the variances and covariances. We have

$$E\{r_{1i}\} = \sum{'} r_{1i} P(r_{11}, r_{12}, \cdots),$$

where the summation is over all positive integers $r_{11}, r_{12}, \cdots$ such that $\sum ir_{1i} = n_1$.

$$E(r_{1i}) = \sideset{}{'}\sum r_{1i} \frac{r_1!}{r_{11}! \, r_{12}! \cdots} \frac{\binom{n_2+1}{r_1}}{\binom{n_1+n_2}{n_1}}$$

(7.7)

$$= \sideset{}{''}\sum \frac{r_1!}{r_{11}! \, r_{12}! \cdots (r_{1i}-1)! \cdots} \frac{\binom{n_2+1}{r_1}}{\binom{n_1+n_2}{n_1}},$$

where the summation Σ'' is the same as Σ' only excluding cases for which $r_{1i} = 0$.

$$E\{r_{1i}\} = \sideset{}{''}\sum \frac{(r_1-1)!}{r_{11}! \, r_{12}! \cdots (r_{1i}-1)! \cdots} \frac{(n_2+1)\binom{n_2}{r_1-1}}{\binom{n_1+n_2}{n_1}}$$

$$= (n_2+1)^{(2)} \frac{n_1^{(i)}}{(n_1+n_2)^{(i+1)}} \sideset{}{''}\sum \frac{(r_1-1)!}{r_{11}! \, r_{12}! \cdots (r_{1i}-1)! \cdots}$$

$$\frac{\binom{n_2-1+1}{r_1-1}}{\binom{n_1-i+n_2-1}{n_1-i}}$$

This last is obtained from the relation

$$\binom{n_1+n_2}{n_1} = \frac{(n_1+n_2)^{(i+1)}}{n_1^{(i)} n_2} \binom{n_1-i+n_2-1}{n_1-1}.$$

But the summation in the expression above produces a total 1 since the terms being added are the probabilities (7.4) with n_1 replaced by $n_1 - i$ and n_2 replaced by $n_2 - 1$. Therefore

(7.8)
$$E\{r_{1i}\} = \frac{(n_1+1)^{(2)} n_1^{(i)}}{(n_1+n_2)^{(i+1)}},$$

and by symmetry

(7.9)
$$E\{r_{2i}\} = \frac{(n_1+1)^{(2)} n_2^{(i)}}{(n_1+n_2)^{(i+1)}}.$$

The variance and covariance are obtained similarly but with somewhat more work for cov $\{r_{1j}\, r_{2k}\}$.

$$(7.10)\quad \text{var}\,(r_{1i}) = \frac{n_2^{(2)}(n_2+1)^{(2)}\,n_1^{(2i)}}{(n_1+n_2)^{(2i+2)}} + \frac{(n_2+1)^{(2)}n_1^{(i)}}{(n_1+n_2)^{(i+1)}}\left[1 - \frac{(n_2+1)^{(2)}n_1^{(i)}}{(n_1+n_2)^{(i+1)}}\right],$$

$$(7.11)\quad \text{cov}\,\{r_{1i}, r_{1j}\} = \frac{n_2^{(2)}(n_2+1)^{(2)}n_1^{(i+j)}}{(n_1+n_2)^{(i+j+2)}} - \frac{n_2^{(2)}(n_2+1)^{(2)}n_1^{(i)}n_2^{(j)}}{(n_1+n_2)^{(i+1)}(n_1+n_2)^{(j+1)}},$$

$$\text{cov}\,\{r_{1i}, r_{2j}\} = \frac{n_1^{(i+2)}n_2^{(j+2)}}{(n_1+n_2)^{(i+j+2)}} + 4\,\frac{n_1^{(i+1)}n_2^{(j+1)}}{(n_1+n_2)^{(i+j+1)}}$$

$$(7.12)\qquad\qquad + 2\,\frac{n_1^{(i)}n_2^{(j)}}{(n_1+n_2)^{(i+j)}} - \frac{(n_1+1)^{(2)}(n_2+1)^{(2)}n_1^{(i)}n_2^{(j)}}{(n_1+n_2)^{(i+1)}(n_1+n_2)^{(j+1)}}.$$

The formula for var $\{r_{2i}\}$ and cov $\{r_{2i}, r_{2j}\}$ are obtained from (7.10) and (7.11) by interchanging the subscripts 1, 2.

By obtaining the probability expression for $(r_{11}, \cdots, r_{1k-1}\, r'_{1k}; r_{21}, \cdots, r_{2h-1}\, r'_{2h})$ and by an analysis similar to that above, Mood [1] obtains the formulas

$$(7.13)\qquad\qquad E\{r'_{1k}\} = \frac{(n_2+1)\,n_1^{(k)}}{(n_1+n_2)^{(k)}},$$

$$(7.14)\quad \text{cov}\,\{r_{1i}, r'_{1k}\} = \frac{n_2^2(n_2+1)n_1^{(i+k)}}{(n_1+n_2)^{(i+k+1)}} - \frac{n_2(n_2+1)^2 n_1^{(i)}n_1^{(k)}}{(n_1+n_2)^{(i+1)}(n_1+n_2)^{(k)}},$$

$$(7.15)\quad \text{var}\,\{r'_{1k}\} = \frac{(n_2+1)^{(2)}n_1^{(2k)}}{(n_1+n_2)^{(2k)}} + \frac{(n_2+1)n_1^{(k)}}{(n_1+n_2)^{(k)}}\left[1 - \frac{(n_2+1)n_1^{(k)}}{(n_1+n_2)^{(k)}}\right],$$

$$(7.16)\quad \text{cov}\,\{r'_{1k}, r_{2j}\} = \frac{n_1^{(k+2)}n_2^{(j+1)} + 2n_1^{(k+1)}n_2^{(j+1)}}{(n_1+n_2)^{(k+j+1)}}$$

$$+ 2\,\frac{n_1^{(k+1)}n_2^{(j)} + n_1^{(k)}n_2^{(j)}}{(n_1+n_2)^{(k+j)}}$$

$$- \frac{(n_1+1)^{(2)}(n_2+1)^{(2)}n_1^{(k)}n_2^{(j)}}{(n_1+n_2)^{(k)}(n_1+n_2)^{(j+1)}},$$

$$(7.17)\quad \text{cov}\,\{r'_{1k}, r'_{2h}\} = \frac{n_1^{(k+1)}n_2^{(h+1)}}{(n_1+n_2)^{(h+k)}} + 2\,\frac{n_1^{(k)}n_2^{(h)}}{(n_1+n_2)^{(k+h-1)}}$$

$$- \frac{(n_1+1)(n_2+1)n_1^{(k)}n_2^{(h)}}{(n_1+n_2)^{(k)}(n_1+n_2)^{(h)}}.$$

Also, we have

$$(7.18)\qquad\qquad E\{r_1\} = \frac{(n_2+1)n_1}{(n_1+n_2)},$$

$$(7.19)\qquad\qquad \text{var}\,\{r_1\} = \frac{(n_1+1)^{(2)}n_1^{(2)}}{(n_1+n_2)(n_1+n_2)^{(2)}}.$$

We consider now the limiting distribution of the r_{ij} as n_1 and n_2 approach infinity in a fixed ratio. Let

$$\frac{n_1}{n_1 + n_2} = e_1,$$

$$\frac{n_2}{n_1 + n_2} = e_2,$$

with $0 < e_1, e_2 < 1$. Then, of course, we have $e_1 + e_2 = 1$.

THEOREM 7.1. (MOOD). As $n_1 + n_2 \to \infty$, the limiting distribution of any finite set of the random variables $r_{11}, r_{12}, \cdots, r_{21}, r_{22}, \cdots$ is normal with means and variances given by the formulas above.

Note. As $n_1 + n_2$ become large, the relation $|r_1 - r_2| \leq 1$ becomes equivalent to the linear relation $r_1 = r_2$. The limiting normal distribution will be degenerate if the variables chosen satisfy a linear relationship obtained from $r_1 = r_2$.

Proof. The proof is given in Mood [1]. The method is essentially that used to show the binomial distribution approaches the normal distribution The r_{ij} are expressed in terms of the standardized variables

$$\frac{r_{ij} - E(r_{ij})}{\sigma_{r_{ij}}},$$

and a substitution is made in the probability expression. Stirling's formula is used to replace the factorials. The logarithm of the probability expression is then shown to approach the logarithm of the multivariate normal density (uniform convergence is not necessary; see Scheffé [13]).

Wolfowitz in [2] introduces a statistic called an additive partition function. Let $f(x)$, $g(x)$ be real-valued functions defined for all positive integers, and consider the function

$$l(r_{11}, \cdots, r_{21}, \cdots) = \sum_{j=1} r_{1j} f(j) + \sum_{j=1} r_{2j} g(j).$$

In terms of the sequence $v = (v_1, \cdots, v_{n_1+n_2})$ which produced the values $r_{11}, r_{12}, \cdots, r_{21}, r_{22}, \cdots$, $1(r_{11}, \cdots)$ can be obtained by adding a number for each run, the number being $f(j)$ if the run is of 1's and of length j and $g(j)$ if the run is of 2's and of length j. Thus $1(r_{11}, \cdots, r_{21}, \cdots)$ can be expressed as an additive function of the partition of 1's and 2's into runs and accordingly is called an *additive partition function*.

THEOREM 7.2. (WOLFOWITZ). If $f(x)$ and $g(x)$ are not proportional to x, and if the series

$$\sum_{i=1}^{\infty} |f(i)| e_m^{i/2}$$

and

$$\sum_{i=1}^{\infty} |g(i)| e_m^{i/2}$$

converge where $e_m = \max\{e_1, e_2\}$, then the additive partition function

$$\sum_{j=1}^{\infty} r_{1j} f(j) + \sum_{j=1}^{\infty} r_{2j} g(j)$$

has a limiting normal distribution as $n_1 + n_2 \to \infty$ with $n_1 = e_1(n_1 + n_2)$ and $n_2 = e_2(n_1 + n_2)$.

Proof. See Wolfowitz [2]. The basic idea in the proof is that the additive partition function can be approximated by

(7.20) $$\sum_{j=1}^{k} r_{1j} f(j) + \sum_{j=1}^{h} r_{2j} g(j)$$

as $n_1 + n_2 \to \infty$, and by choosing k, h large the stochastic approximation can be made as close as desired. (7.20) has a limiting normal distribution by Theorems 7.1 and 2.8.

8. PROBLEMS FOR SOLUTION

1. Show that the moments of a normal distribution satisfy the criterion in Theorem 2.2.
2. Show that p-lim $X_n = c$ is equivalent to the convergence of the corresponding distribution functions to $F(x)$, defined by

$$F(x) = 1 \quad \text{if} \quad x \geq c$$
$$= 0 \quad\quad\quad < c.$$

3. Show that, if $\lim_{n \to \infty} E\{X_n\} = c$ and $\lim_{n \to \infty} \operatorname{var}\{X_n\} = 0$, then $\underset{n \to \infty}{\text{p-lim}} X_n = c$. Use Tchebycheff's inequality.
4. $X_1, X_2, \cdots$ is a sequence of independent and identically distributed random variables. Give conditions under which $\sum_{1}^{n} (X_i - \bar{X})^2$ has asymptotically a normal distribution. What mean? What variance?

5. Let $X_1, X_2, \cdots$ be a sequence of independent and identically distributed random variables. By using the obvious trivariate extension of Theorem 2.7, show that under suitable conditions the limiting distribution of

$$n^{1/2} \frac{X_1 X_2 + X_2 X_3 + \cdots + X_n X_{n+1} - n^{-1} \left(\sum_1^n X_i \right)^2}{X_1^2 + \cdots + X_n^2 - n^{-1} \left(\sum_1^n X_i \right)^2}$$

is normal with mean 0 and variance 1. What conditions? This random variable is of interest in tests of randomness against the alternative of serial correlation.

6. What are conditions under which the conditional distribution of $\sum_1^n X_i X_{i+1}(X_{n+1}$ $= X_1)$, given the order statistic for $X_1, \cdots, X_n$, approaches the normal distribution as $n \to \infty$? What is the limiting conditional distribution of $\sum_1^{n-1} x_i x_{i+1}$? These two statistics are linear combinations, respectively, of the circular and noncircular serial correlation coefficients, the linear function being constant, given the order statistic.

7. By using Theorem 2.4 in Chapter 2, show that $\zeta_c \leq \zeta_m$ ($c = 1, \cdots, m$). ζ_c is defined in Section 5.

8. Prove Theorem 5.6. For this define

$$f^*_{c_1 c_2}(x_1, \cdots, (x_{c_1}; y_1, \cdots, y_{c_2}) = E\{f^*(x_1, \cdots, x_{c_1}, X_{c_1+1}, \cdots, X_{m_1};$$

$$y_1, \cdots, y_{c_2}; Y_{c_2+1}, \cdots, Y_{m_2})\},$$

$$\zeta_{c_1 c_2} = \text{var} \{f^*_{c_1 c_2}(X_1, \cdots, X_{c_1}; Y_1, \cdots, Y_{c_2})\},$$

$$\zeta_{00} = 0.$$

Prove

$$(8.1) \quad \text{var} \{U\} = \frac{1}{\binom{n_1}{m_1}\binom{n_2}{m_2}} \sum_{c_1=0}^{m_1} \sum_{c_2=0}^{m_2} \binom{m_1}{c_1}\binom{n_1 - m_1}{m_1 - c_1}\binom{m_2}{c_2}\binom{n_2 - m_2}{m_2 - c_2} \zeta_{c_1 c_2}.$$

In analogy with the proof of Theorem (5.1) let

$$Z_n = n_1^{1/2}(U - \eta),$$

$$Y_n = \frac{m_1}{n_1^{1/2}} \sum_{\alpha=1}^{n_1} f^*_{10}(X_\alpha) + \frac{m_2 n_1^{1/2}}{n_2} \sum_{\beta=1}^{n_2} f^*_{01}(Y_\beta).$$

Prove that the limiting variance of Z_n is

$$m_1^2 \zeta_{10} + m_2^2 \left(\lim \frac{n_1}{n_2} \right) \zeta_{01}.$$

9. Let $Y_1, \cdots, Y_n$ be positive-valued random variables which are independent and identically distributed. Gini ([13], Chapter 4) defines a coefficient of concentration

$$g = \frac{d}{2\bar{y}},$$

where d is defined by (5.21) and $\bar{y} = n^{-1} \sum_{i=1}^{n} y_i$. Prove that, if $E\{Y^2\}$ exists and if $\mu = E\{Y\} > 0$, then

$$n^{1/2} \left(g - \frac{\Delta}{2u} \right)$$

has a limiting normal distribution with mean 0 and variance

$$\frac{2}{4\mu^4} \zeta_1(\bar{y}) - \frac{\Delta}{\mu^3} \zeta_1(\bar{y}, d) + \frac{1}{\mu^2} \zeta_1(d)$$

where $\zeta_1(d)$ is given by (5.23), and

$$\zeta_1(\bar{y}) = E\{Y^2\} - \mu^2$$
$$= \text{var}\,\{Y\}$$

$$\zeta_1(\bar{y}, d) = \int\int y_1 |y_1 - y_2|\, dF(y_1)dF(y_2) - \mu\Delta.$$

This requires the obvious vector extension of Theorem 5.1.

10. Let $U^{(1)}$, $U^{(2)}$ be two U statistics based on the symmetric kernels, respectively, $f^{*(1)}(x_1, \cdots, x_{m_1}), f^{*(2)}(x_1, \cdots, x_{m_2})$. Prove that the covariance of $U^{(1)}$ and $U^{(2)}$ is given by

$$\text{cov}\,\{U^{(1)}, U^{(2)}\} = \binom{n}{m_{12}} \sum_{c=1}^{m_{12}} \binom{m_{12}}{c}\binom{n - m_{12}}{m_{12} - c} \zeta_c^{(1,2)},$$

where $m_{12} = \min\,\{m_1, m_2\}$ and $\zeta_c^{(1,2)}$ is the covariance between $f_c^{*(1)}(X_1, \cdots, X_c)$ and $f_c^{*(2)}(X_1, \cdots, X_c)$.

11. For a sequence $(x_1^{(1)}, x_1^{(2)}), \cdots, (x_n^{(1)}, x_n^{(2)})$ let $(r_1^{(1)}, r_1^{(2)}), \cdots, (r_n^{(1)}, r_n^{(2)})$ be the ranks as defined in Example 5.2. Show that, if all the first coordinate x's are different and all the second coordinate x's are different, then the correlation coefficient between the first and second coordinate ranks is

(8.2)
$$k' = \frac{12}{n^3 - n} \sum_{\alpha=1}^{n} \left(r_\alpha^{(1)} - \frac{n+1}{2} \right)\left(r_\alpha^{(2)} - \frac{n+1}{2} \right)$$

$$= \frac{3}{n^3 - n} \sum_{\alpha=1}^{n} \sum_{\beta=1}^{n} \sum_{\gamma=1}^{n} s(x_\alpha^{(1)} - x_\beta^{(1)})\, s(x_\alpha^{(2)} - x_\gamma^{(2)})$$

$$= \frac{(n-2)k + 3t}{n+1},$$

where t is the difference-sign covariance (5.27) and k is given by

(8.3)
$$k = \frac{3}{n(n-1)(n-2)} \sum' s(x_\alpha^{(1)} - x_\beta^{(1)})s(x_\alpha^{(2)} - x_\gamma^{(2)}),$$

where the summation is over all α, β, γ which are different. k' is called the *rank correlation coefficient*.

12. If $(X_1^{(1)}, X_1^{(2)})$, $\cdots$, $(X_n^{(1)}, X_n^{(2)})$ are independent and have the same continuous distribution function $F(x^{(1)}, x^{(2)})$, show that k defined above is an unbiased estimate of κ where

$$\kappa = 3 \int \int [2F(x^{(1)}, \infty) - 1][2F(\infty, x^{(2)}) - 1] \, dF(x^{(1)}, x^{(2)}).$$

Show that κ is the coefficient of correlation between $U^{(1)} = F(X^{(1)}, \infty)$ and $U^{(2)} = F(\infty, X^{(2)})$. $U^{(i)}$ has been called the grade of the random variable $X^{(i)}$ and hence κ is called the *grade correlation coefficient*.

13. k defined in Problem 11 is a U statistic and has a kernel $g(x_1, x_2, x_3)$,

$$g(x_1, x_2, x_3) = 3s(x_1^{(1)} - x_2^{(1)}) s(x_1^{(2)} - x_3^{(2)}).$$

A symmetric kernel is

$$g^*(x_1, x_2, x_3) = \frac{1}{2} \sum_{\substack{\alpha \neq \beta \neq \gamma \\ \alpha \neq \gamma}}^{1,2,3} s(x^{(1)} - x^{(1)}) s(x^{(2)} - x^{(2)}).$$

We shall say the *pair* $(x_1^{(1)}, x_1^{(2)})$, $(x_2^{(1)}, x_2^{(2)})$ *is concordant if* $x_1^{(1)} - x_2^{(1)}$ *and* $x_1^{(2)} - x_2^{(2)}$ *are of the same sign.* For computing κ and var $\{k\}$, it is convenient to introduce a real parameter γ, the probability that at least two of the three pairs which can be chosen from $(X_1^{(1)}, X_1^{(2)})$, $(X_2^{(1)}, X_2^{(2)})$, $(X_3^{(1)}, X_3^{(2)})$ are concordant. Show that the U statistic for estimating γ when $F(x)$ belongs to the class of continuous distribution functions has symmetric kernel $h^*(x_1, x_2, x_3)$ where $h^*(x_1, x_2, x_3) = 1$ if at least two of the three expressions

$$(x_\alpha^{(1)} - \tilde{x}_\beta^{(1)})(x_\alpha^{(2)} - x_\beta^{(2)}) \qquad \alpha < \beta;\ \alpha,\ \ \beta = 1, 2, 3$$

are positive and $h^*(x_1, x_2, x_3) = 0$ otherwise.

Assuming that $F(x)$ is continuous, show that

$$h^*(x_1, x_2, x_3) = c_{12,12}c_{23,23}c_{31,31} + c_{12,12}c_{23,23}c_{31,13} + c_{12,12}c_{23,32}c_{31,31} + c_{12,21}c_{23,23}c_{31,31},$$

where

$$c_{\alpha\beta,\gamma\delta} = c((x_\alpha^{(1)} - x_\beta^{(1)})(x_\gamma^{(2)} - x_\delta^{(2)})),$$

and $c(u)$ is defined by (5.25). Prove that

$$g^*(x_1, x_2, x_3) = 2h^*(x_1, x_2, x_3) - 1,$$

and hence show that

$$\kappa = 2\gamma - 1.$$

14. In the notation of Problem 13, prove that

$$g_2^*(x_1, x_2) = 1 + 2F(x_1^{(1)}, x_2^{(2)}) + 2F(x_2^{(1)}, x_1^{(1)})$$
$$- 2c(x_2^{(2)} - x_1^{(2)}) F(x_1^{(1)}, \infty) - 2c(x_1^{(2)} - x_2^{(2)}) F(x_2^{(1)}, \infty)$$
$$- 2c(x_2^{(1)} - x_1^{(1)}) F(\infty, x_1^{(2)}) - 2c(x_1^{(1)} - x_2^{(1)}) F(\infty, x_2^{(2)}),$$

$$g_1^*(x_1) = [1 - 2F(x_1^{(1)}, \infty)][1 - 2F(\infty, x_1^{(2)})]$$
$$- 2F_1^{(1)}(x, \infty) - 2F(\infty, x_1^{(2)})$$
$$+ 4 \int F(x_1^{(1)}, y^{(2)}) \, dF(\infty, y^{(2)}) + 4 \int F(y^{(1)}, x_{(2)}^1) \, dF(y^{(1)}, \infty).$$

Let $\zeta_1(g)$, $\zeta_2(g)$, $\zeta_3(g)$ stand for the variances, respectively, of g_1^*, g_2, g_3^*; prove that

$$\zeta_3(g) = 1 - \kappa^2.$$

Prove that $n^{1/2}(k - \kappa)$ has a limiting normal distribution with mean 0 and variance ζ_1. Prove that

$$(8.4) \quad \text{var } \{k\} = \frac{6}{n(n-1)(n-2)} \left\{ 3 \binom{n-3}{2} \zeta_1(g) + 3(n-3) \zeta_2(g) + \zeta_3(g) \right\}.$$

If $X^{(1)}$ and $X^{(2)}$ are independent, prove that $\kappa = 0$, $\zeta_1(g) = 1/9$, $\zeta_2(g) = 7/18$, $\zeta_3 = 1$, and hence that

$$\text{var } \{k\} = \frac{n^2 - 3}{n(n-1)(n-2)}.$$

15. The rank correlation coefficient k' was defined in Problem 11. Prove that

$$(8.5) \qquad \text{var } \{k'\} = \frac{(n-2)^2 \text{ var } \{k\} + 6(n-2) \text{ cov } \{t, k\} + 9 \text{ var } t}{(n+1)^2}.$$

Prove that

$$\text{cov } \{t, k\} = \frac{6}{n(n-1)} \{(n-3)\zeta_1(t, k) + \zeta_2(t, k)\},$$

where

$$\zeta_1(t, k) = \text{cov } \{f_1^*(X_1), g_2^*(X_1)\},$$
$$\zeta_2(t, k) = \text{cov } \{f_2^*(X_1, X_2), g_2^*(X_1, X_2)\},$$

where f^*, g^* refer to symmetric kernels, respectively, of t, of k.

Prove that, if the bivariate distribution of $\mathbf{X} = (X^{(1)}, X^{(2)})$ is continuous and corresponds to independence of $X^{(1)}$ and $X^{(2)}$, then

$$\zeta_1(k) = \zeta_1(t) = \zeta_1(t, k) = 1/9,$$
$$\zeta_2(t, k) = 5/9,$$

$$(8.6) \qquad\qquad \text{cov } \{t, k\} = \frac{2(n+2)}{3n(n-1)},$$

and hence

$$(8.7) \qquad\qquad \text{var } \{k'\} = \frac{1}{n-1}.$$

Prove that $n^{1/2}(k' - K)$ is asymptotically normal with mean 0. Prove that

$$[n^{1/2}(t - \tau), \quad n^{1/2}(k - \kappa) \quad (\text{or } n^{1/2}(k' - \kappa))]$$

has a limiting normal distribution with means 0, variances $4\zeta_1(t)$, $9\zeta_1(k)$, and covariance $6\zeta_1(t, k)$. It is interesting to note that, in the case of independence as $n \to \infty$, the correlation between t and k approaches one, and the limiting functional relationship $3t = 2k$ holds.

16. Let $X_1, \cdots, X_n$ be independent real random variables, X_i having the continuous distribution function $F_{\theta_i}(x_i)$, where $\theta, \in \Omega$ indexes the continuous distribution functions. The problem of randomness with downward trend is

$$\text{Hypothesis: } F_{\theta_1}(x) = F_{\theta_2}(x) = \cdots = F_{\theta_n}(x); \quad \theta_1 \in \Omega,$$
$$\text{Alternative: } F_{\theta_1}(x) < \cdots < F_{\theta_n}(x); \quad (\theta_1, \cdots, \theta_n) \in \Omega^n.$$

Mann [19] has suggested for this problem a test based on the number T of inequalities $x_\alpha < x_\beta$ for $\alpha < \beta$. Show that

$$2T - \frac{n(n-1)}{2} = \sum_{\alpha < \beta} s(\alpha - \beta)\, s(x_\alpha - x_\beta).$$

The U statistic,

$$t = \frac{4T}{n(n-1)} - 1$$

$$= \frac{2}{n(n-1)} \sum_{\alpha < \beta} s(\alpha - \beta)\, s(x_\alpha - x_\beta),$$

is the difference-sign correlation between $1, \cdots, n$ and $x_1, \cdots, x_n$. Show that it is an unbiased estimate of the parameter

$$\tau = \frac{2}{n(n-1)} \sum_{\alpha < \beta} \tau_{\alpha\beta},$$

where

$$\tau_{\alpha\beta} = s(\alpha - \beta)[2 \int F_{\theta_\beta}(x)\, dF_{\theta_\alpha}(x) - 1].$$

Prove that $\tau = 0, < 0$ according as $(\theta_1, \cdots, \theta_n)$ belongs to the hypothesis, the alternative.

The random variables for the application of Hoeffding's theorem are $(1, X_1), \cdots$, (n, X_n), and hence, for both the hypothesis and alternative limiting distribution of t, Theorem 5.5 is needed. Mann's test is to reject the hypothesis if $t < a_n$ where a_n is chosen to give the test size α. Prove that the test is consistent. Find a limiting form for the constant a_n. What condition is needed to assure asymptotic normality of $(t - \tau)/$ [var $\{t\}]^{1/2}$ under the alternative?

17. Consider the sequence $(x_1^{(1)}, x_1^{(2)}, x_1^{(3)}), \cdots, (x_n^{(1)}, x_n^{(2)}, x_n^{(3)})$ and the $n(n-1)$ triplets of difference signs,

$$s(x_\alpha^{(1)} - x_\beta^{(1)}),\ s(x_\alpha^{(2)} - x_\beta^{(2)}),\ s(x_\alpha^{(3)} - x_\beta^{(3)}),$$

for $\alpha \neq \beta$, $\alpha, \beta = 1, \cdots, n$, and assume that all $x^{(1)}$'s are different, all $x^{(2)}$'s are different, all $x^{(3)}$'s are different. Prove that the regression functions for the trivariate "sign" sample of size $n(n-1)$ are linear.

Let t_{12}, t_{13}, t_{23} be the difference-sign correlation between coordinates 1, 2, coordinates 1, 3, and coordinates 2, 3. Let $t_{12\cdot3}$ be the partial correlation of $s(x_\alpha^{(1)} - x_\beta^{(1)})$ and $s(x_\alpha^{(2)} - x_\beta^{(2)})$ re $s(x_\alpha^{(3)} - x_\beta^{(3)})$.

$$t_{12\cdot3} = \frac{t_{12} - t_{13}t_{23}}{(1 - t_{13}^2)^{1/2}(1 - t_{23}^2)^{1/2}}.$$

Similarly, if $\mathbf{X}_1 = (X_1^{(1)}, X_1^{(2)}, X_1^{(3)})$, $\mathbf{X}_2 = (X_2^{(1)}, X_2^{(2)}, X_2^{(3)})$ are independent vectors having the same continuous distribution over R^3, then we can define correlations τ_{12}, τ_{13}, τ_{23} between the difference sign $s(X_1^{(i)} - X_2^{(i)})$ $(i = 1, 2, 3)$, and also a partial difference-sign correlation

$$\tau_{12\cdot3} = \frac{\tau_{12} - \tau_{13}\tau_{23}}{(1 - \tau_{13}^2)^{1/2}(1 - \tau_{23}^2)^{1/2}}.$$

If $(X_1^{(1)}, X_1^{(2)}, X_1^{(3)}), \cdots, (X_n^{(1)} X_n^{(2)} X_n^{(3)})$ are independent and identically distributed according to a continuous trivariate distribution function, and if $\tau_{23}^2 \neq 1$, $\tau_{23}^2 \neq 1$, then prove that

$$n^{1/2}(t_{12\cdot3} - \tau_{12\cdot3})$$

has a limiting normal distribution with mean 0 and variance

$$\frac{4}{(1 - \tau_{13}^2)(1 - \tau_{23}^2)} \left\{ \zeta_1(t_{12}) + \frac{(\tau_{23} - \tau_{12}\tau_{13})^2}{(1 - \tau_{13}^2)} \zeta_1(t_{13}) \right.$$

$$+ \frac{(\tau_{13} - \tau_{12}\tau_{23})^2}{(1 - \tau_{23}^2)^2} \zeta_1(t_{23}) - 2\frac{\tau_{23} - \tau_{12}\tau_{13}}{1 - \tau_{13}^2} \zeta_1(t_{12}, t_{13})$$

$$\left. - 2\frac{\tau_{13} - \tau_{12}\tau_{23}}{1 - \tau_{23}^2} \zeta_1(t_{12}, t_{23}) + 2\frac{(\tau_{23} - \tau_{12}\tau_{13})(\tau_{13} - \tau_{12}\tau_{23})}{(1 - \tau_{13}^2)(1 - \tau_{23}^2)} \zeta_1(t_{13}, t_{23}) \right\}$$

Use Theorem 2.7.

18. Prove the relations (6.4) and (6.5).

19. Prove the relations (6.25) and (6.26).

20. Prove that the second statistic in Example 6.1 satisfies the conditions of Theorem 6.6.

21. The randomized-block problem was introduced in Section 4.1, Chapter 3. We consider the formulation (4.2). Pitman proposed a conditional test, given the order statistic for each block, that is, given $(x_{1(1)}, \cdots, x_{1(c)}), \cdots, (x_{b(1)}, \cdots, x_{b(c)})$. The test was based on the usual F statistic. Prove that, given the order statistics above, a statistic that is equivalent to the F statistic is

$$(8.8) \qquad \sum_1^c (\bar{x}_{\cdot j} - \bar{x}_{\cdot\cdot})^2$$

where $\bar{x}_{\cdot j} = b^{-1} \sum_{i=1}^b x_{ij}$ and $\bar{x}_{\cdot\cdot} = (bc)^{-1} \sum_{ij} x_{ij}$. On the basis of Theorems 3.4 and 2.8,

give conditions on the x_{ij} sufficient to prove, under the hypothesis of no treatment effects, that the condition distribution of the statistic (8.8), given the order statistics, has as $b \to \infty$ the limiting distribution of a constant times a χ^2 variable on $c - 1$ degrees of freedom. What constant?

22. We consider another test for the randomized-block problem which is of correct size for hypothesis (4.5) or any previous hypothesis of Section (4.1) in Chapter 3. In each block the numbers $x_{i1}, \cdots, x_{ic}$ are replaced by their ranks $r_{i1}, \cdots, r_{ic}$, and then the ordinary F statistic is calculated. Show that an equivalent statistic is

$$\sum_{j=1}^c \left(r_{\cdot j} - \frac{c+1}{2} \right)^2,$$

where

$$\bar{r}_{\cdot j} = b^{-1} \sum_{i=1}^b r_{ij}.$$

Under the hypothesis of no treatment effects find the limiting distribution of this statistic as $b \to \infty$.

23. Another test similar in construction to the one above is to replace in each block the numbers $x_{i1}, \cdots, x_{ic}$ by $E\{Z_{(r_{i1})}\}, \cdots, E\{Z_{(r_{ic})}\}$, where $E\{Z_{(j)}\}$ is the expected valued of the jth order statistic in a sample of c from the normal distribution with mean 0 and variance 1. Do an analysis similar to that in the previous problem.

24. Consider the multivariate analog of the two-sample problem: $(X_1^{(1)}, \cdots, X_1^{(k)})$, $\cdots, (X_{n_1}^{(1)}, \cdots, X_{n_1}^{(k)})$ are independent, and each has the same continuous distribution over R^k. $(X_{n_1+1}^{(1)}, \cdots, X_{n_1+1}^{(k)}), \cdots, (X_{n_1+n_2}^{(1)}, \cdots, X_{n_1+n_2}^{(k)})$ are independent, and each has the same continuous distribution over R^k. The hypothesis is that the two distributions over R^k are identical. For the corresponding problem, assuming normal distributions and the same variance-covariance matrix in the two distributions, Hotelling has suggested the test which is to reject for large values of the statistic T^2:

$$T^2 = \frac{n_1 n_2}{n_1 + n_2} \sum_{ij=1}^{k} s^{ij}(\bar{x}^{(i)} - \bar{x}'^{(i)})(\bar{x}^{(j)} - \bar{x}'^{(j)}),$$

where

$$\bar{x}^{(i)} = n_1^{-1} \sum_{\alpha=1}^{n_1} x_\alpha^{(i)},$$

$$\bar{x}'^{(i)} = n_2^{-1} \sum_{\alpha=1}^{n_2} x_{n_1+\alpha}^{(i)},$$

and $\| s^{ij} \|$ is the inverse of the matrix $\| s_{ij} \|$, given by

$$s_{ij} = \frac{1}{n_1 + n_2 - 2} Q_{ij},$$

$$Q_{ij} = \sum_{\alpha=1}^{n_1} (x_\alpha^{(i)} - \bar{x}^{(i)})(x_\alpha^{(j)} - \bar{x}^{(j)})$$

$$+ \sum_{\alpha=1}^{n_2} (x_{n_1+\alpha}^{(i)} - \bar{x}'^{(i)})(x_{n_1+\alpha}^{(j)} - \bar{x}'^{(j)}).$$

Prove that

$$\frac{|Q_{ij}^*|}{|Q_{ij}|} = 1 + (n_1 + n_2 - 2)T^2,$$

where

$$Q_{ij}^* = Q_{ij} + \frac{n_1 n_2}{n_1 + n_2} (\bar{x}^{(i)} - \bar{x}'^{(i)})(\bar{x}^{(j)} - \bar{x}'^{(j)}),$$

and hence prove that T^2 is a monotone-increasing function of

$$T^{*2} = \sum_{ij=1}^{2} s^{*ij}(\bar{x}^{(i)} - \bar{x}'^{(i)})(\bar{x}^{(j)} - \bar{x}'^{(j)}),$$

where $\| s^{*ij} \|$ is the inverse of

$$\| s_{ij}^* \| = \left\| \frac{1}{n_1 + n_2 - 1} Q_{ij}^* \right\|.$$

For the nonparametric problem with alternatives involving only differences of location of the two distributions, a test suggested by Wald and Wolfowitz is a conditional test, given the order statistic $\{(x_1^{(1)}, \cdots, x_1^{(k)}), \cdots, (x_{n_1+n_2}^{(1)}, \cdots, x_{n_1+n_2}^{(k)})\}$, and rejects for large values of T^{*2}. Prove, using mild restrictions, that under the hypothesis with probability one the limiting conditional distributions of T^{*2} is χ^2 with $k - 1$ degrees of freedom. Under what restrictions? For simplicity treat the case $k = 2$.

25. For the run theory in Section 7 prove that

$$E\{r_{11}^{(a_1)} r_{12}^{(a_2)} \cdots\} = \frac{(n_2 + 1)^{(\Sigma a_i)} \dbinom{n_1 + n_2 - \Sigma(i + 1)a_i}{n_1 - \Sigma i a_i}}{\dbinom{n_1 + n_2}{n_1}}.$$

25. In Section 4, Chapter 5, the likelihood-ratio method was used to produce a test for the two-sample problem. Prove that the statistic on which the test is based has a limiting normal distribution.

REFERENCES AND BIBLIOGRAPHY

1. A. M. Mood, "The distribution theory of runs," *Ann. Math. Stat.*, Vol. 11 (1940), p. 367.

2. J. Wolfowitz, "Additive partition functions and a class of statistical hypotheses," *Ann. Math. Stat.*, Vol. 13 (1942), p. 247.

3. A. Wald and J. Wolfowitz, "Statistical tests based on permutations of the observations," *Ann. Math. Stat.*, Vol. 15 (1944), p. 358.

4. W. Hoeffding and H. Robbins, "The central limit theorem for dependent random variables," *Duke Math. J.*, Vol. 15 (1948), p. 773.

5. W. Hoeffding, "A class of statistics with asymptotically normal distribution," *Ann. Math. Stat.*, Vol. 19 (1948), p. 293.

6. G. E. Noether, "On a theorem by Wald and Wolfowitz," *Ann. Math. Stat.*, Vol. 20 (1949), p. 455.

7. W. Hoeffding, "A combinatorial central limit theorem," *Ann. Math. Stat.*, Vol. 22 (1951), p. 558.

8. W. Hoeffding, "The large sample power of tests based on permutations of observations," *Ann. Math. Stat.*, Vol. 23 (1952), p. 169.

9. W. Feller, *Introduction to Probability Theory*, John Wiley & Sons, 1950.

10. P. R. Halmos, *Measure Theory*, D. Van Nostrand Co., 1950.

11. M. Dwass, "On the asymptotic normality of certain rank order statistics," *Ann. Math. Stat.*, Vol. 24 (1953), p. 303.

12. M. N. Ghosh, "Asymptotic distribution of serial statistics and applications to problems of nonparametric hypotheses," *Ann. Math. Stat.*, Vol. 25 (1954), p. 218.

13. H. Scheffé, "A useful convergence theorem for probability distributions," *Ann. Math. Stat.*, Vol. 18 (1947), p. 434.

14. M. G. Kendall, *The Advanced Theory of Statistics*, Vol. 1, 3d Ed., Charles Griffin and Co., London, 1947.

15. H. Cramér, *Mathematical Methods of Statistics*, Princeton University Press, 1946.

16. J. V. Uspensky, *Introduction to Mathematical Probability*, McGraw-Hill Book Co., New York, 1937.

17. M. V. E. Monroe, *Introduction to Measure and Integration*, Addison and Wesley.

18. U. S. Nair, "The standard error of Gini's mean difference," *Biometrika*, Vol. 28 (1936), p. 428.

19. H. B. Mann, "Nonparametric tests against trend," *Econometrica*, Vol. 13 (1945), p. 245.

20. H. Cramér, *Random variables and probability distributions*, Cambridge University Press, 1937.

CHAPTER 7

Large-Sample Properties of Tests

1. INTRODUCTION

For most of the problems outlined in Chapter 3, the outcome can be represented as the result of a number of repetitions of a component experiment. It is convenient to call this number of repetitions the sample size. For small samples the theory of Chapter 5 can usually be applied directly to produce the constants determining a test's size and to produce values of the power function for particular distributions of the alternative hypothesis. Also, for large samples the theory of limiting distributions developed in the foregoing chapter frequently gives approximations to these values. However, the accuracy of the approximation is often in doubt and depends on the speed with which a distribution approaches its limiting form. Unfortunately, for medium sample sizes, direct calculations frequently lead to very tedious numerical work. Where these extensive calculations are unwarranted, a partial solution to bridging the gap between the results for small samples and the results for samples large enough for application of limiting distribution theory may in individual cases be obtained by experimental sampling from distributions constructed by the statistician. This is the *Monte Carlo method*.

In this chapter we consider some general theory and some particular results for the power of tests when the sample size is large.

2. CONSISTENCY

If we are to consider the effect of letting the sample size increase, we must have a test defined for each sample size; that is, we must have a sequence of tests. Each of the tests developed in Chapter 5 was defined for any sample size, and hence each could be considered as a sequence of

266

tests. For those distributions in the alternative hypothesis which are of particular interest, the minimum we can really expect of a sequence of tests is that the power should approach one as the sample size increases. This property was mentioned briefly in Chapter 2, Section 3.9, and was called consistency. However, in nonparametric theory, the classes of distributions are frequently of quite general mathematical form, and it is possible for some quite useful sequences of tests to construct mathematically peculiar distributions belonging to the alternative such that this requirement is not satisfied. For this reason we introduce a qualified definition of consistency.

Let $\mathscr{X}^n$ be the sample space, and $\{P_\theta^{\mathbf{X}} | \theta \in \Omega\}$ be the class of probability measures over $\mathscr{X}^n$. Also, for the hypothesis testing problem,

$$\text{Hypothesis:} \quad \theta \in \omega,$$
$$\text{Alternative:} \quad \theta \in \Omega - \omega,$$

let $\phi_n(\mathbf{x})$ be a test of size α. Then

The sequence of size-α tests $\{\phi_n(\mathbf{x})\}$ is consistent for $\zeta \subset \Omega - \omega$ if

$$(2.1) \qquad \qquad \lim_{n \to \infty} \mathbf{P}_{\phi_n}(\theta) = 1$$

for $\theta \in \zeta$.

We now consider some criteria for consistency. Let $g(\theta)$ be a real valued parameter defined over Ω, and suppose that this parameter distinguishes between the hypothesis and the subclass ζ of the alternative in the following simple manner

$$(2.2) \qquad \qquad g(\theta) = g_0 \quad \text{if} \quad \theta \in \omega$$
$$> g_0 \qquad \qquad \in \zeta.$$

THEOREM 2.1. (LEHMANN). If $t_n(x_1, \cdots, x_n)$ is a real-valued statistic defined over $\mathscr{X}^n$ for each n, and if for all $\theta \in \Omega$,

$$(2.3) \qquad \qquad E_\theta\{t_n(X_1, \cdots, X_n)\} = g(\theta),$$
$$(2.4) \qquad \qquad \lim_{n \to \infty} \text{var}_\theta \{t_n(X_1, \cdots, X_n)\} = 0,$$

where the limit is uniform for $\theta \in \omega$, then the sequence of tests $\{\phi_n(x)\}$ of exact size α,

$$(2.5) \qquad \qquad \phi_n(\mathbf{x}) = 1 \qquad t_n(\mathbf{x}) - g_0 > c_n$$
$$= 0 \qquad \qquad < c_n$$

is consistent for ζ.

Proof. Since $\text{var}_\theta \{t_n(X)\}$ approaches zero uniformly for $\theta \in \omega$, it is easily seen by an application of Tchebycheff's inequality that, for any positive c,

$$\text{Pr}_\theta \{t_n(X) - g_0 > c\}$$

approaches zero uniformly for $\theta \in \omega$. Hence

$$\sup_{\theta \in \omega} \mathrm{Pr}_\theta \left\{ t_n(X) - g_0 > c \right\}$$

approaches zero as n approaches infinity. Then, since the tests are of exact size α, we have that

$$\limsup_{n \to \infty} c_n \leq 0.$$

By a similar argument it is easily shown that, for each $\theta \in \zeta$,

$$\mathrm{Pr}_\theta \left\{ t_n(X) - g_0 > c \right\}$$

approaches one for positive values of c less than $g(\theta)$. It follows then that, for $\theta \in \zeta$, the power of the test $\phi_n(x)$,

$$\mathbf{P}_{\phi_n}(\theta) = \mathrm{Pr}_\theta \left\{ t_n(X) - g_0 > c_n \right\}$$

must approach one as $n \to \infty$.

This theorem can be extended in a number of simple ways. For example, the conclusions remain valid for two-sided tests of the form

(2.6) $\qquad \phi_n(X) = 1 \qquad$ if $\quad \left| t_n(x) - g_0 \right| > c_n$

$\qquad\qquad\qquad = 0 \qquad\qquad\qquad\quad < c_n.$

Also conditions (2.5) and (2.4) can be replaced by convergence in probability

(2.7) $\qquad\qquad \text{p-}\lim_{n \to \infty} t_n(X_1, \cdots, X_n) = g(\theta),$

provided this convergence is uniform for θ in ω; that is, provided

(2.8) $\qquad\qquad \mathrm{Pr}_\theta \left\{ g_0 - \varepsilon \leq t_n(X_1, \cdots, X_n) \leq g_0 + \varepsilon \right\}$

converges to one uniformly for $\theta \in \omega$. There is also an immediate analog for the two-sample problems where the limits are taken as the smaller sample size approaches infinity.

EXAMPLE 2.1. THE TWO-SAMPLE PROBLEM. We consider the Mann–Whitney test which was discussed in Examples 1.1 and 3.1 in Chapter 5. This test is to reject, for large values of the statistic,

(2.9) $\qquad V = \dfrac{1}{n_1 n_2}$ [number of pairs (x_i, x_{n_1+j}) with $x_i < x_{n_1+j}$

$\qquad\qquad (i = 1, \cdots, n_1;\ j = 1, \cdots, n_2)].$

By using the function $c'(u)$ defined by

(2.10) $$c'(u) = 1 \quad \text{if} \quad u > 0$$

$$= 0 \qquad\qquad \leq 0,$$

we can write

$$V = \frac{1}{n_1 n_2} \sum_{i=1}^{n_1} \sum_{j=1}^{n_2} c'(x_{n_1+j} - x_i).$$

Then, by the theory of Chapter 4 as applied in Example 2.4 of that chapter, it is easily seen that V is a minimum-variance unbiased estimate of the parameter

$$g(F, G) = E\{c'(X_{n_1+1} - X_1)\}$$

$$= \Pr\{X_{n_1+1} - X_1 > 0\},$$

where X_1, X_{n_1+1} are independent and have the distribution functions $F(x)$, $G(x)$.

From the minimum-variance property of V, it follows that the variance of V is less than the variance of the unbiased estimate

$$\frac{1}{\min(n_1, n_2)} \sum_{i=1}^{\min(n_1,n_2)} c(X_{n_1+i} - X_i).$$

The variance of this last expression is bounded by

$$\frac{1}{\min(n_1, n_2)}$$

Hence, the variance of V approaches zero uniformly as the smaller sample size approaches infinity. Then, by the two-sample extension of Theorem 2.1, the one-sided Mann–Whitney test is consistent against alternatives having

$$\Pr\{X_{n_1+1} - X_1 > 0\} > 1/2,$$

and similarly the two-sided test is consistent against alternatives having

$$\Pr\{X_{n_1+1} - X_1 > 0\} \neq 1/2.$$

In this example we have assumed that the class of probability measures corresponds to all pairs $(F(x), G(x))$ of continuous or absolutely continuous distribution functions. The extension to include distributions having discrete probabilities is straightforward.

3. A CRITERION FOR THE RELATIVE EFFICIENCY OF TESTS

As we remarked in the previous section, most of the standard tests are consistent—consistent at least for those alternatives of particular interest. However, if we wish to compare two sequences of tests, we could examine the way in which powers approach the limit one. In Section 3.9 of Chapter 2 we proposed an expression to measure the relative efficiency, and it was based on the limiting behaviors of the power. Essentially the expression was the limiting ratio of sample sizes such that the power functions were equivalent.

In general for nonparametric tests there is no simple measure of the relative efficiency based on the behavior of the power function for all parameter values of the alternative. Often, though, the statistician is particularly interested in the behavior of tests for some simple parametric class of alternatives. For most of the problems outlined in Chapter 3, this parametric class is the set of normal distributions used as the alternative for the problem as given in normal theory. For these, the power usually approaches one. It seems reasonable then to choose from the parametric class a sequence that gets closer and closer to the distribution of the hypothesis. Let $\{\theta_i\}$ be such a sequence. Also let $\{\phi_n\}$, $\{\phi_n^*\}$ be two sequences of tests all of the same size α, and let $\{n_i\}$, $\{n_i^*\}$ be two increasing sequences of integers such that

$$(3.1) \qquad \lim_{i \to \infty} \mathbf{P}_{\phi_{n_i}}(\theta_i) = \lim_{i \to \infty} \mathbf{P}_{\phi_{n_i}^*}(\theta_i),$$

with the two limits existing not equal zero or one (the limiting power of ϕ_{n_i} at θ_i must be the same as the limiting power of $\phi_{n_i}^*$ at θ_i). Then *the relative efficiency of $\{\phi_n\}$ with respect to $\{\phi_n^*\}$* is defined to be

$$(3.2) \qquad e(\{\phi_n\}, \{\phi_n^*\}) = \lim_{i \to \infty} \frac{n_i^*}{n_i},$$

if this limit exists the same for all sequences $\{n_i\}$, $\{n_i^*\}$ satisfying (3.1). This is a definition of the relative efficiency corresponding to the sequence of alternatives θ_i and is based on the reciprocal of the ratio of sample sizes giving the same power for that sequence.

Under moderate assumptions the theorems in this section give a simple expression for the relative efficiency of two sequences of tests. For this we introduce some notation. Let ζ be a subset of the parameter space Ω, and assume that ζ is indexed by a real parameter δ. Further, assume that $\delta = 0$ gives a distribution in the hypothesis ω, and that other δ's correspond to distributions in the alternative $\Omega - \omega$. Now let $t_n(\mathbf{x})$, $t_n^*(\mathbf{x})$ be two real-valued statistics defined over R^n, and designate by $E_\delta\{T_n\}$, $\sigma_\delta^2\{T_n\}$

and $E_\delta\{T_n^*\}$, $\sigma_\delta^2\{T_n^*\}$ the mean and variance of $t_n(\mathbf{X})$ and $t_n^*(\mathbf{X})$, respectively. The theorems on efficiency will be concerned with the sequences of tests $\{\phi_n(\mathbf{x})\}$, $\{\phi_n^*(\mathbf{x})\}$ defined by

(3.3)
$$\phi_n(\mathbf{x}) = 1 \qquad \text{if} \quad t_n(\mathbf{x}) > t_{n,\alpha}$$
$$= a \qquad\qquad = t_{n,\alpha}$$
$$= 0 \qquad\qquad < t_{n,\alpha},$$

(3.4)
$$\phi_n^*(\mathbf{x}) = 1 \qquad \text{if} \quad t_n^*(\mathbf{x}) > t_{n,\alpha}^*$$
$$= b \qquad\qquad = t_{n,\alpha}^*$$
$$= 0 \qquad\qquad < t_{n,\alpha}^*,$$

where $t_{n,\alpha}$, $t_{n,\alpha}^*$ are chosen to give the tests size α according to the distribution given by $\delta = 0$.

First we have two theorems on the limiting power of a sequence of tests $\{\phi_n(\mathbf{x})\}$.

THEOREM 3.1. If for $\delta = 0$,

(3.5)
$$\frac{d}{d\delta}E_\delta\{T_n\} > 0,$$

(3.6)
$$\lim_{n \to \infty} \frac{\frac{d}{d\delta}E_\delta\{T_n\}\big|_{\delta=\delta_n}}{n^{1/2}\sigma_0\{T_n\}} = c,$$

and, if for the sequence of alternatives $\delta_n = k/n^{1/2}$,

(3.7)
$$\lim_{n \to \infty} \frac{\frac{d}{d\delta}E_\delta\{T_n\}\big|_{\delta=\delta_n}}{\frac{d}{d\delta}E_\delta\{T_n\}\big|_{\delta=0}} = 1,$$

(3.8)
$$\lim_{n \to \infty} \frac{\sigma_{\delta_n}\{T_n\}}{\sigma_0\{T_n\}} = 1,$$

and, if corresponding to the parameter value $\delta_n = k/n^{1/2}$ (with $k \geq 0$) T_n is asymptotically normal with mean $E_{\delta_n}\{T_n\}$ and variance $\sigma_{\delta_n}^2\{T_n\}$, then the limiting power of the size-α test $\phi_n(\mathbf{x})$ is

(3.9)
$$1 - \Phi(z_\alpha - kc)$$

where $1 - \Phi(z_\alpha) = \alpha$ and $\Phi(x)$ is the standardized normal distribution function.

Proof. Because T_n is asymptotically normal for $k = 0$, we have

$$\lim_{n \to \infty} \frac{t_{n,\alpha} - E_0\{T_n\}}{\sigma_0\{T_n\}} = \lambda_\alpha.$$

Also, because T_n is asymptotically for $k > 0$, we have that the limiting power is

$$1 - \Phi(\hat{z}),$$

where

$$\hat{z} = \lim_{n \to \infty} \frac{t_{n,\alpha} - E_{\delta_n}\{T_n\}}{\sigma_{\delta_n}\{T_n\}}.$$

Now, since

$$E_{\delta_n}\{T_n\} = E_0\{T_n\} + \frac{k}{n^{1/2}}\left[\frac{d}{d\delta} E_\delta\{T_n\}\right]_{\delta=\hat{\delta}} \qquad 0 < \hat{\delta} < \delta_n,$$

then

$$\hat{z} = \lim_{n \to \infty} \frac{t_{n,\alpha} - E_0\{T_n\} - \dfrac{k}{n^{1/2}}\left[\dfrac{d}{d\delta} E_\delta\{T_n\}\right]_{\delta=\hat{\delta}}}{\sigma_{\delta_n}\{T_n\}}$$

$$= \lim_{n \to \infty} \frac{t_{n,\alpha} - E_0\{T_n\}}{\sigma_0\{T_n\}} \frac{\sigma_0\{T_n\}}{\sigma_{\delta_n}\{T_n\}} - \lim_{n \to \infty} \frac{\dfrac{k}{n^{1/2}}\left[\dfrac{d}{d\delta} E_\delta\{T_n\}\right]_{\delta=\hat{\delta}}}{\sigma_{\delta_n}\{T_n\}}$$

$$= \lambda_\alpha - kc.$$

This completes the proof.

As a generalization of this theorem we have

THEOREM 3.2. (NOETHER). If for $\delta = 0$,

(3.10) $\quad \dfrac{d}{d\delta} E_\delta\{T_n\} = \cdots = \dfrac{d^{m-1}}{d\delta^{m-1}} E_\delta\{T_n\} = 0, \qquad \dfrac{d^m}{d\delta^m} E_\delta\{T_n\} > 0,$

(3.11) $\quad \displaystyle\lim_{n \to \infty} \frac{\dfrac{d^m}{d\delta^m} E_\delta\{T_n\}\big|_{\delta=0}}{n^{m\gamma}\sigma_0\{T_n\}} = c \qquad \text{for some} \quad \gamma > 0,$

and, if for the sequence $\delta_n = k/n^\gamma$,

(3.12) $\quad \displaystyle\lim_{n \to \infty} \frac{\dfrac{d^m}{d\delta^m} E_\delta\{T_n\}}{\dfrac{d^m}{d\delta^m} E_0\{T_n\}} = 1,$

(3.13) $\quad \displaystyle\lim_{n \to \infty} \frac{\sigma_{\delta_n}\{T_n\}}{\sigma_0\{T_n\}} = 1,$

and, if corresponding to the parameter value $\delta_n = k/n^\nu$ for $k \geq 0$, T_n is asymptotically normal with mean $E_{\delta_n}\{T_n\}$ and variance $\sigma^2_{\delta_n}\{T_n\}$, then the limiting power of the size-α test $\phi_n(\mathbf{x})$ is

(3.14) $$1 - \Phi\left(z_\alpha - \frac{k^m c}{m!}\right).$$

Proof. The proof corresponds to that for the previous theorem.

The next two theorems are concerned with the relative efficiency of sequences of tests.

THEOREM 3.3. (PITMAN). If $\{T_n\}$ and $\{T_n^*\}$ satisfy the conditions of Theorem 3.1, then the relative efficiency of $\{\phi_n\}$ re $\{\phi_n^*\}$ is

(3.15) $$\lim_{n \to \infty} \left[\frac{\frac{d}{d\delta} E_\delta\{T_n\}|_{\delta=0}}{\frac{d}{d\delta} E_\delta\{T_n^*\}|_{\delta=0}}\right]^2 \frac{\sigma^2_0\{T_n^*\}}{\{\sigma^2_0 T_n\}}.$$

Proof. The two tests will have the same limiting power if

$$kc = k^* c^*.$$

The sequences of alternatives will be the same if

$$\frac{k}{n^{1/2}} = \frac{k^*}{n^{*1/2}}.$$

It follows then that

$$\frac{n^*}{n} = \left(\frac{c}{c^*}\right)^2$$

$$= \lim_{n \to \infty} \left[\frac{\frac{d}{d\delta} E_\delta\{T_n\}|_{\delta=0}}{\frac{d}{d\delta} E_\delta\{T_n^*\}|_{\delta=0}}\right]^2 \frac{\sigma^2_0\{T_n^*\}}{\sigma^2_0\{T_n\}}.$$

THEOREM 3.4. (NOETHER). If $\{T_n\}$ and $\{T_n^*\}$ satisfy the conditions of Theorem 3.2, and if $\gamma = \gamma^*$, $m = m^*$, then the relative efficiency of $\{\phi_n\}$ re $\{\phi_n^*\}$ is

$$\lim_{n \to \infty} \left[\frac{\frac{d^m}{d\delta^m} E_\delta\{T_n\}|_{\delta=0}}{\sigma_0\{T_n\}} \cdot \frac{\sigma_0\{T_n^*\}}{\frac{d^m}{d\delta^m} E_\delta\{T_n^*\}|_{\delta=0}}\right]^{\frac{1}{m\gamma}}.$$

Proof. The proof corresponds to that for Theorem 3.3.

THEOREM 3.5.   Theorems 3.3 and 3.4 remain valid as stated if the tests are two-sided tests of the form

$$\phi_n(\mathbf{x}) = 1 \qquad \text{if} \quad t_n(\mathbf{x}) > t_{n',\,\alpha''}$$
$$= 1 \qquad \text{if} \quad t_{n,\alpha'} > t_n(\mathbf{x})$$
$$= 0 \qquad \text{if} \quad t_{n,\alpha''} > t_n(\mathbf{x}) > t_{n,\alpha'}$$

where α', α'' are fixed proportions, the same for each sequence of tests.

Proof.   Straightforward.

In the statement of Theorems 3.3 and 3.4 there is nothing essential in the requirement that the limiting distribution be normal.   It could be any other distribution form having scale and location parameters.

EXAMPLE 3.1.   THE SINGLE-SAMPLE PROBLEM OF LOCATION.   Let $X_1, \cdots, X_n$ be independent and each have the same continuous distribution function $F_\theta(x)$.   The usual form of the location problem uses the median as location parameter and is given by

$$(3.16) \qquad \text{Hypothesis:} \quad \xi_{.5}(F_\theta) = \xi_0,$$
$$\text{Alternative:} \quad \xi_{.5}(F_\theta) > \xi_0.$$

In parametric theory, when the distributions are assumed normal, the usual test for this problem is the t-test.   From Chapter 2 we know that it is most powerful similar, most powerful invariant, and most stringent. The most powerful test for the nonparametric formulation was derived in Section 2.1 of Chapter 5.   It is the sign test.   We calculate now the large-sample efficiency of the sign test with respect to the t test when the underlying distributions are normal.

Both tests are invariant under a change of scale about the origin.   Hence it suffices to evaluate efficiency when the underlying distribution being sampled is normal with mean δ and variance 1.   Also, without loss of generality, we can let $\xi_0 = 0$.

If we use the function $c'(u)$ defined by (2.10), the sign test is to reject for large values of the statistic

$$(3.17) \qquad v_n = \frac{1}{n} \sum_{i=1}^{n} c'(x_i).$$

We have

$$(3.18) \qquad E_\delta(V_n) = E_\delta\{c'(X)\}$$

$$= \frac{1}{(2\pi)^{1/2}} \int_{-\infty}^{\infty} c'(x) \exp\left[-\frac{(x-\delta)^2}{2}\right] dx$$

$$= \frac{1}{(2\pi)^{1/2}} \int_{-\delta}^{\infty} \exp\left(-\frac{x^2}{2}\right) dx$$

(3.19)
$$\frac{\partial}{\partial \delta} E_\delta(V_n)\Big|_{\delta=0} = \frac{+1}{(2\pi)^{1/2}} e^0$$

$$= (2\pi)^{-1/2}.$$

We calculate the variance of V_n:

$$\sigma_\delta^2(V_n) = \frac{n}{n^2} \sigma_{c'(X)}^2$$

$$= \frac{1}{n} p(1-p),$$

where p is given by the expression (3.18). If $\delta = 0$, then $p = 1/2$ and

$$\sigma_0^2(V_n) = \frac{1}{4n}.$$

Also by Theorem 3.5 in Chapter 6 it is straightforward to show that the induced distribution of the statistic v is normal.

The t test is to reject for large values of the statistic

$$w = \frac{\bar{x}}{\left[\frac{1}{n} \sum_{i=1}^{n} (x_i - \bar{x})^2\right]^{1/2}},$$

where

$$\bar{x} = \frac{1}{n} \sum_{i=1}^{n} x_i.$$

The denominator of w converges stochastically to 1, and hence an asymptotically equivalent statistic is

$$w' = \bar{x}.$$

We have

$$E_\delta(W') = \delta,$$

$$\frac{\partial}{\partial \delta} E_\delta(W') = 1.$$

Also we have

$$\sigma_\delta^2(W') = \frac{1}{n}.$$

By Theorem 3.5 in Chapter 6 it follows that the induced distribution of $\bar{x}$ is normal.

Then by Theorem 3.1 the large-sample efficiency of the sign test with respect to the t test for normal alternatives is

$$\left[\frac{(2\pi)^{-1/2}}{1}\right]^2 \frac{1/n}{1/4n} = \frac{2}{\pi}.$$

In [4] Dixon considers the power function of the sign test for small samples and shows that, for approximate agreement of the power functions, the ratio of sample sizes is approximately 0.95 when the sign test is based on a sample of 5, 0.80 for a sample of 10, 0.70 for a sample of 20. This indicates a high efficiency for small samples which gradually decreases to a limiting efficiency of 0.637.

4. THE EFFICIENCY OF SOME CONDITIONAL TESTS

In Chapter 3, Section 2.2, we developed a technique for finding similar tests most powerful for simple alternatives. This technique depended on having a statistic that was sufficient and complete under the distributions of the hypothesis. The resultant test could be described as a conditional test, given the statistic. In this section we develop some theory which enables us to show that a number of these conditional tests are asymptotically as efficient, when the distributions are normal, as the corresponding tests of parametric theory.

Consider the sample space $\mathcal{X}(\mathcal{A})$, the class of probability measures $\{P_\theta \,|\, \theta \in \Omega\}$, and the hypothesis testing problem

(4.1)
$$\text{Hypothesis: } \theta \in \omega,$$
$$\text{Alternative: } \theta \in \Omega - \omega.$$

Suppose that $t(x)$ is a statistic which is sufficient for the probability measures of the hypothesis, $\{P_\theta \,|\, \theta \in \omega\}$. Let $s(x)$ be a real-valued statistic. Then the type of test mentioned above has the following form

(4.2)
$$
\begin{aligned}
\phi(x) &= 1 &&\text{if}\quad s(x) > c_{t(x)} \\
&= a_{t(x)} && \qquad\;\; = c_{t(x)} \\
&= 0 && \qquad\;\; < c_{t(x)},
\end{aligned}
$$

where the 'constants' $a_{t(x)}$, $c_{t(x)}$ are chosen so that, under the hypothesis, the test has conditional size α, given the statistic $t(x)$.

For convenience we introduce some additional notation to describe the test (4.2). From the assumptions above it follows that, under the hypothesis, the conditional distribution, given the statistic $t(x)$, does not depend on the parameter $\theta \in \omega$. Hence, under the hypothesis, there is a single conditional distribution for $s(x)$, given a value for $t(x)$. This conditional distribution is important because it is with respect to it that the test was given size α. Let $F(s; x)$ be the distribution function for this conditional distribution; we have

$$(4.3) \qquad F(s; x) = \mathrm{Pr}_\omega \{s(X) \le s | t(x)\},$$

where the subscript ω is used to indicate the single hypothesis distribution, given a value for $t(x)$. We introduce a symbol $S(x)$ designating a random variable having the conditional distribution $F(s; x)$:

$$(4.4) \qquad F(s; x) = \mathrm{Pr} \{S(x) \le s\}.$$

Also we wish a symbol to designate a certain percentage point of this distribution. In Chapter 2, Section 2.1, we introduced the symbol $\xi_p(Y)$ to designate the p percentile of the distribution of the real random variable Y. However, for a description of the test (4.2) we need a point exceeded with probability α; hence with some apology for the notation we define

$$(4.5) \qquad \xi_\alpha(x) = \xi_{1-\alpha}(S(x)).$$

The test (4.2) then takes the form

$$(4.6) \qquad \begin{aligned} \phi(x) &= 1 & s(x) &> \xi_\alpha(x) \\ &= a_{t(x)} & &= \xi_\alpha(x) \\ &= 0 & &< \xi_\alpha(x), \end{aligned}$$

where $a_{t(x)}$ is chosen to give the test size α under the hypothesis and is given explicitly by

$$(4.7) \qquad a_{t(x)} = \frac{\alpha - \mathrm{Pr} \{S(x) > \xi_\alpha(x)\}}{\mathrm{Pr} \{S(x) = \xi_\alpha(x)\}}.$$

To illustrate this notation we refer to Example 2.1 in Chapter 5. There the Pitman two-sample test was derived as the most powerful similar test against alternatives involving normal distributions. The statistic $t(x)$ was the order statistic for the combined sample. A number of definitions for $s(x)$ were considered, but at the end of the example it was taken to be the usual two-sample t statistic, and this is the most convenient form for our purposes here. The conditional distribution, given a value for $t(x)$, is equal probability to each of the points obtained by permuting the coordinates in the order statistic. There are $(n_1 + n_2)!$ such permutations. Under the hypothesis that the two samples come from the same distribution, it is seen that the induced conditional distribution is discrete—is equal probability to each of $(n_1 + n_2)!$ values of $s(x)$ derived under permutations of the coordinates in the order statistic (of, course, not all of these values are different).

We use the framework of this example to indicate the direction in which we shall develop the theory in this section. The statistic $s(x)$ is the two-sample t statistic. For the two-sample problem *involving normal distributions* and a one-sided alternative, the most powerful similar test is the t test and is given by

$$\phi^*(x) = 1 \qquad s(x) > s_\alpha$$
$$= 0 \qquad < s_\alpha,$$

where s_α is the point exceeded with probability α according to the t distribution with $n_1 + n_2 - 2$ degrees of freedom. We shall show for a class of alternatives including some normal distributions that $\xi_\alpha(X)$ converges in probability to s_α as the sample sizes increase; also that the limiting distribution of $s(X)$ is continuous at the limiting value of s_α. From this it follows quite easily that, for this class of distributions, the tests $\phi(x)$ and $\phi^*(x)$ are asymptotically equivalent and hence have the same limiting power function. This then almost immediately implies that Pitman's test for normal alternatives is asymptotically as efficient as the usual t test..

We return to the general model introduced earlier. Our results in this section are concerned with limiting distributions and relative efficiency as a parameter n approaches ∞. Each of the symbols introduced can depend on n; however, it is not convenient to put a subscript n on every symbol introduced, but we shall try to use it where it is most essential. Hence the test (4.6) for sample size n is given by

$$\text{(4.8)} \qquad \begin{aligned} \phi_n(x) &= 1 & s_n(x) &> \xi_{\alpha,n}(x) \\ &= a_{t(x)} & &= \xi_{\alpha,n}(x) \\ &= 0 & &< \xi_{\alpha,n}(x). \end{aligned}$$

Also suppose that $\phi_n^*(x)$ is a related test of the form found in parametric theory,

$$\text{(4.9)} \qquad \begin{aligned} \phi_n^*(x) &= 1 & s_n(x) &> s_{\alpha,n} \\ &= a^0 & &= s_{\alpha,n} \\ &= 0 & &< s_{\alpha,n}, \end{aligned}$$

where the constant $s_{\alpha,n}$ is chosen to give the test size α for a distribution θ_n^0 in the hypothesis ω_n.

THEOREM 4.1. (HOEFFDING). For the sequence of distributions $\{\theta_n'\}$ for X_n, if $F_n(s; X_n)$ converges in probability to a distribution function $F(s)$ at every point of continuity of $F(s)$, if $F(s) = 1 - \alpha$ has a unique solution

$s = s_\alpha$, a point of continuity of $F(s)$, then $\xi_{\alpha,n}(X)$ converges in probability to s_α. And, if there exists a function $H(s)$ continuous at s_α such that

$$(4.10) \qquad \mathrm{Pr}_{\theta'_n}\{s_n(X_n) \leq s\} \to H(s)$$

at every continuity point of $H(s)$, then, for the sequence of distributions $\{\theta'_n\}$, the power of $\phi_n(x)$ converges to $1 - H(s_\alpha)$. And, if $s_{\alpha,n}$ converges to s_α then, for the sequence $\{\theta'_n\}$, the power of ϕ_n^* converges also to $1 - H(s_\alpha)$.

Note. It is of interest to emphasize that $F_n(s; x)$ is the distribution function corresponding to the hypothesis conditional distribution of $s(X)$, given $t(x)$. On the other hand, $H(s)$ is the limiting form of the marginal distribution of $s_n(X)$ under the sequence of alternative distributions $\{\theta'_n\}$.

Also the assumptions of the theorem are much stronger than necessary for the equality of limiting powers for the sequence $\{\theta'_n\}$. The proof will indicate the modifications that can be made with the results remaining valid.

Proof. We first show that $\xi_{\alpha,n}(X_n)$ converges in probability to s_α. From the definitions of $\xi_{\alpha,n}(x)$ and $F_n(s; x)$, it follows that

$$\alpha < F_n(s, x)$$

implies that

$$\xi_{\alpha,n}(x) \leq s,$$

which implies that

$$\alpha \leq F_n(s, x);$$

hence

$$(4.11) \quad \mathrm{Pr}_{\theta'_n}\{F_n(s; X_n) > \alpha\} \leq \mathrm{Pr}_{\theta'_n}\{\xi_{\alpha,n}(X_n) \leq s\} \leq \mathrm{Pr}_{\theta'_n}\{F_n(s; X_n) \geq \alpha\}.$$

Now, if s is a continuity point of $F(s)$ and if $s < s_\alpha$, then from the assumptions we have

$$(4.12) \qquad \underset{n \to \infty}{\text{p-lim}}\, F_n(s; X_n) = F(s) < F(s_\alpha) = \alpha,$$

and hence the outside terms of (4.11) approach zero; hence

$$\mathrm{Pr}_{\theta'_n}\{\xi_{\alpha,n}(X_n) \leq s\} \to 0,$$

if $s < s_\alpha$. And, if s is a continuity point of $F(s)$ and if $s > s_\alpha$, then from the assumptions we have

$$(4.13) \qquad \underset{n \to \infty}{\text{p-lim}}\, F_n(s; X_n) = F(s) > F(s_\alpha) = \alpha,$$

and hence the outside terms of (4.11) approach one; hence

$$\mathrm{Pr}_{\theta'_n}\{\xi_{\alpha,n}(X_n) \leq s\} \to 1,$$

if $s > s_\alpha$. It follows then that $\xi_{\alpha,n}(X_n)$ converges in probability to s_α.

We now show that the power of $\phi_n(x)$ approaches $1 - H(s_\alpha)$. From the definition of $\phi_n(x)$ in (4.8), we have

$$(4.14) \ \text{Pr}_{\theta'_n}\{s_n(X_n) > \xi_{\alpha,n}(X_n)\} \leq E_{\theta'_n}\{\phi_n(X_n)\} \leq \text{Pr}_{\theta'_n}\{s_n(X_n) \geq \xi_{\alpha,n}(X_n)\}.$$

From the assumptions, we have that $H(s)$ is continuous at s_α and $\text{Pr}\{s_n\{X_n\} > s\}$, $\text{Pr}\{s_n(X_n) \geq s\}$ converge to $1 - H(s)$ for continuity points s. Hence $\text{Pr}\{s_n(X_n) > s\}$, $\text{Pr}\{s_n(X_n) \geq s\}$ can be made arbitrarily close to $1 - H(s_\alpha)$ by choosing n large enough and s close enough to s_α. Then, since $\xi_{\alpha,n}(X_n)$ converges in probability to s_α, it follows that the outside terms of (4.14) converge to $1 - H(s_\alpha)$, and hence that

$$\lim_{n \to \infty} E_{\theta'_n}\{\phi_n(X_n)\} = 1 - H(s_\alpha),$$

Since it is assumed that $s_{\alpha,n}$ converged to s_α, it follows trivially that the power of $\phi_n^*(x)$ converges also to $1 - H(s_\alpha)$. This completes the proof.

The theorem above has been stated for one-sided tests, but it extends in a straightforward manner to cover the two-sided tests.

The next theorem gives a simple procedure for checking whether a distribution function $F_n(s; X)$ converges in probability to a distribution function $F(s)$.

THEOREM 4.2. (HOEFFDING). A necessary and sufficient condition that $F_n(s; X)$ converge in probability to $F(s)$ is that

$$(4.15) \qquad \text{Pr}\{S_n(X_n) \leq s\} \to F(s),$$

$$(4.16) \qquad \text{Pr}\{S_n(X_n) \leq s, \ S_n'(X_n) \leq s\} \to F^2(s).$$

where $S_n(x)$, $S_n'(x)$ are independent and identically distributed random variables defined by (4.4).

Proof. Problem 3 in Chapter 6 was to show that, if the mean and variance of a random variable Y_n converge, respectively, to c and 0, then the random variable Y_n converges in probability to c. An equivalent condition is that $E\{Y_n\}$, $E\{Y_n^2\}$ converge, respectively, to c, c^2. If the random variables are uniformly bounded, then it is trivial to show that the converse also holds. Then, since $0 \leq F_n(s; X) \leq 1$, the convergence in probability of $F_n(s; X_n)$ to $F(s)$ is equivalent to

$$E\{F_n(s; X_n)\} \to F(s)$$

$$E\{[F_n(s; X_n)]^2\} \to F^2(s).$$

The theorem then follows by noting that

$$(4.17) \qquad F_n(s; x) = \text{Pr}\{S_n(x) \leq s\}$$

$$(4.18) \qquad F_n^2(s; x) = \text{Pr}\{S_n(x) \leq s, S_n'(x) \leq s\}.$$

EXAMPLE 4.1. THE PROBLEM OF LOCATION, GIVEN SYMMETRY. The problem of location, given symmetry, was described in Section 2.2 of Chapter 3 and was designated by (2.7) and (2.8). Let $X_1, \cdots, X_n$ be independent and each have the same absolutely continuous distribution which is symmetric about the median. The problem is to test the hypothesis that the median is zero against the alternative that it is larger (one-sided problem), or that it is not equal to zero (two-sided problem).

Problem 11 of Chapter 5 was to apply the theory of Section 2.2 of that chapter to finding the most powerful similar test for the one-sided problem against a normal alternative and a most stringent similar test for the two-sided problem with normal alternative. The test was a conditional test, given the statistic $t'_n(\mathbf{x}) = \{|x_1|, \cdots, |x_n|\}$, and was to reject for large values of the statistic $s'_n(\mathbf{x}) = \Sigma x_i$ for the one-sided problem and large values of $|s'_n(\mathbf{x})|$ for the two-sided problem. Since both $t'_n(\mathbf{x})$ and $s'_n(\mathbf{x})$ are symmetric in the x's, it is equivalent to construct the test as a conditional test, given $t_n(x) = (|x_1|, \cdots, |x_n|)$. Under the hypothesis the conditional distribution, given $t_n(x) = (|x_1|, \cdots, |x_n|)$, is equal probability to each of the 2^n values of $(\pm x_1, \cdots, \pm x_n)$. If we let G_i be a random variable taking the values $+1, -1$ each with probability $1/2$, then the random variable $S_n(\mathbf{x})$ can be described by

(4.19)
$$S_n(\mathbf{x}) = (G_1 x_1, \cdots, G_n x_n).$$

We now replace the statistic $s'_n(\mathbf{x})$ by an equivalent statistic so chosen that its conditional distribution under the hypothesis has mean 0 and variance 1 (unless all the x_i's $= 0$):

(4.20)
$$s_n(\mathbf{x}) = \sum_1^n x_i \left(\Sigma x_i^2 \right)^{-1/2}.$$

We designate by $\phi_n(\mathbf{x})$ the one-sided conditional test based on $s_n(\mathbf{x})$, and for normal alternatives we compare its power with the power of the t test which is of course most powerful similar for the problem in terms of normal distributions.

Let $Y_i = G_i X_i$ and $Y'_i = G'_i X_i$, where $G_1, \cdots, G_n, G'_1, \cdots, G'_n$ are independent and identically distributed with probability $1/2$ at each of $+1, -1$. Then $Y_i^2 = Y_i'^2 = X_i^2$, and

(4.21)
$$S_n(X) = n^{-1/2} \sum_{i=1}^n Y_i \left[n^{-1} \sum_{j=1}^n X_i^2 \right]^{-1/2},$$

(4.22)
$$S'_n(X) = n^{-1/2} \sum_{i=1}^n Y'_i \left[n^{-1} \sum_{j=1}^n X_i^2 \right]^{-1/2}.$$

Now consider the case where the common distribution of the X_i is normal with mean μ and variance σ^2. By Theorem 3.1 in Chapter 6, $n^{-1} \Sigma X_i^2$ converges in probability to $\sigma^2 + \mu^2$. Hence, by Theorem 2.6, Chapter 6, $(S_n(\mathbf{X}), S_n'(\mathbf{X}))$ has the same limiting distribution (if any) as

$$(4.23) \qquad \left[(\sigma^2 + \mu^2)^{-1/2} n^{-1/2} \sum_{i=1}^{n} Y_i, (\sigma^2 + \mu^2)^{-1/2} n^{-1/2} \Sigma Y_i' \right].$$

The vectors $(Y_1, Y_1'), \cdots, (Y_n, Y_n')$ are independent and identically distributed, and

$$E(Y_i) = E(Y_i') = 0,$$

$$E(Y_i^2) = E(Y_i'^2) = \sigma^2 + \mu^2,$$

$$E(Y_i Y_i') = 0.$$

Then, by Theorem 3.5 in Chapter 6, the random vector (4.23) has the limiting distribution function $\Phi(s) \Phi(s')$, where $\Phi(s)$ is the normal distribution function with mean 0 and variance 1. Then, by Theorem 2.8 in Chapter 6, the limiting distribution of

$$(\sigma^2 + \mu^2)^{-1/2} n^{-1/2} \Sigma Y_i$$

has the distribution function $\Phi(s)$. Hence, by Theorem 4.2, $F_n(s; \mathbf{X}_n)$ converges in probability to $\Phi(s)$, and, by Theorem 4.1, $\xi_{\alpha,n}(\mathbf{X}_n)$ converges in probability to s_α, where $1 - \Phi(s_\alpha) = \alpha$.

By the same type of argument, we find that the limiting distribution of

$$(4.24) \qquad \frac{s_n(\mathbf{X}_n) - n^{1/2}\mu/(\sigma^2 + \mu^2)^{1/2}}{[1 + (\mu/\sigma)^2]^{-1/2}}$$

is normal with mean 0 and variance 1. Then, if μ/σ is positive, it follows that

$$H(s) = \lim_{n \to \infty} \Pr \{s_n(\mathbf{X}_n) \le s\}$$

$$= 0,$$

and hence the power of the test tends to one.

Now let μ, σ depend on n in such a manner that $(\mu/\sigma)n^{1/2}$ approaches a constant δ. The distribution of the (Y_i, Y_i') depends on n, but we are able to repeat the above argument, using the more general central-limit Theorem 3.5 in Chapter 6. Since $E\{|X_i|^3\}\sigma^{-3} = o(n^{1/2})$, the conditions of the theorem are satisfied, and we obtain

$$H(s) = \Phi(s - \delta).$$

The most powerful similar test of normal theory is the t test, and is based on the statistic

(4.25)
$$\frac{n^{1/2}\bar{x}}{\left[\dfrac{1}{n-1}\Sigma(x_i-\bar{x})^2\right]^{1/2}}.$$

But, since

$$s_n(\mathbf{x}) = \frac{\Sigma x_i}{(\Sigma x_i^2)^{1/2}}$$

$$= \frac{n\bar{x}/[\Sigma(x_i-\bar{x})^2]^{1/2}}{1+n\bar{x}^2/\Sigma(x_i-\bar{x})^2}$$

$$= \frac{\left(\dfrac{n}{n-1}\right)^{1/2}\dfrac{n^{1/2}\bar{x}}{\left[\dfrac{1}{n-1}\Sigma(x_i-\bar{x})^2\right]^{1/2}}}{1+(n-1)^{-1}\left\{\dfrac{n^{1/2}\bar{x}}{\left[\dfrac{1}{n-1}\Sigma(x_i-\bar{x})^2\right]^{1/2}}\right\}^2},$$

it follows that $s_n(\mathbf{x})$ is a monotone-increasing function of the t statistic and hence can be used equivalently to form the normal theory test which we designate by $\phi_n^0(\mathbf{x})$ in accordance with our formula (4.9).

Our argument above shows that, under the hypothesis normal distribution with mean 0, the limiting distribution of $s_n(\mathbf{X})$ is normal with mean 0 and variance 1. Hence $s_{\alpha,n}$ converges to s_α, defined by $1-\Phi(s_\alpha)=\alpha$. By Theorem 4.1 the tests $\phi_n(\mathbf{x})$ and $\phi_n^0(\mathbf{x})$ have the same limiting power. Then by Theorem 4.1 it follows that, for normal alternatives, the relative efficiency of the nonparametric test $\phi_n(\mathbf{x})$ with respect to the t test is *one*.

EXAMPLE 4.2. THE RANDOMIZED-BLOCK PROBLEM. The randomized-block problem was described in Section 4.1 of Chapter 3. Let $\mathbf{X}=(X_1,\cdots,X_n)$, where $X_i=(X_{i1},\cdots,X_{ic})$ $(i=1,\cdots,n)$ are n independent random variables with absolutely continuous distributions over R^c $(c\geq 2)$, and let the hypothesis be one of those designated by (4.1), (4.2), (4.3), (4.4). Each of these hypotheses implies that the distribution of each X_i is invariant under the $c!$ permutations of its coordinates $(X_{i1},\cdots,X_{ic})$. In accordance with the theory of Section 2.2 of Chapter 5, a similar size-α test can be constructed as a conditional size-α test, given the statistic

$$t_n(\mathbf{x})=(\{x_{11},\cdots,x_{1c}\},\cdots,\{x_{n1},\cdots,x_{nc}\}).$$

Also it can be shown that, for a suitable class of distributions for the hypothesis, all similar tests have this conditional form.

A test $\phi_n(\mathbf{x})$ proposed by Pitman [7] is a conditional test given $t_n(\mathbf{x})$, and is to reject for large values of the ordinary F statistic for testing treatment against error. This F statistic,

$$(4.26) \quad \frac{\sum_{j=1}^{c} n^{-1}\left[\sum_{i=1}^{n}(x_{ij} - \bar{x}_{i.})\right]^2 (c-1)^{-1}}{\left\{\sum_{i=1}^{n}\sum_{j=1}^{c}(x_{ij} - \bar{x}_{i.})^2 - \sum_{j=1}^{c} n^{-1}\left[\sum_{i=1}^{n}(x_{ij} - \bar{x}_{i.})\right]^2\right\}(n-1)^{-1}(c-1)^{-1}},$$

varies both in numerator and denominator, given $t_n(\mathbf{x})$. However, it can be written in the form

$$\frac{s_n'(\mathbf{x})}{1 - s_n'(\mathbf{x})}\frac{(c-1)^{-1}}{(n-1)^{-1}(c-1)^{-1}},$$

where $\bar{x}_{i.} = c^{-1}\sum_{j=1}^{c} x_{ij}$, and

$$(4.27) \quad s_n'(\mathbf{x}) = \frac{\sum_{j=1}^{c} n^{-1}\left[\sum_{i=1}^{n}(x_{ij} - \bar{x}_{i.})\right]^2}{\sum_{i=1}^{n}\sum_{j=1}^{c}(x_{ij} - \bar{x}_{i.})^2}.$$

From this it is easily seen that $s_n'(\mathbf{x})$ is an equivalent statistic to use both for the ordinary analysis of variance test and for the conditional test. Also for the conditional test it has the added advantage that the denominator is constant-valued under the permutations of the conditional distribution, given $t_n(\mathbf{x})$. To fit in with the use of the theorems of this section, it is convenient to make a further trivial modification and use the statistic

$$(4.28) \quad s_n(\mathbf{x}) = \frac{\sum_{j=1}^{c} u_j^2(\mathbf{x})}{n^{-1}\sum_{i=1}^{n}(c-1)^{-1}\sum_{j=1}^{c}(x_{ij} - \bar{x}_{i.})^2},$$

where $u_j(\mathbf{x}) = n^{-1/2}\sum_{i=1}^{n}(x_{ij} - \bar{x}_{i.})$ for $j = 1, \cdots, c$.

We now use the theory of this section to evaluate the limiting power under the normal distributions of the usual analysis of variance alternative. For this we now let

$$(4.29) \quad X_{ij} = Y_{ij} + \beta_i + \tau_j,$$

where the Y_{ij} are independent and identically distributed with means 0 and variances σ^2, and the β_i and the τ_j are the block and the treatment effect constants. Also we take c fixed and let $n \to \infty$.

Consider the denominator of $s_n(\mathbf{x})$. The random variables

$$(c-1)^{-1} \sum_{j=1}^{c} (X_{ij} - \bar{X}_{i.})^2 \qquad (i = 1, \cdots, n),$$

are independent and identically distributed with mean $\sigma^2(1 + \delta^2)$, where

$$\delta^2 = \sigma^{-2}(c-1)^{-1} \sum_{j=1}^{c} (t_j - \bar{t})^2,$$

and

$$t = c^{-1} \sum_{j=1}^{c} t_j.$$

By Theorem 3.1 in Chapter 5, it follows that

$$n^{-1} \sum_{j=1}^{n} (c-1)^{-1} \sum_{j=1}^{c} (X_{ij} - \bar{x}_{i.})^2$$

converges in probability to $\sigma^2(1 + \delta^2)$. Also it is invariant under the conditional distribution permutations.

Now to apply Theorem 4.2 we need the limiting distribution of

$$(S_n(\mathbf{X}), S_n'(\mathbf{X})),$$

where

$$S_n(\mathbf{X}) = s_n(G\mathbf{X}),$$
$$S_n'(\mathbf{X}) = s_n(G'\mathbf{X}),$$

and G, G' are independent and identically distributed random variables and are such that G applies to $\mathbf{x}$ with equal probability each of the $(c!)^n$ permutations of the hypothesis conditional distribution, given $t_n(\mathbf{x})$. By the above paragraph it follows that

$$(S_n(\mathbf{X}), S_n'(\mathbf{X}))$$

has the same limiting distribution (if any) as does

$$(s_n^*(G\mathbf{X}), s_n^*(G'\mathbf{X})),$$

where

$$s^*(\mathbf{x}) = \sigma^{-2}(1 + \delta^2)^{-1} \sum_{j=1}^{c} u_j^2(\mathbf{x}).$$

We can write

$$u_j(\mathbf{x}) = \sum_{k=1}^{c} \left(\delta_{jk} - \frac{1}{c} \right) v_k(\mathbf{x}),$$

where δ_{jk} is Kronecker's delta and

$$v_k(\mathbf{x}) = n^{-1/2} \sum_{i=1}^{n} (x_{ik} - b_i).$$

Let $V_j = v_j(G\mathbf{X})$, $V_j' = v_j(G'\mathbf{X})$. Toward finding the limiting distribution of $(s_n^*(G\mathbf{X}), s_n^*(G'\mathbf{X}))$, we now investigate the limiting distribution of $V_1, \cdots, V_c, V_1', \cdots, V_c'$. The random vector $n^{1/2}\mathbf{V} = n^{1/2}(V_1, \cdots, V_c, V_1', \cdots, V_c')$ is the sum of n independent random vectors, each of which has the distribution of

$$\mathbf{Z} = (Z_{R_1}, \cdots, Z_{R_c}, Z_{R_1'}, \cdots, Z_{R_c'}),$$

where $Z_1, \cdots, Z_c$ are independent, Z_j has the distribution of $Y_{ij} + t_j$, and $(R_1, \cdots, R_c)$ and $(R_1', \cdots, R_c')$ are two independent random variables whose values are the $c!$ permutations of $(1, \cdots, c)$, each taken with the same probability. By the central-limit Theorem 3.3 in Chapter 6, it follows that $\mathbf{V} - E(\mathbf{V})$ has a limiting normal distribution with means 0 and the same covariance matrix as $\mathbf{Z}$. If δ^2 and σ^2 are allowed to depend on n, then the more general Theorem 3.5 in Chapter 6 is needed. Then by Theorem 2.8 in Chapter 6 it is straightforward to show that the limiting distribution of $(s_n^*(G\mathbf{X}), s_n^*(G'\mathbf{X}))$ is that of two independent χ^2 random variables with $c - 1$ degrees of freedom. (See Problem 6.) Now, applying Theorems 4.1 and 4.2, we find that $\xi_\alpha(\mathbf{X})$ converges in probability to s_α, the point exceeded with probability α by a χ^2 random variable with $c - 1$ degrees of freedom.

The results in the paragraph above also remain valid when $\delta = n^{-1/2}k$ and k is independent of n. The limiting distribution of $s_n^*(\mathbf{X})$, for this sequence of alternatives can be obtained in the manner used above and is a noncentral χ^2. The usual test of normal theory has the general form given by (4.9). Therefore, when the alternative distribution is normal as defined at the beginning of this example, Theorem 4.1 proves that Pitman's conditional test has the same limiting power function as does the ordinary F test, and hence the relative efficiency is *one*.

EXAMPLE 4.3. THE PROBLEM OF RANDOMNESS WITH REGRESSION ALTERNATIVE. THE TWO-SAMPLE PROBLEM. The problem of randomness was described in Section 3.3 of Chapter 3. In this Section we consider a conditional test designed for the problem of randomness with regression alternative. The test is an analog of Pitman's two-sample test, Example 2.1 in Chapter 5, and was mentioned in Problem 10 of that chapter.

Let $X_1, \cdots, X_n$ be n real-valued random variables defined by

(4.30) $X_i = \xi c_i + Y_i,$

where $Y_1, \cdots, Y_n$ are independent and each has the same absolutely continuous distribution. The n constants c_i are the values of the independent regression variable. The hypothesis that $\xi = 0$ is to be tested against the one-sided $\xi > 0$ or the two-sided alternative $\xi \neq 0$.

Let the statistic $t_n(\mathbf{x})$ be the order statistic for the set of n numbers $x_1, \cdots, x_n$:

$$t_n(\mathbf{x}) = (x_{(1)}, \cdots, x_{(n)}).$$

Under the hypothesis the conditional distribution, given $t_n(\mathbf{x})$, is equal probability to each of the $n!$ permutations of the numbers in $t_n(\mathbf{x})$. The Pitman test is a conditional test, given $t_n(\mathbf{x})$, and is to reject for large values of the statistic $s_n(\mathbf{x})$ for the one-sided alternative and for large values of $|s_n(\mathbf{x})|$ for two-sided alternatives, where

$$(4.31) \qquad s_n(\mathbf{x}) = \frac{\sum_1^n (c_i - \bar{c}) x_i}{[\Sigma(c_i - \bar{c})^2 (n-1)^{-1} \Sigma(x_i - \bar{x})^2]^{1/2}}$$

and $\bar{c} = n^{-1} \Sigma c_i$, $\bar{x} = n^{-1} \Sigma x_i$. The one-sided test then has the form

$$\phi_n(\mathbf{x}) = 1 \qquad \text{if} \quad s_n(x) > \xi_{\alpha n}(\mathbf{x})$$
$$= a_{t_n(\mathbf{x})} \qquad\qquad = \xi_{\alpha n}(\mathbf{x})$$
$$= 0 \qquad\qquad < \xi_{\alpha n}(\mathbf{x}),$$

and $\xi_{\alpha n}(\mathbf{x})$ is chosen to give the test size α according to the hypothesis conditional distribution of $s_n(\mathbf{x})$, given $t_n(\mathbf{x})$.

The usual t test for the analog of this problem in normal theory can also be expressed in terms of $s_n(\mathbf{x})$. For we can write the t statistic as follows:

$$\frac{\Sigma(c_i - \bar{c}) x_i}{[\Sigma(c_i - \bar{c})^2]^{1/2}} \cdot \frac{1}{\left[\Sigma(x_i - \bar{x})^2 - \dfrac{[\Sigma(c_i - \bar{c}) x_i]^2}{\Sigma(c_i - \bar{c})^2} \right]^{1/2}} (n-2)^{-1/2}$$

$$= (n-2)^{1/2} \frac{s_n(\mathbf{x})}{[(n-1) - s_n^2(\mathbf{x})]^{1/2}}.$$

Then, because $-(n-1)^{1/2} \leq s_n(\mathbf{x}) \leq (n-1)^{1/2}$, this expression for the t statistic is a monotone-increasing function of $s_n(\mathbf{x})$. Also it follows that the absolute value of the t statistic is an increasing function of $|s_n(\mathbf{x})|$. Hence the one-sided test of normal theory can be written

$$(4.32) \qquad \phi^0(\mathbf{x}) = 1 \qquad \text{if} \quad s_n(\mathbf{x}) > s_{n\alpha}$$
$$= 0 \qquad\qquad < s_{n\alpha},$$

where $s_{n\alpha}$ is chosen to give the test size α under the hypothesis using normal distributions.

We consider the limiting value (if any) for $\xi_{\alpha n}(\mathbf{X})$ under sampling from a hypothesis distribution. Let $\xi = 0$, var $\{Y_i\} > 0$, and $E|Y_i|^3 < \infty$. Then by Theorem 6.8 in Chapter 6 it follows that, if either

$$(4.33) \qquad \frac{\max (c_i - \bar{c})^2}{\Sigma(c_i - \bar{c})^2} \to 0,$$

or Y_i is normally distributed, then

$$(4.34) \qquad F_n(s; \mathbf{X}) \to \Phi(s) \quad \text{in probability}$$

as $n \to \infty$, where $\Phi(s)$ is the cumulative for the normal distribution with mean 0 and variance 1. From this it follows that, under the above assumptions,

$$(4.35) \qquad \text{p-lim}_{n \to \infty} \xi_{\alpha n}(\mathbf{X}) = z_\alpha,$$

where z_α is the point exceeded with probability α according to the standardized normal distribution. It also follows immediately that $s_{n\alpha} \to z_\alpha$ as n approaches infinity.

We consider the limiting values of $\xi_{\alpha n}(\mathbf{X})$ (if any) under distributions of the alternative. Assume that $X_i = d_i + Y_i$, where $Y_1, \cdots, Y_n$ are independent and identically distributed, $E\{|Y_i|^3\} < \infty$, var $\{Y_i\} > 0$. By Theorem 6.9 in Chapter 6 it follows that, if

(a)

$$(4.36) \qquad Y_i \text{ is normal}$$

or

$$(4.37) \qquad \frac{\max (c_i - \bar{c})^2}{\Sigma(c_i - \bar{c})^2} \to 0,$$

and

(b)

$$(4.38) \qquad n \frac{\max (c_i - \bar{c})^2}{\Sigma(c_i - \bar{c})^2} \cdot \frac{\max (d_i - \bar{d})^2}{\Sigma(d_i - \bar{d})^2} \to 0,$$

then, as $n \to \infty$

$$F_n(s; \mathbf{x}) \to \Phi(s) \quad \text{in probability};$$

that is, the probability approaches one that the distribution function of $S_n(\mathbf{x})$ is within any preassigned amount of the normal distribution with mean 0 and variance 1. $S_n(\mathbf{x})$ was defined in general notation by formula (4.4). From this it follows by Theorem 4.1 that, under the assumptions above,

$$(4.39) \qquad \text{p-lim}_{n \to \infty} \xi_{\alpha n}(\mathbf{X}) = z_\alpha.$$

We now consider the limiting distribution of $s_n(\mathbf{X})$ under the distributions of the alternative mentioned above. If $E\{|Y_1|^3\} < \infty$, var $\{Y_1\} > 0$ and either X_i is normal or

$$\frac{\max (c_i - \bar{c})^2}{\Sigma(c_i - \bar{c})^2} \to 0,$$

then it follows easily from the central-limit Theorem 3.4 in Chapter 6 that the limiting distribution of $s_n(\mathbf{X})$ is normal. The limiting power of the conditional test can then be obtained by using Theorem 4.1.

We now compare the t test with Pitman's test when the distributions are normal. Let $X_i = d_i + Y_i$, where $Y_1, \cdots, Y_n$ are independent, and each has the same normal distribution. It follows by Theorem 4.1 and the results above that, if the power of the t test tends to a finite limit, then Pitman's conditional test converges to the same limit. Hence the relative efficiency of the two tests is *one*.

5. THE EFFICIENCY OF A RANK TEST

In Chapter 5, Example 3.2, the invariance method was applied to the two-sample problem. From the invariant or rank tests a test was chosen having locally maximum power against normal alternatives; it was the c_1 test developed by Terry. In this section we prove that the c_1 test is asymptotically as powerful as the best test; the t test of normal theory. Following Hoeffding [8], however, we prove the stronger result that the analog of the c_1 test for the problem of randomness with regression alternative is asymptotically as efficient as the t test for this regression alternative. This more general c_1 test was introduced in Problem 16 of Chapter 5.

Let $X_1, \cdots, X_n$ be independent, and let X_i be normally distributed with mean $\xi c_i + \eta$ and variance σ^2. For the analogous nonparametric formulation see Section 3.3 in Chapter 3. The hypothesis testing problem is to test the hypothesis; $\xi = 0$, against the alternative; $\xi > 0$, or the alternative, $\xi \neq 0$. When σ is known, the standard test of parametric theory is based on the statistic

$$(5.1) \qquad t_n(\mathbf{x}) = \frac{\Sigma_i(c_i - \bar{c})x_i}{\sigma[\Sigma_i(c_i - \bar{c})^2]^{1/2}}$$

where $\bar{c} = \sum_{i=1}^{n} c_i$. It is easily seen that the induced distribution of this statistic is normal with mean

$$(5.2) \qquad \delta_n = \frac{\xi}{\sigma} [\Sigma(c_i - \bar{c})^2]^{1/2}$$

and variance 1. When σ is unknown, the standard test is based on $t_n(\mathbf{x})$ with σ replaced by its unbiased estimate based on the x_i's. By the results in Example 4.3, this modification of $t_n(\mathbf{x})$ has an induced distribution which is asymptotically normal with mean (5.2) and variance 1. The c_1 test of Problem 16 in Chapter 5 is based on the statistic

$$(5.3) \qquad c_1(\mathbf{r}) = \frac{\Sigma_i(c_i - \bar{c})E\{Z_{(r_i)}\}}{[\Sigma_i(c_i - \bar{c})^2]^{1/2}},$$

where $\mathbf{r} = \mathbf{r}(\mathbf{x}) = (r_1, \cdots, r_n)$ is the rank statistic, giving the ranks of $x_1, \cdots, x_n$ and where $Z_{(1)}, \cdots, Z_{(n)}$ are the order-statistic random variables for a sample of n from the standardized normal distribution. In the remainder of this section we shall prove that, if δ_n is bounded then $c_1(\mathbf{r})$ also has an induced distribution which is asymptotically normal with mean δ_n and variance 1. This equivalence of the limiting distributions of the two statistics implies that the c_1 test is asymptotically as efficient as the usual t test.

By observing the form of (5.3) we see that we can assume that $\bar{c} = 0$ and $\Sigma c_i^2 = 1$. Also without loss of generality we assume that $\eta = 0$ and $\sigma^2 = 1$. Now, applying Theorem 3.3 Chapter 5 in the same manner used in Example 3.2 of that chapter, we find

$$(5.4) \qquad \Pr\{\mathbf{r}(X) = \mathbf{r}\} = \frac{1}{n!} E\left\{\prod_{i=1}^{n} \frac{\exp[-\tfrac{1}{2}(Z_{(r)} - \xi c_i)^2]}{\exp[-\tfrac{1}{2}Z_{(r_i)}^2]}\right\}$$

$$= \frac{1}{n!} \exp(-\tfrac{1}{2}\xi^2 \Sigma c_i^2) E\{\exp[\Sigma c_i Z_{(r_i)}]\}$$

$$= \frac{1}{n!} \exp\left(-\frac{\delta_n^2}{2}\right) E\{\exp[\delta_n \Sigma c_i Z_{(r_i)}]\}.$$

Also, if $\phi_n(t, \delta_n)$ designates the characteristic function of $c_1(\mathbf{r}(X)) - \delta_n$, then we have

$$(5.5) \qquad \phi_n(t, \delta_n) = \Sigma_\mathbf{r} \exp[itc_1(\mathbf{r}) - it\delta_n] \Pr\{\mathbf{r}(X) = \mathbf{r}\}.$$

To prove that, when δ_n is bounded, $c_1(\mathbf{r}(X))$ has a limiting normal distribution with mean 0 and variance 1, we shall prove that, for every $t \in R^1$,

$$(5.6) \qquad \lim_{n \to \infty} \phi_n(t, d) = \exp(-t^2/2),$$

and that the convergence is uniform for d bounded. Then, since $\exp(-t^2/2)$ is the characteristic function for the standardized normal, the limiting normality of $c_1(\mathbf{r}(X))$ follows from the use of Theorem 6.6 in Chapter 6.

From (5.4) and (5.5) it follows that we can write

(5.7) $\quad \phi_n(t,d) = \dfrac{1}{n!} \Sigma_{\mathbf{r}} \exp\left[itc_1(\mathbf{r}) - itd - d^2/2\right] E\{\exp\left[d\Sigma c_i Z_{(r_i)}\right]\}$

$\quad\quad\quad = \dfrac{1}{n!} \exp\left(-itd - d^2/2\right)\Sigma_{\mathbf{r}} E\{\exp\left[itc_1(\mathbf{r}) + d\Sigma c_i Z_{(r_i)}\right]\}$

$\quad\quad\quad = \exp\left(-itd - d^2/2\right) \dfrac{1}{n!} \Sigma_{\mathbf{r}} E\{\exp\left[(it + d)\Sigma c_i Z_{(r_i)}\right]$

$\quad\quad\quad\quad \exp\left[-it(\Sigma c_i Z_{(r_i)} - c_1(\mathbf{r}))\right]\}$

$\quad\quad\quad = \exp\left(-itd - d^2/2\right) E\{\exp\left[(it + d)\Sigma c_i Z_{(R_i)}\right]$

$\quad\quad\quad\quad \exp\left(-itU_R\right)\}$

where

$$U_{\mathbf{r}} = \sum_{i=1}^{n} c_i Z_{(r_i)} - c_1(\mathbf{r}) = \sum_{i=1}^{n} c_i(Z_{(r_i)} - E\{Z_{(r_i)}\}),$$

and where $\mathbf{R} = (R_1, \cdots, R_n)$ designates a random variable which takes each permutation of $(1, \cdots, n)$ with the same probability $1/n!$. From the definition of $\mathbf{R}$ it follows that $(Z_{(R_1)}, \cdots, Z_{(R_n)})$ is a random sample of n from the standardized normal; hence $\sum_{i=1}^{n} c_i Z_{(R_i)}$ has the standardized normal distribution. Now, letting θ stand for a complex-valued quantity with absolute value less than one, we can rewrite (5.7)

(5.8) $\quad \phi_n(t, d) = \exp\left(-itd - d^2/2\right) E\{\exp\left[(it + d)\Sigma c_i Z_{(R_i)}\right](1 + \theta|tU_{\mathbf{R}}|)\}$

$\quad\quad\quad = \exp\left(-itd - d^2/2\right)\exp\left[(it + d)^2/2\right] + \exp\left(-itd + d^2/2\right)$

$\quad\quad\quad\quad E\{\exp\left[(it + d)\Sigma c_i Z_{(R_i)}\right]\theta|tU_{\mathbf{R}}|\}$

$\quad\quad\quad = \exp\left(-t^2/2\right) + \theta|t|\exp\left(-d^2/2\right)E\{|U_{\mathbf{R}}|\exp\left[d\Sigma c_i Z_{(R_i)}\right]\}.$

By Schwarz's inequality we obtain

$E\{|U_{\mathbf{R}}|\exp\left[d\Sigma c_i Z_{(R_i)}\right]\} \leq [E\{U_{\mathbf{R}}^2\}]^{1/2}[E\{\exp\left[2d\Sigma c_i Z_{(R_i)}\right]\}]^{1/2}$

$\quad\quad\quad\quad = [E\{U_{\mathbf{R}}^2\}]^{1/2}[\exp\left(4d^2/2\right)]^{1/2}$

$\quad\quad\quad\quad = [E\{U_{\mathbf{R}}^2\}]^{1/2} e^{d^2}.$

Therefore

(5.9) $\quad\quad |\phi_n(t, d) - \exp\left(-t^2/2\right)| \leq |t| \exp\left(d^2/2\right) E\{U_{\mathbf{R}}^2\}.$

The convergence and uniform convergence of (5.6) are now obtained by showing that $\lim E\{U_R^2\} = 0$. We have $E\{[\Sigma c_i Z_{(R_i)}]^2\} = 1$ and $E\{\Sigma c_i Z_{(r_i)}\}$ $= \Sigma c_i E(Z_{(r_i)}) = c_1(\mathbf{r})$; therefore

(5.10) $\qquad E\{U_R^2\} = E\{[\Sigma c_i Z_{(R_i)} - c_1(\mathbf{R})]^2\}$

$\qquad\qquad = 1 - 2E\{\Sigma c_i Z_{(R_i)} c_i(\mathbf{R})\} + E\{(c_1(\mathbf{R}))^2\}$

$\qquad\qquad = 1 - E\{(c_1(\mathbf{R}))^2\}.$

Then, by formula (6.5) in Chapter 6,

(5.11) $\qquad\qquad E\{[c_1(\mathbf{R})]^2\} = (n-1)^{-1}\Sigma_i(EZ_{(i)})^2.$

This last expression stands for the variance of the c_1 statistic as calculated under the hypothesis of randomness. This variance approaches the limiting value one as was proved by Terry [9]. It also obtains from a general theorem by Hoeffding which we quote at the end of this section. It follows then that (5.11) approaches one, (5.10) approaches zero, and the limiting normality follows from (5.9) and the succeeding remarks.

We complete this section by quoting a theorem proved by Hoeffding [10]. Let $X_1, X_2, \cdots$ be independent and each have the same distribution function $F(x)$. Also let $(x_{(1)}, \cdots, x_{(n)})$ be the order statistic for the first n x's. Then the theorem is concerned with the distribution obtained when a value is chosen at random (equal probability) from the n numbers in the set $\{E(X_{(1)}), \cdots, E(X_{(n)})\}$. As n becomes large, this distribution approximates that given by $F(x)$. We quote the theorem:

THEOREM 5.1. (HOEFFDING). If $\int_{-\infty}^{\infty} |x|\, dF(x) < \infty$, and if $g(x)$ is a real-valued continuous function bounded by $h(x)$, where $h(x)$ is convex and $\int_{-\infty}^{\infty} h(x)\, dF(x) < \infty$, then

(5.12) $\qquad\qquad \lim_{n\to\infty} \frac{1}{n} \sum_{i=1}^{n} g(EX_{(i)}) = \int_{-\infty}^{\infty} g(x)\, dF(x).$

By taking $g(x) = x^r$ and applying the theorem to the order-statistic random variable $(Z_{(1)}, \cdots, Z_{(n)})$ for a sample of n from the standardized normal distribution, we obtain that

$$n^{-1} \sum_{i=1}^{n} [E(Z_{(i)})]^r$$

converges to the rth moment of the standardized normal distribution. With $n = 2$ this proves that (5.11) converges to one.

6. PROBLEMS FOR SOLUTION

1. Show that the one-sided sign test, Section 2.1 in Chapter 5, is consistent against alternatives for which the p percentile is positive. Also show that the two-sided sign test is consistent against alternatives for which the p percentile is not equal zero.

2. For the two-sample scale problem (3.6) in Chapter 3, show that the unbiased test proposed in Problem 2 of Chapter 5 is consistent against the alternatives for which

$$\Pr\{|X_{n_1+2} - X_{n_1+1}| > |X_2 - X_1|\} > \tfrac{1}{2}.$$

3. Consider the randomized-block problem, (4.3), (4.4), or (4.5) in Chapter 3, when the number of treatments is two. In Section 2.1 and Problem 6 of Chapter 5 the sign test was shown to be most powerful for formulation (4.5) against one-sided alternatives. Also the two-sided sign test has optimum properties—Problems 8 and 9 in Chapter 5. Against alternatives for which treatment differences in each block all have the same normal distribution, show that the sign test has an efficiency $2/\pi$ with respect to the usual t test.

4. The problem of randomness was described (3.3) and (3.4) in Chapter 3. Let $X_i = \xi d_i + Z_i$ ($i = 1, \cdots, n$) where the $Z_1, \cdots, Z_n$ are independent, each Z_i has the same absolutely continuous distribution, and $d_1, \cdots, d_n$ are given constants. Consider the case where the d_i's are equally spaced and occur in order of magnitude, and hence without loss of generality can be replaced by the integers $1, \cdots, n$. For the parametric class of distributions corresponding to each Z_i having the same normal distribution, compare the efficiency of the following tests. For convenience let

$$r(t) = \frac{\left[\dfrac{\partial}{\partial \xi} E\{t(\mathbf{X})\}\,\big|_{\xi=0}\right]^2}{\operatorname{var}\{t(\mathbf{X})\}\big|_{\xi=0}};$$

then the efficiency of t_1 re t_2 is given by

$$e(t_1, t_2) = \lim_{n \to \infty} \frac{r(t_1)}{r(t_2)}.$$

(a) *The difference-sign test* (*Moore and Wallis* [5]). The difference sign test is based on D, the number of positive first differences in the sequence $x_1, \cdots, x_n$. Using the function $c'(u)$ defined by (2.10), we can write

$$D = \sum_{i=2}^{n} c'(x_i - x_{i-1}).$$

The one- and two-sided tests are to reject for large values of D and $\left|D - \dfrac{n-1}{2}\right|$, respectively. Prove that

$$r(D) \sim 3n/\pi.$$

(b) *The difference-sign correlation coefficient test.* A test can be based on the difference-sign correlation coefficient, t, between the x sequence and the d sequence. See (5.27) in Chapter 6. Show that, for our special form of a sequence, t can be written

$$t = 1 - \frac{4Q}{n(n-1)},$$

where

$$Q = \sum_{i<j} c'(x_i - x_j).$$

Prove that

$$r(Q) \sim n^3/4\pi.$$

(c) *The rank correlation coefficient test.* The rank correlation coefficient k' was defined in Problem 11, Chapter 6. Show that the coefficient k' for the x and d sequences can be written

$$k' = 1 - \frac{12V}{n(n^2 - 1)},$$

where

$$V = \sum_{i<j} (j - 1)c(x_i - x_j).$$

Prove that

$$r(V) \sim n^3/4\pi.$$

(d) *The turning-point test.* This test proposed in [6] is based on the number of runs up and down or equivalently on T the number of "peaks" and "troughs" in the x sequence:

$$T = \sum_{i=3}^{n} T_i,$$

where

$$T_i = 1 \qquad (x_i - x_{i-1})(x_{i-1} - x_{i-2}) < 0$$
$$= -1 \qquad \text{otherwise.}$$

Prove that

$$\frac{\partial}{\partial \xi} E(T) \big|_{\delta=0} = 0.$$

(e) *The t test.* The usual t test is based on the statistic

$$b = \frac{\Sigma(x_i - \bar{x})(d_i - \bar{d})}{(\Sigma(x_i - \bar{x})^2)^{1/2}}.$$

Prove that

$$r(b) \sim n^3/12.$$

5. The two-sample problem was described in Section 3.1 of Chapter 3. Let $X_1, \cdots,$ X_{n_1} be independent and each have an absolutely continuous distribution function $F(x)$ on the real line. Also let $X_{n_1+1}, \cdots, X_{n_1+n_2}$ be independent and each X_{n_1+j} have an absolutely continuous distribution function $G(x)$ on the real line. For the parametric class of distributions corresponding to normal distributions with the same variance but different means, find the relative efficiency of the following tests. Use the function $r(t)$ defined in Problem 4, and for convenience and no loss of generality consider the normal distributions with variance 1, first sample mean 0, and second sample mean ξ.

(a) *The t test.* The t test is based on the statistic

$$t = \frac{\bar{x} - \bar{x}'}{\left[\dfrac{\displaystyle\sum_{1}^{n_1}(x_i - \bar{x})^2 + \sum_{1}^{n_2}(x_{n_1+j} - \bar{x}')^2}{n_1 + n_2 - 2} \right]^{1/2}},$$

where

$$x = n_1^{-1} \Sigma x_i,$$

$$x' = n_2^{-1} \Sigma x_{n_1+j}.$$

Show that

$$r(t) = \frac{1}{1/n_1 + 1/n_2} = \frac{n_1 n_2}{n_1 + n_2}$$

(*b*) *The Mann–Whitney test.* The Mann–Whitney test was defined in Example 1.1 in Chapter 5 and can be based on the statistic V^*.

$$V^* = \sum_{i=1}^{n_1} \sum_{j=1}^{n_2} c'(x_{n_1+j} - x_i),$$

where $c'(u)$ was defined in (2.10). Prove that

$$r(V^*) = \left(\frac{n_1 n_2}{2\pi^{1/2}} \right)^2 \cdot \frac{12}{n_1 n_2 (n_1 + n_2 + 1)}.$$

(*c*) *The median test.* The median test is based on the number, u, of first-sample values smaller than the median, z, of the combined sample. Make the inessential restriction that the combined sample size is odd, say equal to $2r + 1$. By using the hypergeometric distribution, show that the joint probability density for u, z is given by

$$h(u, z) = n_1 \binom{n_1 - 1}{u} \binom{n_2}{r - u} F^u(z)(1 - F(z))^{n_1-u-1} G(z)^{-u}(1 - G(z))^{n_2-r+u} \frac{dF(z)}{dz}$$

$$+ n_2 \binom{n_1}{u} \binom{n_2 - 1}{r - u} F^u(z)(1 - F(z))^{n_1-u} G(z)^{r-u}(1 - G(z))^{n_2-r+u-1} \frac{dG(z)}{dz}.$$

Show how that (u, z) has a limiting bivariate normal distribution. For this let

$$u = n_1 F(c) + n_1^{1/2} v,$$

$$z = c + w n_1^{-1/2},$$

where c satisfies

$$n_1 F(c) + n_2 G(c) = \frac{n_1 + n_2}{2}.$$

Use Stirling's formula, and work with the logarithm of the density element. The quadratic form of the limiting distribution is

$$v^2 \left[\frac{1}{F(c)(1 - F(c))} + \frac{n_1}{n_2 G(c)(1 - G(c))} \right]$$

$$- 2vw \left[\frac{f(c)}{F(c)(1 - F(c))} \frac{g(c)}{G(c)(1 - G(c))} \right]$$

$$+ w^2 \left[\frac{f^2(c)}{F(c)(1 - F(c))} \frac{n_2 g^2(c)}{G(c)(1 - G(c))} \right],$$

where $f(x) = dF(x)/dx$, $g(x) = dG(x)/dx$. Show that under the hypothesis the large-sample variance of v is given by

$$\frac{n_1 n_2}{4(n_1 + n_2)}.$$

Hence show that

$$r(v) = \frac{4(n_1 + n_2)}{n_1 n_2} \left[\frac{n_1 n_2}{(2\pi)^{1/2}(n_1 + n_2)} \right]^2.$$

6. For the theory in Example 4.2 find the covariance matrix of $\mathbf{Z}$. From this, by using Theorem 2.8 in Chapter 6, show that $(s_n^*(GX), s_n^*(G'X))$ has the limiting distribution of two independent χ^2 random variables with $c - 1$ degrees of freedom.

7. The problem of randomness with regression alternative was defined in Section 3.3 of Chapter 3. In Section 5 of this chapter a rank test, the c_1 test of Terry, was proved asymptotically as efficient as the standard t test. Prove that the following randomized rank test also has limiting efficiency one. Proceed as in Terry's test, but use the randomized statistic

$$c_1^*(\mathbf{r}) = \frac{\Sigma_i (c_i - \bar{c}) Z_{(r_i)}}{[\Sigma(c_i - \bar{c})^2]^{1/2}},$$

where $(Z_{(1)}, \cdots, Z_{(n)})$ is the order-statistic random variable for an independent sample of n from the standardized normal distribution.

REFERENCES AND BIBLIOGRAPHY

1. E. L. Lehmann, "Consistency and unbiasedness of certain nonparametric tests," *Ann. Math. Stat.*, Vol. 22 (1951), p. 165.

2. A. Stuart, "Asymptotic relative efficiencies of distribution-free tests of randomness against normal alternatives," *J. Am. Stat. Assoc.*, Vol. 49 (1954), p. 147.

3. W. Hoeffding, "The large sample power of tests based on permutations of observations," *Ann. Math. Stat.*, Vol. 23 (1952), p. 169.

4. W. J. Dixon, "Power functions of the sign test and power efficiency for normal alternatives," *Ann. Math. Stat.*, Vol. 24 (1953), p. 467.

5. G. H. Moore and W. A. Wallis, "Time series significance tests based on signs of differences," *J. Am. Stat. Assoc.*, Vol. 38 (1943), p. 153.

6. W. A. Wallis and G. H. Moore, "A significance test for time series analysis," *J. Am. Stat. Assoc.*, Vol. 36 (1941), p. 401.

7. E. J. G. Pitman, "Significance tests which may be applied to samples from any population. III. The analysis of variance test," *Biometrika*, Vol. 29 (1938), p. 322.

8. W. Hoeffding, "The large sample power of Fisher-Yates rank tests," unpublished.

9. M. E. Terry, "Some rank order tests which are most powerful against specific parametric alternatives," *Ann. Math. Stat.*, Vol. 23 (1952), p. 346.

10. W. Hoeffding, "On the distribution of the expected values of the order statistics," *Ann. Math. Stat.*, Vol. 24 (1953), p. 93.

Index

Criminology
Dr. Grygier
Octior

Applied Statistics (Continued)

HALD · Statistical Theory with Engineering Applications
HANSEN, HURWITZ, and MADOW · Sample Survey Methods and Theory, **Volume I**
HOEL · Elementary Statistics
KEMPTHORNE · An Introduction to Genetic Statistics
MEYER · Symposium on Monte Carlo Methods
MUDGETT · Index Numbers
RICE · Control Charts
ROMIG · 50–100 Binomial Tables
SARHAN and GREENBERG · Contributions to Order Statistics
TIPPETT · Technological Applications of Statistics
WILLIAMS · Regression Analysis
WOLD and JURÉEN · Demand Analysis
YOUDEN · Statistical Methods for Chemists

Books of Related Interest

ALLEN and ELY · International Trade Statistics
ARLEY and BUCH · Introduction to the Theory of Probability and Statistics
CHERNOFF and MOSES · Elementary Decision Theory
HAUSER and LEONARD · Government Statistics for Business Use, *Second Edition*
STEPHAN and McCARTHY · Sampling Opinions—An Analysis of Survey Procedures

T